aerospace:
THE CHALLENGE
SECOND EDITION

BY:
HAROLD R. BACON
WARREN H. GARTHRIGHT
ROBERT O. DAHL

DESIGN AND PRODUCTION:
WILLIAM J. DePAOLA
HARLEY A. SAMFORD, JR.
ISAAC E. VASS

EDITED BY:
PATRICIA S. SMITHSON

CENTER FOR AEROSPACE EDUCATION DEVELOPMENT
CIVIL AIR PATROL
Maxwell AFB, Alabama

I

Civil Air Patrol National Headquarters
Maxwell Air Force Base, Alabama 36112

Published 1979   Second Edition 1983

Printed in the United States of America

CONTRIBUTORS:

Mrs. Jeanne M. Wilson, Mrs. Rita C. Ricks, Mr. Louis N. Neeley, Headquarters CAP-USAF

Capt. John C. Sampson, USAF, Lt. Donna M. Graham, USAF, Lt. Lynne M. Tirpak, USAF, AIC James C. Benkoczy, USAF, Headquarters USAFROTC

PREFACE

Aerospace: The Challenge has been prepared to provide young people with a basic aerospace education so that they can better understand and appreciate their aerospace world. Our purpose is not to train these students to become pilots, astronauts, engineers, or flight attendants. Rather, we want to provide them with the basic knowledge, skills, and attitudes about aerospace that will enable them to live and function in tomorrow's society.

Only a few of these students will choose a career in aviation or space. However, *all* of them are citizens of the leading aerospace nation on Earth. This citizenship provides them with the many benefits which come with freedom and affluence. It also requires certain responsibilities and obligations. These young people, in today's schools, will become tomorrow's taxpayers and voters. It is vital that they understand the importance of aerospace developments both present and potential so that their decisions can be based on an informed viewpoint rather than on ignorance.

Our youth today are active and involved in their society. They are looking for worthwhile causes to serve and ways in which to contribute. This course of study will help them understand the contributions that aerospace is making toward solving many of today's social and economic problems. It may also "turn them on" to becoming personally involved in aerospace.

To many of our youth today, the future looks very bleak. At every turn, they see and hear about the energy crisis, shortages of many natural resources, pollution, population and hunger problems, world unrest, and armed confrontations. The result of this is that many of them question their future and damn the legacy left them by the present generation. However, the future shines brightly in aerospace. We have just begun our journey on this new ocean, and our aerospace leaders view these world issues not as problems but as challenges.

In the brief span of only twenty-five years, they have developed instantaneous communications via satellite. Satellites also perform constant worldwide weather forecasting and monitoring of Earth's resources. We have investigated the near planets, man has set foot on another heavenly body, and the Space Shuttle program is now operational and will open new vistas in the utilization of space for mankind's benefit.

Doctor Robert H. Goddard, the "Father of Modern Rocketry," put it as well any anyone has when, in 1904, he said:

"It is difficult to say what is impossible, for the dreams of yesterday are the hopes of today and the realities of tomorrow."

Table of Contents

PART ONE: *The Heritage of Flight*

CHAPTER

PART TWO: *Rocketry and Spacecraft*

CHAPTER

PART THREE: *The Aerospace Community*

CHAPTER

PART ONE

THE HERITAGE OF FLIGHT

To many people in today's world, particularly in America, flight has become commonplace and seemingly very natural. They board today's flying carpets (jet airliners) and are whisked across the country at speeds considered impossible less than 100 years ago. Modern air travelers either have never thought about mankind's centuries-long struggle to fly or have passed it off as something unimportant.

Mankind's ability to fly was accomplished only by years of trial and error, success and failure, and by overcoming many natural laws. Many hundreds of skilled and dedicated men and women have slowly, step-by-step, built the base upon which our present-day capabilities rest. These individuals came from different nations and varied backgrounds, but they all had one thing in common—the imagination to look into the future and the genius to mold their ideas into concrete form.

It is to these aerospace pioneers that we owe our heritage of flight and it is fitting that Part One of our book is devoted to this heritage.

The main learning objective of this Part is for you to Know the Heritage of Flight. Upon completing your study of all six chapters in this Part, you should:

1. know the origins of flight,
2. know the important developments in aviation during the 1904-1919 time period,
3. know aviation developments during the Golden Age: 1919-1939,
4. know aviation developments during World War II,
5. know aviation developments in the postwar years: 1945-1958,
6. know significant developments and events in the Aerospace Age: 1958-present.

THE ORIGINS OF FLIGHT

T hroughout the history of flight there have been many milestones and many great accomplishments. This chapter deals with the first 6,000 years of that history. The first 5,500 years of the history of flight deals with mankind's desire to fly, and only for the last 500 years has this desire led to actual accomplishment. The chapter ends with the achievement of powered flight by the Wright brothers, only 80 years ago.

The general learning objective for this chapter is for you to know the origins of flight. To reach this objective, you must pattern your study of the material according to the *specific learning objectives* listed in the Appendix of this textbook.

WHAT IS AEROSPACE?

Aerospace is considered to be everything above the Earth's surface, including both the atmosphere and space beyond. It is now believed that aerospace is one medium, not two. There is no clear line where the atmosphere ends and space begins, but rather, as you go higher, the atmosphere becomes thinner and thinner until you reach a point where you are considered to be in space.

It is safe to say that this vast expanse has always been there. Long before man appeared on this planet, other forms of life which included birds, mammals (bats), and reptiles (pterodactyls) had learned to travel through the atmosphere. It is also believed by some scientists that, many centuries ago, life from other planets may have developed the capability of traveling through space. But for man here on Earth, aerospace travel is a very recent occurrence. Only within this century have we been able to fly through the atmosphere and, of course, space flight has occurred within your own lifetime. However, in another sense, mankind has probably traveled through the air and space for as long as they have been on Earth—at least, in their imagination they have (see fig.1).

THOUGHTS AND LEGENDS

THE DESIRE TO FLY

In looking at the very earliest records of mankind, we see references to flight and to people's desire to fly. In these early records, from all parts of the world, flight is shown as a supernatural event, something only gods or demons could do. From the beginning, all races of man have worshipped gods,

FIGURE 1   CHRONOLOGY OF AEROSPACE EVENTS

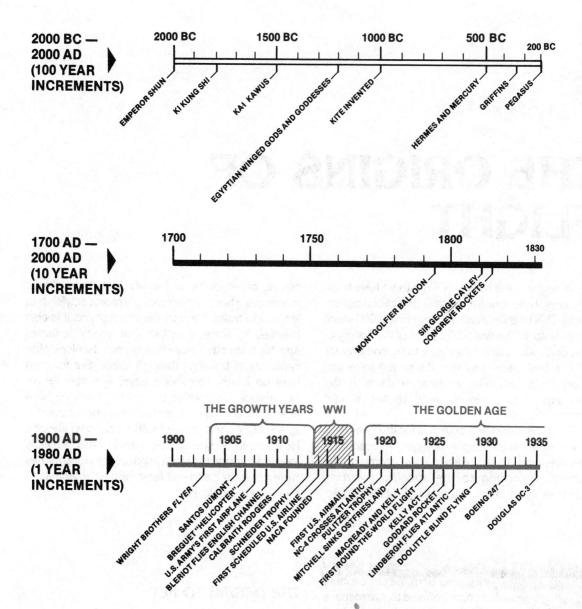

2000 BC — 2000 AD (100 YEAR INCREMENTS)

2000 BC · 1500 BC · 1000 BC · 500 BC · 200 BC

EMPEROR SHUN · KI KUNG SHI · KAI KAWUS · EGYPTIAN WINGED GODS AND GODDESSES · KITE INVENTED · HERMES AND MERCURY · GRIFFINS · PEGASUS

1700 AD — 2000 AD (10 YEAR INCREMENTS)

1700 · 1750 · 1800 · 1830

MONTGOLFIER BALLOON · SIR GEORGE CAYLEY · CONGREVE ROCKETS

THE GROWTH YEARS   WWI   THE GOLDEN AGE

1900 AD — 1980 AD (1 YEAR INCREMENTS)

1900 · 1905 · 1910 · 1915 · 1920 · 1925 · 1930 · 1935

WRIGHT BROTHERS FLYER · SANTOS DUMONT · BREGUET "HELICOPTER" · U.S. ARMY'S FIRST AIRPLANE · BLERIOT FLIES ENGLISH CHANNEL · CALBRAITH RODGERS · SCHNEIDER TROPHY · FIRST SCHEDULED U.S. AIRLINE · NACA FOUNDED · FIRST U.S. AIRMAIL · NC-4 CROSSES ATLANTIC · PULITZER TROPHY · MITCHELL SINKS OSTFRIESLAND · MACREADY AND KELLY · FIRST ROUND-THE-WORLD FLIGHT · KELLY ACT · GODDARD ROCKET · LINDBERGH FLIES ATLANTIC · DOOLITTLE BLIND FLYING · BOEING 247 · DOUGLAS DC-3

THERE ARE THREE CHRONOLOGICAL LINES REPRESENTED ABOVE, EXTENDING ACROSS BOTH PAGES. THE TOP ONE, FROM 2000 BC TO 2000 AD, REPRESENTS 4000 YEARS OF HUMANITY'S DREAM OF FLIGHT TO THE ULTIMATE ACHIEVEMENT OF THAT DREAM. THE MIDDLE ONE,

FIGURE 1 CHRONOLOGY OF AEROSPACE EVENTS
(continued)

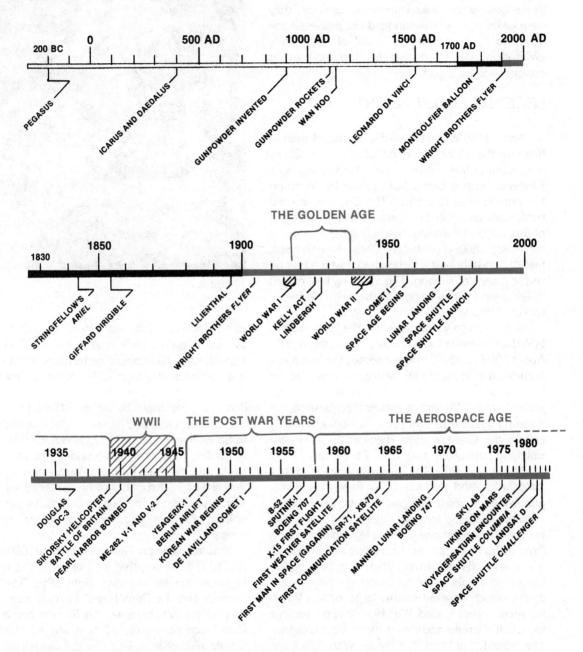

FROM 1700 AD TO 2000 AD, REPRESENTS THE LAST 300 YEARS IN THE DEVELOPMENT OF FLIGHT. THE BOTTOM ONE REPRESENTS THE PAST 80 YEARS OF ACTUAL MANNED FLIGHT IN BOTH THE ATMOSPHERE AND "OUTER" SPACE.

both good and bad. These gods were used to explain those things mankind could not understand. Since gods were looked upon as supreme, they were given a power mankind did not possess—the ability to fly. It seems that, in all of these early civilizations, to fly meant to dominate or to conquer—to be a god.

LEGENDS ABOUT FLIGHT

Among the earliest recorded stories of man in flight is the Chinese legend of Emperor Shun. According to this legend, nearly 4,000 years ago, Emperor Shun escaped from prison by "donning the work clothes of a bird." The Chinese seemed particularly enchanted by flight. Kei Kung, their god of thunder and lightning, flew using the wings of a bat. Also, 1,800 years before Christ, legend has it that Ki-Kung-Shi built a flying chariot which had no visible means of support. This is the earliest record of levitation (to rise or float in the air). This feat is repeated throughout legendary history.

In addition to writing legends, the Chinese also built the first devices which would enable them to fly. About 100 B.C., the Chinese invented the kite, and it is known that some of their kites were huge. Did the Chinese use kites to carry man aloft back in those ancient times? We cannot answer this question, but it seems possible that they may have. We are fairly certain the Chinese used man-carrying kites for watching enemy troops in the 17th century.

About A.D. 900, the Chinese also invented gunpowder, and by A.D. 1100 they were using gunpowder to build simple rockets. These early rockets were used for celebrations and in warfare, but there is at least one Chinese legend of manned flight using rocket power. According to this legend, a Chinese official named Wan Hoo (see fig. 2) attempted a flight to the moon using a large wicker chair to which were fastened 47 large rockets. When the rockets were ignited, Wan Hoo disappeared in a large ball of smoke and fire—never to be seen again. The legend concludes that maybe Wan Hoo is the man in the moon.

From throughout the world come other folklore or legends. One of the earliest illustrations of flight is found on a seal from Babylonia which was made in

Figure 2.

about 3500 B.C. This seal pictures King Etena flying to heaven on the back of an eagle. In 1500 B.C. a Persian King, Kai Kawus, had a flying throne which was carried aloft by four eagles. Alexander the Great, King of Macedonia in 336 B.C., is said to have ridden in a cage drawn by winged griffins (a fabulous animal, half eagle and half lion). The Inca civilization in South America dates from about 2500 B.C. and, according to legend, was founded and led by four brothers. One of the brothers, Auca, was winged and flew like a bird. From Egypt, twelve centuries before Christ, we have numerous art objects, including the sphinx, showing gods and goddesses who are winged.

It is from ancient Greece and Rome (800 B.C.—A.D. 527) however, that we get our most familiar legends and art showing flight. The Greek god Hermes and the Roman god Mercury traveled on winged sandals. Eros and his Roman counterpart, Cupid, are both pictured as a winged child. The Greeks also gave us Pegasus, the winged horse. Of course, the most famous myth of all is that of Icarus and Daedalus. According to this myth, Daedalus (an architect and mechanic) and his son, Icarus, were imprisoned by King Minos of Crete. Determined to escape, Daedalus made a large set of wings for himself and his son. These wings were made of feathers and attached to their bodies with wax. With these wings, they flew speedily away from the island prison. Despite his father's warning, Icarus flew too near the sun; the wax melted, and he fell to his death in the sea (see fig. 3). We find these same types of legends in the civilizations of Africa and Europe and even in the folklore of the American Indian.

In tracing the history of flight, there are two traits that appear over and over in all parts of the world. First, it appears that people have always had the desire to fly. And second, since they did not have the natural ability to fly like the birds, flight has always depended on their own ability to build machines to carry them aloft. The history of flight is really a history of mankind's ability to invent and perfect these machines.

Figure 3.

The ancient civilizations had no flying machines, nor even the knowledge to conceive them. Therefore, their gods and demons flew using the only devices for flight which they knew—the wings of birds. As we continue our study of the history of flight, we will see that, as knowledge increased, mankind's ability to build better flying machines improved. These two traits—desire and ability—are important to a much larger concept, which will be

discussed in a later chapter of this textbook.

FROM DESIRE TO ACCOMPLISHMENT

EARLY ATTEMPTS AT FLIGHT

While most early people only dreamed about flight, there were a few that were determined to understand and do something about it.

The first record of man attempting to fly dates back to A.D. 852. At that time a Moor, Armen Firman, donned a huge cloak and jumped from a tower in Cordoba, Spain. Naturally, Firman didn't glide in flight, but instead fell to his death while performing what turned out to be an unsuccessful, primitive parachute jump.

When we think about the myths and legends of flight, it isn't too difficult to understand why mankind's first ventures into flight were attempts to imitate the flight of the birds. As early as the eleventh century there are records of people who tried to fly by attaching large wings to their bodies and jumping from high places. Many of these wings were immovable and merely allowed the wearer to glide. Others, however, were attached to the arms or legs, or both, and flight was attempted by flapping them. All of these attempts to fly by "flapping their wings" were failures and led either to the death or serious injury of the wearer. However, even today there are still attempts to fly by this method.

EARLY SCIENTIFIC ATTEMPTS

The great Italian artist, architect, and man of science—Leonardo da Vinci (1452-1519)—made the first scientific experiments in the field of aviation. He devoted many years of his life to understanding the mysteries of flight and left the world 160 pages of descriptions and sketches of flying machines. Among these descriptions and pictures are the world's first known designs of the parachute and the helicopter. From his notes, it appears that he made models of both and may even have flown them successfully. He understood and wrote about the

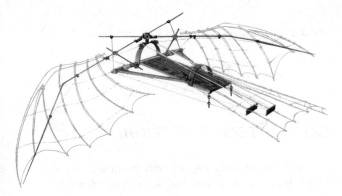

Figure 4.

importance of the center of gravity, center of pressure, and streamlining. These principles are vital in designing and building modern aircraft and spacecraft.

It seems certain that, if da Vinci had concentrated his research only in these areas, he could have constructed a workable manned glider four hundred years before the first one was actually built and flown. But, like so many before and since, he was obsessed with the idea of man flying like a bird. He described, sketched, and built models of many types of ornithopters (flying machines which are kept aloft and propelled by flapping wings). He left detailed sketches of wing mechanisms which used levers and pulleys to allow man's muscle power to flap the artificial wings (see fig. 4).

It is important to note here that Leonardo da Vinci was a brilliant scientist whose work could have changed the entire history of flight—except for one tragic fact. It was three hundred years after his death before his manuscripts were published and made known to the world. As a result, this knowledge was lost to the world for these three hundred years and prevented progress in flight.

LIGHTER-THAN-AIR FLIGHT

Basic Scientific Research. Beginning in the late 1500s and continuing through the 1700s, there were many stories and books written about flight—including some that were partially based on scientific principles. In the 1600s, a great deal of scientific research took place which was not directly related to flight; however, it provided knowledge that

would be used later to accomplish flight. Three European scientists (Torricelli from Italy, Von Guericke from Germany, and a Frenchman named Pascal) perfomed scientific studies of the atmosphere. They learned that the atmosphere is a fluid and that atmospheric pressure decreases the higher you climb. They invented the barometer, which measured the pressure of the atmosphere, and the air pump, which allowed them to study vacuums. This knowledge eventually led to successful lighter-than-air flight.

In 1670, a Jesuit priest, Francesco de Lana, who was a professor of mathematics, wrote about an "aerial ship." This airship would be carried aloft by four large spheres (see fig. 5) from which all air had been removed to make them lighter than the surrounding air. He proposed to make the spheres out of very thin copper. The principle was sound but the spheres, of course, would have been immediately crushed by the pressure of the surrounding air. Francesco de Lana's writings are the first scientific records of a vacuum balloon. He also discussed the need for ballast (a heavy substance) for controlling ascent and the need to let air enter the spheres gradually to control descent. Francesco de Lana also wrote about military uses for balloons.

Several developments made the first successful lighter-than-air flight possible. None were more important than the developments which reduced the cost of printing. These developments made the wide distribution of books and other written documents possible. For the first time, scientists

Figure 5.

throughout Europe could benefit from the work done by others, and scientific knowledge began to accumulate.

Another Jesuit priest, Laurenco de Gusmao, is credited with inventing the hot-air balloon. There is no evidence that he did anything but make small models. However, we know that in 1709 he demonstrated a small hot-air balloon for the King of Portugal. We also know that records of this demonstration were printed and widely read throughout Europe.

In 1766, an English chemist, Henry Cavendish, made an important contribution to flight when he discovered a gas which he called "flammable air." Later named hydrogen, this gas is important because it is fourteen and one-half times lighter than air. Cavendish himself didn't recognize its importance to flight, but Doctor Joseph Black, Professor of Chemistry at Glasgow University, did. He realized that if this light gas were enclosed in a thin bladder, it would weigh less than the surrounding air and would therefore rise. Doctor Black's records show that he intended to experiment with this idea, but dropped it because of his heavy teaching schedule.

The next scientist to work in the area of lighter-than-air flight was Tiberius Cavallo, an Italian. He had heard of Doctor Black's work, and in 1781 set out to perform Black's experiments. He tried using various types of animal bladders and thin films, but they were all too heavy. Finally, he blew hydrogen gas into soapy water, forming hydrogen–filled soap bubbles. These bubbles rose into the air but they were very fragile and broke easily. He next attempted to use thin paper bags, but the paper was too porous to contain the gas, and Cavallo gave up his experiments.

Hot-air Balloons. The accomplishment of manned flight was made, not by scientists, but by two brothers who were papermakers in Annonay, France. Joseph and Etienne Montgolfier were well educated eighteenth century gentlemen who were very interested in science and in flight. They had read the works of the English scientist Joseph Priestley, who, in 1774, had discovered oxygen and had written scientific papers on the properties of air.

In 1782, while watching a fire in his fireplace, Joseph Montgolfier became interested in the "force" that caused the sparks and smoke to rise. He made a small bag out of fine silk and lighted a fire under the opening at the bottom. The bag swelled and rose to the ceiling of the room. The Montgolfiers soon moved their experiments outdoors, building and flying larger and larger bags made of paper and linen (see fig. 6).

In June 1783, the brothers were ready for a public demonstration using a paper-lined linen bag thirty-eight feet in diameter. On June 5th, in the marketplace, they built a fire of straw and wood under their balloon, and when it was released, the balloon rose to an altitude of 6,000 feet. It traveled over a mile before landing. The Montgolfiers had no idea that their balloon rose because it contained heated air which was lighter than the surrounding air. They thought the balloon's ascent was caused by a lighter-than-air gas which was created by the burning fuel. They called the gas "Montgolfier gas."

An account of this demonstration was sent to the Academy of Science in Paris, and the Montgolfiers were invited to demonstrate their balloon before this scientific body. Again, the demonstration was a success, and on September 19, 1783, the Montgolfiers were asked to demonstrate their balloon for King Louis XVI and Marie Antoinette. For this demonstration, the Montgolfiers attached a cage to their balloon and the first living passengers— a sheep, a rooster, and a duck—were carried aloft and returned safely to Earth.

The first men to fly in a lighter-than-air craft rode a Montgolfier balloon into the air over Paris on November 21, 1783. The two men who made this historic flight were Pilatre de Rozier,* a young physician, and the Marquis d'Arlandes, a young infantry officer. The flight lasted twenty-five minutes and covered a little more than five miles. After centuries of dreaming, flight had become a reality— but we were still a long way from conquering this element.

These hot-air balloons stayed aloft only as long as a fire continued to heat the trapped air, and this made them very dangerous. It also limited the duration of the flight because a great deal of wood and straw had to be carried as fuel.

The honor of being the first woman to fly belongs to a French woman named Madame Thible. On June 4, 1784, she ascended in a hot-air balloon over Lyons, France. However, she rode as a passenger. It was not until 1799 that a woman flew alone in a balloon; and that flight was made in a

*Later, Pilatre de Rozier would become the first man to be killed in an aircraft.

Figure 6.

hydrogen balloon piloted by Madame Jeanne-Genevieve Garnerin. Madame Garnerin was also the first woman to descend in a parachute; however, her niece, Elisa Garnerin, was the first professional woman parachutist—making nearly 40 descents between 1815 and 1836.

Hydrogen Balloons in Europe. When the Montgolfiers demonstrated their hot-air balloon for the Academy of Science, they made such an impression that they hired a young scientist, J.A.C. Charles, to carry out further research on balloons. Charles was familiar with the "flammable air" isolated by Cavendish. He also realized that whatever "Montgolfier gas" was, it was not as light and, therefore, not as efficient as hydrogen. Charles had read of Cavallo's experiments and his difficulties in containing hydrogen. Therefore, for his balloon he selected a small globe of rubberized silk. On August 23, 1783, the globe was inflated with hydrogen and rose into the air. One of the spectators at this event was Benjamin Franklin. He was so impressed that he immediately

wrote to scientists in the United States stressing the military importance of this new invention. On December 1, 1783, Charles and another passenger made the first manned flight in a hydrogen balloon. This flight lasted for over two hours and covered more than twenty-seven miles.

Following these early flights, ballooning became very popular in Europe. Between 1783 and 1790, seventy-six flights were recorded in France alone. In 1793, the French government formed an air arm to the army and balloons were used for reconnaissance during the French Revolution. In 1797, Andre-Jacques Garnerin made the first parachute jump from a balloon flying at an altitude of 3,000 feet. During this time period the hydrogen balloon became much more popular than the hot-air balloon. In fact, by the end of the 1700s, the hot-air balloon had disappeared and its popularity would not return until the advent of modern day sport balloons.

On January 7, 1785, a French aeronaut (balloonist), Jean Pierre Blanchard, and an American passenger, Doctor John Jeffries, made the first balloon flight from one nation to another. They flew across the English Channel from England to France. The flight covered about twenty miles and required almost two hours to complete.

The first woman to make ballooning a career was Jean Blanchard's wife, Madeleine Sophie Blanchard. From 1805-1819, she performed exhibitions of ballooning throughout the European continent. Madame Blanchard was also the first woman to be killed in a ballooning accident (1819, at Paris).

Ballooning in the United States. The first balloon flight in the United States took place in Philadelphia, Pennsylvania, on January 9, 1793 (see fig. 7). The "pilot" was the same Jean Pierre Blanchard that had flown across the English Channel. The flight was witnessed by President George Washington, many members of his cabinet, and thousands of spectators. The balloon lifted off at ten o'clock in the morning and landed safely near Woodbury, New Jersey, about forty-six minutes later.

The first use of balloons by the United States military occurred during the Civil War. Several

Figure 7.

professional aeronauts, including Thaddeus S. C. Lowe, volunteered their services to the Union Army. Soon after the war broke out Lowe visited General Winfield Scott to volunteer his services to the Union Army, but he was unable to convince General Scott that there was a real military need for balloons. Lowe told his friend Joseph Henry, first Secretary of the Smithsonian Institution, of his disappointment at the General's reaction. Henry made an appointment with President Abraham Lincoln and went with Lowe to tell the President of the advantages of aerial observation.

To demonstrate the effectiveness of aerial reports, Lowe went up in his balloon from the Smithsonian grounds and used a telegraph wire, which extended from his balloon basket to the White House, to describe the scene below to President Lincoln. After this dramatic demonstration and the discussion with Lowe and Henry, Lincoln sent General Scott a note asking him to consider seriously Lowe's offer.

Lowe was finally allowed to organize the Balloon Signal Service of the Union Army. He and a few other Army aeronauts served in the balloon corps for the first two years of the war, after which time the corps was disbanded for lack of men and money for its upkeep. The aeronauts furnished valuable information to Union forces during several battles (see fig. 8).

The aerial observers had some frustrating experiences, however. They had to struggle to get their salaries, their supplies, their ground and maintenance crews, and even to get permission to make aerial ascents. Lowe headed the corps, but he was never given an official title. He often had to pay for his own ballooning supplies and had spent $500 of his own money before he resigned from the corps shortly before it was disbanded.

The Southerners were well aware of the value of the aeronaut's services to the Union and wanted to start a Confederate balloon force. They made their first balloon of varnished polished cotton and raised it with air heated over a fire of turpentine and pine knots. The second Confederate balloon had to be made from silk dresses donated by Southern women. Each day the crew filled this patchwork balloon at the Richmond gas plant and took it by rail to the battle lines east of the city. Once they mounted the balloon on a James River steamer. The steamer ran aground when the tide went out. The Union troops spotted the helpless vessel, captured it

Figure 8.

and the balloon, and ended Confederate hopes for a balloon corps.

Advantages of Hydrogen over Heated Air. The use of hydrogen gas overcame the major disadvantage of the hot-air balloon—that of carrying a fire and fuel aloft to keep the air heated. However, hydrogen also had a serious disadvantage—it was highly flammable and many people were killed before a safer gas (helium) came into use. In either case, the balloon was a captive of the winds. The problem of changing a free balloon into a dirigible (a lighter-than-air craft which can be propelled and steered) would stump scientific minds for more than a century.

Dirigibles. In 1785, a French general, J.B.M. Meusnier, made several suggestions which would eventually lead to successful dirigibles. First, he suggested changing the shape of a balloon from a sphere to the shape of a football. This would reduce air resistance and also establish a front and rear for the balloon. He also suggested an envelope (container for the gas) made of several compartments and a passenger car shaped like a boat attached to the bottom of the dirigible by a system of ropes. The one problem Meusnier did not solve was how to power the dirigible. He suggested a large propeller turned by eighty men!

The next breakthrough came in 1852 by another Frenchman – Henri Giffard. He built a cigar shaped balloon 114 feet long and 39 feet in diameter. The dirigible was powered by a three-horsepower steam engine which propelled it at a speed of about five miles per hour. This dirigible is generally credited as being the first successful one in the world.

Another dirigible which is sometimes credited with being the first successful one was the "LaFrance" built by Charles Renard and A. C. Krebs in 1884 (see fig. 9). This airship was powered by electric motors and was the first dirigible to be steered back to its takeoff point. However, electric motors were also too heavy and limited the range of the dirigible. It was not until the invention of the internal combustion engine* that dirigibles became

*An engine in which the gases formed by combustion are used directly to produce the engine motion.

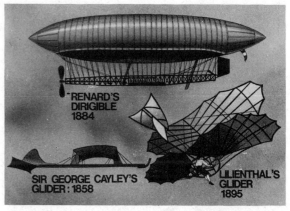

Figure 9.

a real success. The first known internal combustion engine-powered dirigible was built by a German engineer, Paul Haenlein, in 1872. This engine used coal gas taken from the balloon envelope as its fuel. This system had several obvious drawbacks including the fact that the longer it flew, the less lift was developed because the engine was using the gas from the balloon.

These early dirigibles were of the nonrigid type. This means that the shape of the envelope is maintained only by the pressure of the gas inside. If the airship exceeded a certain speed, or if the pressure of the gas went down below a certain point, the balloon envelope would buckle or become distorted.

As balloon technology improved, the envelopes were stiffened by an internal rigid keel. This keel extended along the length of the airship and carried the load of the engines and passenger compartment. These were known as semirigid airships.

As a practical flying machine, the dirigible made its most noteworthy advances with the contributions of Count Ferdinand von Zeppelin in Germany and Alberto Santos-Dumont, a wealthy Brazilian. Both men successfully used internal combustion engines to power lighter-than-air craft. Although von Zeppelin perfected the dirigible for public use, it was Santos-Dumont who ushered in the era of the powered gas bag.

His first nonrigid airship was a small vessel 82 feet long, driven by a three-horsepower gasoline motor. On its first flight, it reached a height of 1,300 feet and responded readily to movements of its rudder. During this period between 1898 and 1907, he constructed and flew 14 gasoline-powered nonrigid airships. On his largest vessel (157 feet) he used a 20-horsepower engine, and, on another, he carried an engine that developed 60 horsepower.

Santos-Dumont became the idol of Paris in 1901, when he piloted a blimp driven by a 12-horsepower motor from St. Cloud around the Eiffel Tower, a distance of nine miles. Despite a side wind of 12 to 13 miles per hour, he developed a speed of 19 miles per hour and covered the distance in less than one-half hour. For this accomplishment, Dumont won a 100,000 franc award put up by the French petroleum magnate Henri Deutsch. About the same time that he completed his fourteenth airship, Santos-Dumont became interested in the flights of the Wright brothers in the United States and he abandoned the airship altogether.

In July 1900, Ferdinand von Zeppelin built and flew the world's first successful rigid dirigible, the LZ-1 (see fig. 10). This began a long period of German domination of this type of aircraft. In fact, Germany so dominated the rigid airships that they became known as "Zeppelins." A rigid-type airship has an internal framework of steel or aluminum girders which support the dirigible and give it its shape.

Zeppelin continued to build large rigid airships for the German Government, and on June 22, 1910, the *"Deutschland"* (LZ-7) became the world's first commercial airship. Between 1910 and the beginning of World War I in 1914, German Zeppelins flew 107,208 miles and carried 34,028 passengers (and crew)—entirely without injury.

Most of the early powered dirigible flights were made by men, but some women did fly dirigibles. In 1903, Cuban-born Aida de Acosta made one of the world's first powered dirigible flights, piloting a dirigible over Paris months before the Wright's Kitty Hawk flights.

THE DEVELOPMENT OF ROCKETRY

The history of rocketry began with the ancient Chinese. The first written accounts are dated A.D. 1232 and refer to "Arrows of Flaming Fire," which were rockets used to frighten enemies in battle. In

Figure 10.

A.D. 1242 an English scientist, Roger Bacon, described the chemical components for the first rocket fuel (gunpowder). Rockets were first used for celebrations and then became weapons of war. By about A.D. 1500, the cannon had developed into the primary bombardment weapon. Rockets were once again used as fireworks at celebrations and to signal and carry lines to ships in distress.

In the 1770s, a British Army captain, William Congreve, developed a solid fuel rocket which was more accurate and had a longer range than the cannons of the day. Congreve rockets were used by the British during the War of 1812. The "rocket's red glare" referred to by Francis Scott Key in the "Star Spangled Banner" were Congreve rockets which were used to bombard Fort McHenry during the war.

The first use of rockets as weapons by United States troops occurred during the Civil War. This was another British rocket, built by William Hale, and introduced to the United States Army in 1861. The Civil War also brought about the development of rifled barrels for cannons. These rifled barrels and improved projectiles increased the range and accuracy of cannons and once again forced rockets into the background. In fact, not until the German V-2 rocket of World War II would rockets be used again as a primary bombardment weapon.

THREE BASIC PROBLEMS OF FLIGHT

The basic problems of flight to be solved by both lighter-than-air and heavier-than-air flyers were: First, to develop the lift necessary to rise into the air; second, to sustain that lift; and third, to control the aircraft once it was flying. The balloonists overcame the first two problems by (1) building their aircraft so they were lighter-than-air, and by (2) keeping them lighter-than-air by either dumping ballast or maintaining a fire to heat the trapped air. Therefore, they were faced only with the problem of control. The heavier-than-air pioneers, however, had to struggle with all three problems.

HEAVIER-THAN-AIR FLIGHT

Scientific Study. The 18th century produced many speculators and experimenters in heavier-than-air flight who contributed little to the field of aviation. Two Frenchman, Laundy and Bienvenu, were notable exceptions. In 1784, they constructed the first heavier-than-air craft to rise by self-contained power. This craft (fig. 11) was the first successful model helicopter, and its chief importance was the interest it aroused in other inventors, especially Sir George Cayley.

The first pioneer to enter the area of heavier-than-air flight in the 19th century was a young Englishman named George Cayley. He was nine years old when the Montgolfiers made their first flight, and he immediately began experimenting with small paper balloons. His interest in flight continued into his teens, during which he built small model helicopters to which he applied the airscrew concept. Following this, Cayley neglected his helicopter work until he was sixty years old, when he built a more sophisticated model with a three-bladed metal screw.

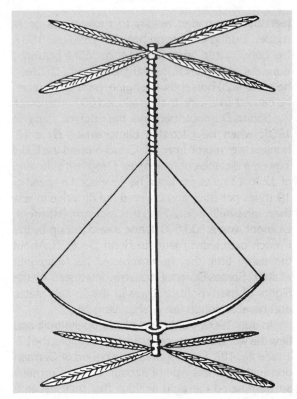

Figure 11.

Like Leonardo da Vinci, Cayley also studied the flight of birds. In 1804, he constructed a whirling-arm device with which he could test the behavior of air pressure on various types of wings. He later built and flew small model gliders (see fig. 9). In 1809, he published the conclusions of his research in a scientific paper. A single sentence in his paper laid the whole foundation for modern aeronautics— "The whole problem is confined within these limits, namely, to make a surface support a given weight by the application of power to the resistance of air."

During his lifetime, Cayley identified the forces of lift, drag, and thrust as they apply to aviation; developed the cambered (curved) upper surface on a wing to increase lift; worked on propellers and power plants; developed the concept of bi-winged and tri-winged aircraft; and built the first successful full-sized, manned gliders (1850).

Other Europeans, particularly the French, tried to unlock the secrets of heavier-than-air flight in the

19th century. In 1857, Felix Du Temple built a model monoplane powered by a clockwork mechanism. The monoplane's flight, although brief, was the first successful flight of a powered airplane of any size. Later, in 1871, another Frenchman, Alphonse Penaud, developed the twisted rubber band to power workable helicopter models and to fly his "planophore," which was a 20-inch model airplane that flew 131 feet in 11 seconds. The "planophore" contained Penaud's greatest contribution to aviation—automatic longitudinal (fore and aft) stability, which he obtained by placing a properly formed tailplane well aft of the main wings. Penaud ranks close to Cayley as one of the most significant 19th century aeronautical thinkers.

Toward the end of the century, Clement Ader built the first manned aircraft to takeoff from level ground under its own power (1890). The craft resembled a huge bat and was driven by a 20-horsepower engine. Although it rose to a height of eight inches and traveled through the air some 165 feet, it was incapable of sustained and controlled flight. Some seven years later he built an improved model, which he called the *Avion III*, that never got off the ground.

Unpowered Gliders. During the second half of the nineteenth century, many men were bitten by the flying bug, and they tried their hands at designing gliders and airplanes. Most of the gliders were unsuccessful as flying machines, but out of some of these failures came knowledge that would contribute to success in aviation. For example, Frances H. Wenham had little practical success with his own gliders, but he became the first person to build a wind tunnel to test various wing shapes (1871); in time, both his invention and his glider work would become useful to Chanute and the Wright brothers. There were, however, three men during this period who made very significant contributions to real gliding. They were an American, John J. Montgomery; a German, Otto Lilienthal; and a French-born American, Octave Chanute. These men all conducted successful gliding experiments.

John Montgomery began his career in aviation research as a boy lying on his back under a barnyard fence. He had chosen this as a good place to study the airborne chickens that his sisters frightened into flight for him. Even more than studying the flight of chickens, he enjoyed flying kites—a sport that he could indulge in frequently because of the good weather in Oakland, California, where he lived on his grandmother's farm. Pieces of tin provided him with primitive airfoils, which he would bend into various shapes and curves and then throw into the air to see which would go the farthest.

By 1884, Montgomery had graduated from St. Ignatius College in San Francisco and from Santa Clara College in Santa Clara, California; had moved with his parents to a farm near San Diego; and had secretly built a man-carrying glider with wings like a sea gull. He was 26 when he and his younger brother loaded the 440-pound glider onto a hayrack and headed for a gently sloping, mile-long hill. To avoid the ridicule of neighbors, they chose to try their first flight in the dead of night, but they had to wait until dawn before a breeze came in from the sea. Montgomery faced the wing surface of the glider into the 12-mile-per-hour breeze, and his brother ran with the pull rope. The glider, carrying Montgomery's 130 pounds, soared up 600 feet before easing to Earth again.

Montgomery made several flights in his glider before it was wrecked in an accident. He built two other gliders, one with flat wings and one with wings that pivoted, but neither flew as well as his first. From 1886 through 1892, Montgomery made thousands of experiments and studies on the wings of soaring birds. He gave to his research every moment he could spare from his job as professor of physics at Santa Clara College.

By 1893 Montgomery had done enough research to design a glider that he thought would be successful. But he had to wait nine years before he had the time and money to turn the plans into a real flying craft. In 1905 he unveiled his glider to the public. Fifteen thousand people gathered at Santa Clara on April 29 to watch Daniel Maloney, who was known for his parachute jumps from hot-air balloons at county fairs, pilot Montgomery's craft.

Maloney climbed aboard the glider, which Montgomery had hitched to a hot-air balloon. After the balloon was cut loose, it rose to 4,000 feet, where

Maloney cut the glider loose. Twenty minutes and eight air miles later, Maloney brought the ship down to a preselected spot, three-fourths of a mile from where the ascent had started. During the flight he had whipped the craft into sharp dives and turns and had reached speeds estimated at 68 miles per hour. Montgomery clearly had put together a successful glider.

During the next year Montgomery exhibited his glider throughout California, raising funds for additional experiments. He built five more gliders and trained men to pilot them. These craft were all extremely maneuverable and capable of all sorts of twists, turns, and somersaults. Then on April 18, 1906, the fruits of his 20 years of labor were demolished in an earthquake—the same one that destroyed San Francisco.

Montgomery was unable to resume his experiments until 1911. On October 31, 1911, his lifelong devotion to gliding and aviation ended. As he was landing his glider, a gust of wind flipped it and hurled him to his death.

The next pioneer, Otto Lilienthal, has been called the "father of modern aviation." This German engineer was the first practical aviator. He brought the theory of flight and the practice of flight together by actually riding his gliders into the air and controlling them. He built many single and bi-winged gliders (see fig. 9) which he flew by running down hill until sufficient speed was built up to allow them to fly. His gliders had cambered wings and fixed tail surfaces. Between 1891 and 1896, he made over 2,000 glides, many of which covered over 700 feet. However, his total flying time was still only five hours.

In 1896 Lilienthal turned to powered flight, choosing to use a biplane patterned after a double-winged glider he had flown successfully the year before. He built an engine to link to the wingtips, which were hinged for flapping. Into both the new and the old biplane, he built a pilot control system for elevating the surfaces of the tailplane. The pilot's head worked the controls by a headband and rope which joined him to the tail. When the pilot lowered his chin, the plane rose, and when he lifted his chin, the place dropped.

Before trying his powered biplane, Lilienthal flew the older biplane glider one last time to practice with the new elevating controls. He took off in a gusty wind. At 50 feet his glider stalled and suddenly dropped like a rock. The fall broke Lilienthal's back, and he died the next day.

Lilienthal's power glider never left the ground. But his book on flying, which he had written during the moments he could spare from his work as an engineer and manufacturer, informed and inspired pioneers in many countries. Also, the development of photography allowed pictures to accompany his writings. Photographs of his aircraft were seen throughout the world and created a great deal of interest in aviation.

One of the people who read Lilienthal's works was an American civil engineer, Octave Chanute. By 1896, Chanute was performing gliding experiments on the sand dunes around Lake Michigan. Chanute was in his sixties when he became interested in flight, and because of his age, did no flying himself. He designed the gliders which were flown by another engineer named A.M. Herring. Chanute is not noted for any outstanding advancement in aeronautics, although he did improve on Lilienthal's work. What he is noted for, is his careful study of aviation history and collection and distribution of aviation information.

Adding Power. The works of Cayley were published and widely read by scientists and aviation enthusiasts throughout the world. Among those who read these documents were two Englishmen who were to make additional contributions to heavier-than-air flight. They were W.S. Henson, an inventor, and John Stringfellow, a skilled engineer. In 1843, they drew up plans and even received a patent for a man-carrying, powered aircraft. This aircraft, named the Ariel (see fig. 12), was to be a monoplane with a 150-foot wingspan. It was powered by a steam engine which drove two six-bladed propellers. This aircraft was never built, but the plans were masterpieces of aviation engineering. The plans for the wing structure showed a front and rear spar with connecting ribs. This same type structure is used for making aircraft wings today. A small model of the Ariel was built and tested, but it failed to fly. Later, Stringfellow built a steam driven

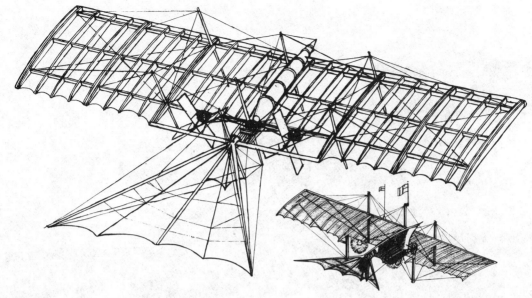

Figure 12.

model which did fly (1848). This was the first successful powered flight of a heavier-than-air craft.

Another American who entered the field of aviation at this time was Samuel Pierpont Langley. Langley was an astronomer and the director of the Smithsonian Institution in Washington, D.C. His major contributions to flight involved attempts at adding a power plant to a glider. In 1896, he successfully built a steam-powered model which flew for three-quarters of a mile before it ran out of fuel. He then set out to build a full-size, man-carrying aircraft. He received a $50,000 grant from Congress to build this airplane.

One problem Langley encountered was the extremely heavy weight of steam engines. He was convinced that the internal combustion gasoline engine held the greatest promise for a lightweight, powerful engine for aircraft. Charles M. Manly, Langley's assistant, designed such an engine. It was a five-cylinder radial engine which weighed only 125 pounds, but produced an amazing fifty-three horsepower. By October 1903, the engine had been placed in a full-size copy of his successful model, and Langley was ready for flight testing.

The *Aerodrome* (see fig. 13), as Langley called his aircraft, was to be launched by catapult from a barge anchored in the Potomac River. The first flight was conducted on 7 October with Manly at the controls. The *Aerodrome* left the catapult. However, it did not fly and fell into the Potomac. The test was repeated on 8 December with exactly the same results. Unfortunately, both attempts were well attended by the press, and their critical reporting caused the government to withdraw its support, and Langley gave up his project.

Langley made some important contributions to flight, but he spent far too much time on the power plant and too little time on how to control the aircraft once it was flying. However, just nine days after his last failure, two brothers who had approached the problem from just the opposite direction would succeed in powered flight on the sand dunes of North Carolina.

The Wright Brothers. A combination of factors helped the Wright brothers (Orville and Wilbur) to achieve success in controlled, sustained, and powered heavier-than-air flight. First, they had access to the knowledge about flight gained by others before them. Second, they lived at a time when the first practical power plant (the gasoline engine) had been developed. Finally, they possessed

Figure 13. Langley's Aerodrome

a combination of attitudes and aptitudes which enabled them to bring the work of all the previous individuals together and combine it into a successful product. They were patient in their approach to solving any type of problem. They were also highly creative, had a great deal of personal integrity, and possessed outstanding mechanical aptitude.

The Wright brothers approach to flight was first to develop an aircraft which would fly and could be controlled in flight, and then to add a power plant. Their observations led them to believe that birds maneuvered in flight chiefly by twisting their wings. Using this information, they built a large box kite with four cords attached to the "wing tips." They found that by pulling these cords, and thus twisting (warping) the wings, they could maneuver the kite from the ground.

Following these successful kite flights, the Wrights realized that the next step must be to get

Samuel Pierpont Langley

into the air themselves to further test their "wing warping" technique. Before beginning their glider tests, they requested information from the weather bureau for a site to conduct their tests. They needed a location which would have steady winds and plenty of open space. They were advised to try the beaches just south of Kitty Hawk, North Carolina.

They selected Kill Devil Hill, North Carolina, for their tests, and in October 1900, their first glider was ready. This glider was a biplane with a horizontal elevator in front, no tail, and cords attached to the wing tips for warping them. In order to reduce wind resistance, the pilot rode lying down between the wings. They made a few successful glides during that first winter, but the winds were generally too light for manned flights. For the most part, this first aircraft was also flown as a kite (see fig. 14).

The following July, they returned with their second glider which had much larger wings. They also had fastened the wing warping cables to a cradle in which the pilot lay. The aircraft was controlled by shifting this cradle with the hips, thus tightening the cables and causing the wings to warp. The cables were arranged so that as the rear of one wing tip was warped downward, the wing tip on the opposite side was warped upward. This caused the aircraft to turn. This was the first of two great contributions the Wright brothers made toward controlling flight. The Wrights had so many problems with the control of their second glider that after only a month they stopped their tests and returned home to Dayton, Ohio.

During the winter of 1901, they built a small wind tunnel and tested many different shapes of wings.

1900

1902

1903

WILBUR & ORVILLE WRIGHT

Figure 14.

These tests gave them the knowledge they needed to overcome the control problems of their second glider.

By September 1902, they built a third glider and returned to North Carolina. This aircraft was basically the same as the first two, with the addition of two fixed vertical fins at the rear. It performed well except that, when turning, the wing which was warped downward would tend to drag and the aircraft would begin to slide sideways through the air. This was corrected by changing the two fixed vertical fins to a single movable rudder which was interconnected with the wing warping cables. This allowed the rudder to be turned so that the air pressure against it would automatically counteract the drag of the downwarped wing. This was the second great contribution they made toward controlling flight. By the time the Wright brothers returned to Dayton in October, they had performed over 1,000 successful flights and had solved all the major problems of control in the air. Now, all that remained was to add a suitable power plant.

Like others before them, the Wrights found no suitable lightweight engine that would meet their needs. Although they had no experience in power plants, they designed and built a four-cylinder, water-cooled gasoline engine which produced about 12 horsepower. Next, they designed and built the two propellers which would be turned by the engine. The propellers were connected to the engine by a pair of bicycle chains and turned in opposite directions.

By September 1903, the engine had been installed and the Wrights returned to North Carolina with their powered aircraft, which they named the *Flyer* (see fig. 14). The *Flyer* had no wheels but landed in the sand on a pair of skids. For takeoff they constructed a long wooden rail upon which ran a small trolley. The skids were set on the trolley and a

Kitty Hawk triumph

wire held the trolley until the aircraft's engine was running at full power. When the wire was released, the aircraft and trolley ran smoothly down the track until the aircraft lifted off, leaving the trolley behind.

Their first attempt was made on December 14, 1903, with Wilbur at the controls. The *Flyer* became airborne, but stalled and fell back into the sand. It was slightly damaged.

Success At Last. Three days later the damage was repaired. The wind was blowing at over 20 mph and this time it was Orville's turn and he fitted himself into the cradle. The engine was started, run up to full power, and the wire was released. The *Flyer* moved down the track picking up speed with Wilbur running alongside. As the *Flyer* neared the end of the track, it rose into the air, and for 12 seconds it flew. One hundred and twenty feet from the end of the track, it slowly settled back onto the sand. It was 10:35 A.M., December 17, 1903.

Three more times that day the *Flyer* left the Earth. The final flight, with Wilbur at the controls, lasted 59 seconds and covered 852 feet. Following the last flight, a gust of wind tipped the *Flyer* and badly damaged it. This small, flimsy, wooden and cloth airplane had made a place in history, but it was never to fly again. Its total useful lifetime lasted but one day.

Previously Stringfellow had flown a powered model airplane which was sustained, but he was not on board to control it; Lilienthal had controlled his glider which could not be sustained since it was not powered; and Ader could not sustain his powered *Avion* in the air even though he produced controlled hops. But with the flight of the Wright *Flyer*, mankind's age-old dream of controlled, sustained, and powered heavier-than-air flight was finally a reality.

This chapter has pointed out the major milestones of the development of flight and the significant accomplishments of the men and women around the world who helped make the flight of the Wright *Flyer* possible. With the *Flyer*, controlled, sustained, and powered heavier-than-air flight was finally achieved—real flight was born. However, it would be a number of years before the powered airplane would be developed to the point of being accepted as a practical, useful tool. In the next chapter we will look at the formative years of flight and the acceptance of the flying machine.

Chapter 1-2

THE FORMATIVE YEARS: 1904-1919

etween 1904 and 1919, flight was in its
formative years. Many people were very
interested in and enthusiastic about flying. Most
people in the United States still looked at airplanes
as toys and couldn't understand that they could be
put to practical use. In Europe, aviation progressed
more rapidly and there was a far greater understanding of aviation as something useful. This chapter
concludes with the end of World War I, the first war in
which the airplane was used as a weapon.

The general learning objective for this chapter is
for you to know the important developments in
aviation during the 1904-1919 time period. To reach
this objective, you must pattern your study of the
material according to the *specific learning
objectives* listed in the Appendix of this textbook.

DEVELOPMENT IN THE UNITED STATES

WRIGHT BROTHERS

The achievement of the first successful powered
flight went almost unnoticed throughout the world.
Only one newspaper published an account of the

flight, and this was poorly written and misleading. To
prevent any further errors, the Wrights issued a
statement to the Associated Press on January 5,
1904, but this statement was either ignored or
hidden deep inside the papers and printed without
comment.

The Wright brothers continued in 1904-1905,
conducting trial flights from a pasture just outside
Dayton, Ohio. They experimented and perfected
their flying machines and in October 1905, in their
new and improved machine, they made a flight
which lasted 38 minutes and covered over 24 miles.
It ended only when the fuel supply was exhausted.

Early in 1905 the Wrights started writing to the
United States Government in Washington, D.C.,
offering to build aircraft that would meet government
needs and to sell them to the United States on a
contract basis. The responses to their offers were, to
say the least, unenthusiastic. After the Langley
failures, the War Department did not want to be
embarrassed again. When the War Department
failed to accept their third offer, the Wrights gave up
on their efforts to sell their invention to their own
government. When Octave Chanute learned of the
third refusal, he said of the War Department officials,
"Those fellows are a bunch of asses."

Figure 15.

Theodore Roosevelt, who as Secretary of the Navy had worked to promote money for Langley's experiments, was elected President of the United States in 1904. In the spring of 1907, he received a clipping in the mail that described the Wrights' work. He then directed the Secretary of War to look into the possibility of testing the Wrights' machine.

President Roosevelt's interest set into motion the contacts necessary for the Wrights to gain a sympathetic ear from the Board of Ordnance and Fortifications. With Wilbur's help, the Board drafted a public request for bids for an aircraft which could carry a pilot, a passenger, and fuel for a 125-mile trip; fly at least 36 miles per hour under perfect control; take off and land in any likely war zone without damage; be disassembled for transport by wagon and be reassembled in one hour. The contract also called for the Wrights to train two pilots for the Army. This public request for bids was merely a "red tape" formality. The Board knew that the Wrights were the only people with the knowledge to build such a craft at that time.

While Orville was busy building a new plane for the Army tests (see fig. 15), Wilbur went to France to demonstrate their aircraft for European governments and businessmen. These demonstrations resulted in Wilbur's signing a $100,000 contract to form a French company.

In September, Orville began his tests at Fort Myers, Virginia. His first flight, on September 3, 1908, astounded official Washington. During the next two weeks, Orville completed eleven more flights, each more successful than the last. But on the thirteenth test, tragedy struck. On September 17, while conducting a test carrying Lieutenant Thomas Selfridge as a passenger, a propeller broke and the airplane crashed. Lieutenant Selfridge was killed. He was the first man to lose his life in an airplane. Orville was seriously hurt in the crash, but by July 1909, he had returned and completed the tests. On August 2, 1909, he was given a $30,000 contract to build the first Army heavier-than-air aircraft.*

During October Wilbur met the final requirements of the Army contract by teaching Lieutenants Frank P. Lahm and Frederic E. Humphreys to fly.

Toward the end of 1909, the Signal Corps Aeronautical Division was established. It had one plane and two pilots. This might well be thought of as the time at which today's United States Air Force actually went into the business of flying.

CURTISS

While the Wright brothers were trying to sell their aircraft, another aviation pioneer was entering the scene. Glenn Curtiss (who as a teenager in Hammondsport, New York, had turned his natural engineering talents to building gasoline engines for the motorcycles he loved to race) was beginning to catch the interest of men in other fields. In 1907, Curtiss became known as the "fastest man on Earth" when he set the motorcycle speed record of 136 mph.

Curtiss' motorcycle engines were so light and powerful that Thomas Baldwin, a balloonist, asked

*In 1902, the first military aircraft, the dirigible SC-1, was purchased for the United States Army.

Curtiss to build an engine for use on an airship. Baldwin's airship, with its Curtiss engine, became the first powered dirigible in the United States. Other balloonists soon followed Baldwin's lead and turned to Curtiss for engines for their ships. Another of his engines was used to power the first U.S. Army aircraft—the dirigible SC-1.

Airplanes soon replaced motorcycles as Glenn Curtiss's first love, and the "fastest man on Earth" went into the business of making flying machines.

In 1907, Curtiss and Alexander Graham Bell (the inventor of the telephone) founded an organization called the Aerial Experiment Association. This organization designed and built several aircraft including the first American aircraft to be equipped with ailerons and the first seaplane to be flown in the United States.

In 1908, Curtiss won the *Scientific American* trophy in the *"June Bug"* for making the first public flight of over 1 kilometer in the United States (see fig. 16).

At the 1909 Rheims Air Meet in France (flying the *"Golden Flyer"* which he had just completed), Curtiss won the Gordon Bennett trophy. Bennett, publisher of the *New York Herald,* offered the prize for the fastest two laps around a triangular 6.21-mile course. The final day of the meet, Glenn Curtiss claimed the coveted prize by averaging 47 miles an hour in his two flights around the course.

1910 EVENTS!

In 1910, both the Wrights and Curtiss opened flying schools. The Wright brothers had delivered their airplane to the Army and trained the first two Army pilots. In November 1910, Eugene Ely made the first flight from the deck of a ship at Hampton Roads, Virginia, in a Curtiss biplane (see fig. 17). He later accomplished the more difficult feat of landing his aircraft on a wooden platform on the U.S.S. *Pennsylvania.* This same year, former President Theodore Roosevelt took an airplane ride in St.

Figure 16.

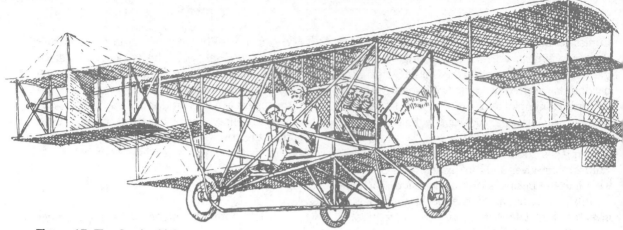

Figure 17. The Curtiss biplane

Louis. He was the first U.S. President to fly.

RODGERS

In 1911, William Randolph Hearst, publisher of the Hearst newspapers, offered a prize of $50,000 for a flight across the United States in 30 days. Calbraith Perry Rodgers, grand-nephew of Commodore Oliver H. Perry (a U.S. Naval hero of the War of 1812), decided to try for the prize.

Rodgers persuaded a firm that made Vin Fiz, a soft drink, that such a flight would have great publicity value. The firm agreed to furnish a Wright plane, which Rodgers named the *"Vin Fiz Flyer,"* and a special train stocked with spare parts to follow Rodgers across the country (see fig. 18).

Realizing the difficulties of the trip ahead, Rodgers knew that he needed the services of a superior mechanic who could be relied on to keep his plane in good repair. He asked Charles Taylor, the Wrights' mechanic, to take the job. The Wrights were extremely reluctant to let Taylor go, but Rodgers had offered him considerably more money than he was getting from the Wrights. Taylor was so eager to go that Orville finally agreed, but only on the condition that Taylor consider himself on a leave of absence.

Rodgers started the flight from Sheepshead Bay, Long Island, on September 17, 1911. The sponsoring firm planned the route. It went roughly

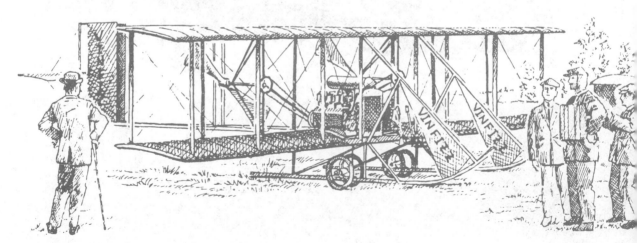

Figure 18. The "Vin Fiz Flyer"

1-26

from New York to Chicago, Kansas City, San Antonio, El Paso, Yuma, and Pasadena—3,390 miles. The limitations of a 40-horsepower engine presented a problem of major proportions when planning a route across the Rocky Mountains. There were few places where Rodgers could even hope to fly across the Rockies.

Day after day Rodgers flew on. Some days he could not make more than 40 miles per hour because of head winds. Before the trip ended, he had to make 68 landings—some of them severe crackups. His plane had to be repaired so many times that the only original parts to make the entire trip were the rudder and one strut.

Rodgers' actual flying distance was 4,251 miles, his longest single flight was 133 miles, and his average flying speed was just under 52 mph. After reaching Pasadena on November 5th, he flew on to the ocean where he rolled his plane along the beach and wet the wheels in the Pacific. He had to hobble from his last landing on crutches, and he had missed the prize because the trip had taken 49 days. An automobile or a train would have made much better time. But the important thing was that he had made the first airplane crossing of the United States.

By today's standards, this flight may not sound like much of an achievement. But in 1911 it was a remarkable feat. Rodgers' plane would not compare favorably with today's sturdy aircraft. He had no prepared landing fields, no advance weather information, no special instruments, and his supplies and facilities were inadequate. Calbraith Perry Rodgers was indeed a skillful and persistent pilot.

AMERICAN WOMEN

Soon after men began flying heavier-than-air aircraft, American women also entered the field. On September 2, 1910, Blanche Scott became America's first woman to solo an aircraft. She soloed in Hammondsport, New York, in what was really an unscheduled takeoff, since it was never established whether the takeoff was accidental or intentional. Ms. Scott, however, never received a pilot's license although she did become an exhibition pilot. On September 16 of the same year,

Bessica Medlar Raiche intentionally soloed without a moment of instruction or trial glide. She was awarded a medal by the Aeronautical Society for being the "first woman aviator of America."

In August of 1911, Harriet Quimby became the first woman in the United States to receive a pilot's certificate. Ms. Quimby was also the first woman to fly across the English Channel alone (April 26, 1912). In the summer of 1912 (July 1), she was killed while performing in an air meet at Boston. However, she was not the first woman to be killed in an airplane accident. Ms. Denise Moore was America's first woman to be killed in an aircraft; she died while taking her license test in November, 1911.

Other women making their mark during this era were: Mathilde Moisant, who flew in the Moisant Flying Circus and was the second American licensed female pilot (August 17, 1910), and Ruth Law, a well-known barnstorming sensation in the post-World War I period who became the third American woman to receive a pilot's license (she also set a new nonstop distance record in 1916 to exemplify the resourcefulness of women pilots). Katherine Stinson, the fourth U.S. woman to become a licensed pilot (1912), and her sister Marjorie (1914), gained fame during World War I with cross-country Liberty Bond and Red Cross flights. Katherine Stinson and Ruth Law both tried to get into the Army Air Service during the war but were rejected.

These, then, were some of the American women who broke the ice for feminine flight and paved the way for the many who were to follow them.

PROGRESS IN EUROPE

AILERONS

The Wright brothers' wing-warping technique was a clumsy method to control the airplane. In Europe, a Frenchman named Robert Esnault-Pelterie built a Wright-style glider in 1904 and used ailerons to replace the wing-warping technique. Although Matthew P.W. Boulton had described the operation of ailerons in his 1868 British patent (No. 392), no one had actually built the devices to control lateral balance and control until Esnault-Pelterie's 1904 glider. His use of ailerons spurred designers in several nations to experiment with their own aileron designs. Esnault-Pelterie also built the first fully enclosed fuselage airplane.

SANTOS-DUMONT

Alberto Santos-Dumont flew the first powered aircraft in Europe. His aircraft (the "14-bis" biplane), which looked like two huge box kites, was successfully flown in Paris on October 23, 1906. Two weeks later, he again flew his aircraft—this time traveling 722 feet. Unlike the negative press reaction in the United States, the press reported this flight, and all of Europe was excited by the news.

BLERIOT

In 1907, Louis Bleriot, after experimenting with biwinged gliders, built and flew the world's first powered monoplane. In 1909, two major events attracted worldwide attention to aviation. The first was the flight across the English Channel performed by Bleriot in his small monoplane (see fig. 19) and the second was the first International Air Meet held in Rheims, France.

Bleriot, a man of great determination, had to build eleven planes before getting one that was good enough to make the trip across the Channel. In testing his planes, he had almost 50 crashes, but he refused to give up. On the morning he took off from the coast of France, near Calais, he had to limp painfully to his aircraft because he had injured his foot in a recent accident. Bleriot had no compass for the 25-mile trip, and ten minutes after his takeoff at sunrise, he was lost. All he could see was sky and water—not a landmark in sight. When he finally saw the cliffs of Dover in the distance, he noticed that his engine was running hot. As Bleriot listened to the roar of his overheated engine, he searched the water below him hoping to find a ship that would be close enough to pick him up if his engine failed before he could reach the coast of England. He saw no ship, but luck was with him. He flew into a shower and the rain cooled the overheated engine. Thirty-seven minutes after taking off in France, Bleriot landed not far from the spot that had been the starting point for

Figure 19.

Figure 20. Sikorsky's "LeGrand"

the balloon crossing of the Channel by Jeffries and Blanchard 124 years earlier.

Word of his historic achievement soon spread throughout Europe and the United States, and he was rewarded with admiration and fame. Even though the British people realized that the planes flying to their homeland in the future would not all necessarily be piloted by friends, they cheered the plucky Frenchman.

INTERNATIONAL AIR MEET

Less than a month after Bleriot crossed the Channel, the first international air meet was held in Rheims, France, between August 22 and 28. Thirty-six planes competed in the contest. During the week of the meet, several of the little planes crashed, but no one was killed or seriously injured. Many of the pilots broke records. An endurance record was set by Henri Farman, who stayed in the air three hours, four minutes and fifty-six seconds. Bleriot made the best time for a single lap—47.8 mph.

WOMEN AVIATORS

It was not long after European men began flying heavier-than-air aircraft that women in Europe took up the challenge. Probably the first woman to go up in a powered airplane was Therese Peltier in July of 1908 (her pilot was Leon Delagrange from Italy). The first European woman to pilot an aircraft was a French baroness, Raymonde de Laroche, on October 22, 1909. She was also the first woman in Europe to earn a pilot's license—on March 8, 1910.

MULTIENGINE AIRPLANES

Another aviation accomplishment worthy of mention which took place in Europe during this period of time was the development of the first multiengine aircraft. There are two reasons for building aircraft with more than one engine—to increase the aircraft's power and to improve reliability and safety. Two engines can provide more power than one, and if one engine fails in flight, there is another to provide power until a safe landing can be made. During the early days of aviation both of these reasons were justified. The engines were very much underpowered for their weight and were notorious for stopping while the aircraft was in flight.

In 1911, the Short brothers of England were granted patents for the world's first multiengine aircraft—the *"Triple Twin."* This unique aircraft flew first time on September 18, 1911. The *Triple Twin* had two engines and three propellers. The two engines were mounted in tandem, one in front of the cockpit and one behind. The front engine drove two propellers attached to the wings. The rear engine drove a single pusher propeller.

The first four engine aircraft was built and flown by the great Russian designer and pilot Igor Sikorsky on May 13, 1913 (see fig. 20). This aircraft was a giant of its time with a wingspan of 92 feet. The aircraft was powered by four 100-horsepower engines, and, because of its large size, its landing gear consisted of 16 wheels. Other innovations were a fully enclosed cockpit which protected the pilot from weather and a passenger cabin with "portholes" for windows. The *LeGrand,* as this aircraft was called, was an imaginative forerunner of the modern airliner.

NEW ENGINES

An important development in aircraft engines was made in Europe during this same period. Early aircraft engines were manufactured out of steel, cast iron, and brass and were water cooled. This resulted in engines which were very heavy, generally weighing about ten pounds for every horsepower they produced. These large, heavy engines not only reduced performance but they required a heavy structure to support the weight of the engine.

In an effort to overcome this problem, in 1907 two French brothers, Laurent and Gustav Seguin, developed an engine they called the *Gnome.* The *Gnome* was an air-cooled engine with the cylinders arranged in a radial fashion. The cylinders had cooling fins machined into them to dissipate the heat into the surrounding air. The Seguins realized that they had to have some way to circulate the air around the cylinders even while the aircraft was sitting still. They accomplished this by fastening the crankshaft solidly to the airframe and allowing the engine and the attached propeller to spin around the fixed crankshaft (this is exactly the opposite of modern radial engines, where the engine is fixed and the propeller is attached to the rotating crankshaft). Because of this unique method of operation, these engines were called rotary engines.

Rotary engines like the *Gnome* and the later *Le Rhone* were an instant success and weighed only about three pounds for each horsepower produced. It was later discovered that it was not necessary to rotate the cylinders in order to achieve cooling, but

many World War I aircraft, such as the Sopwith *Pup* and Sopwith *Camel,* were powered by rotary engines.

AVIATION GROWTH

By the end of 1911, aviation had grown and spread. There were 353 pilots in France, 57 in Britain, 46 in Germany, 32 in Italy, and 27 in Belgium. The United States ranked sixth in the world, with only 26 pilots. Unfortunately, the nation which had given birth to aviation still looked on the airplane as a toy. Aviation industries such as Avro, Sopwith, Fokker, Vickers, Morane, and Handley-Page were springing up in Europe. In the United States, however, aircraft were still largely handmade.

VERTICAL FLIGHT

While the balloon and airplane pioneers were building their "flying machines," other men were experimenting in another area of flight. These men dreamed of being able to take off and land vertically and control their aircraft while in flight. Their experiments would lead to the modern-day helicopter.

We have already mentioned the three basic problems of flight in Chapter 1. Later on you will study how lift is produced and sustained in heavier-than-air craft. Here we will simply say that in heavier-than-air craft the lift is produced by the wing. Also, in order to sustain lift, the wing must continuously move through the air.

In a fixed-wing aircraft, the forward motion of the aircraft causes the wing to move through the air and produce lift. There is another method of moving the wing through the air which is used on helicopters. The large rotor (propeller) on top of a helicopter is made up of a number of blades. Each of these rotor blades is a wing. As the rotor whirls, the blades (wings) move through the air causing lift. Helicopters are called rotary-wing aircraft because the wings (blades) rotate.

Many of the aviation pioneers we have already mentioned, such as Roger Bacon, Leonardo da Vinci, and George Cayley, experimented with

Figure 21.

helicopters. None of them, however, went any further than building and flying models. However, the rotary-wing concept was validated by one of these models. In 1842, W.H. Phillips built and successfully flew a model helicopter powered by steam jets at the rotor tips. This formed a modest milestone in airscrew evolution since the rotors were driven by jet reaction much like the modern-day ramjets on helicopter rotor blades.

The first helicopter to lift a man into the air was flown in 1907. This machine was built and flown by a Frenchman named Louis Breguet. Although it lifted him, it was held steady by four assistants. In that same year another Frenchman, Paul Cornu, also "flew" a helicopter (see fig. 21). In 1909, a father and son—Emile and Henry Berliner—became the first Americans to build and fly a helicopter.

All of these early experimenters were plagued by problems in control of the helicopter while in flight. The major control problem to be overcome was counteracting the torque* of the rotor blade. When the rotor of a helicopter is turning, the rest of the machine tends to spin in the opposite direction. One way to overcome the torque is to have two rotors

which rotate in opposite directions. Another is to provide a small propeller at the end of a long tail boom (tail rotor) which provides thrust to counteract the torque of the main rotor. This problem of control would continue to haunt the designers for more than thirty years before being solved.

COMMERCIAL FLIGHT— A BEGINNING

On January 1, 1914, the world's first regularly scheduled airline service using heavier-than-air craft was inaugurated in the United States. This airline was called the "St. Petersburg-Tampa Airboat Line." It was flown by Tony Jannus in a twin-engine Benoist XIV Flying Boat (see fig. 22), which carried two passengers. The 22 mile flight across Tampa Bay cost $5.00 and took about twenty minutes. The airline flew the route twice a day for about four months and carried over 496 passengers.

PREPARING FOR WAR

By 1912, all the major nations of the world had formed a military flying service. In the United States

*Torque—A turning twisting force.

Figure 22. Benoist XIV Flying Boat

it was present in name only. While other nations of the world made advances in military aviation, almost no progress was made in the United States. The U.S. Army had purchased a single Wright biplane in 1908, and for three years, this one airplane was the entire "Air Force" of the United States. In 1911, Congress appropriated funds to purchase five more airplanes, and by the end of 1913, there were a total of 19 aircraft and 29 pilots in the United States Army.

In 1914, when World War I started in Europe, Germany had about 200 aircraft in its air force. Britain and France possessed about 450 craft. But more important, they also possessed the industries needed to manufacture more aircraft.

The United States did not enter World War I until 1917. Even though we had three years to prepare, the United States did not possess one single combat-worthy aircraft when it entered the war. To make the situation even worse, Curtiss Aircraft was the only company in the United States which could be considered an aviation industry.

In 1917, Congress appropriated $64,000,000 for construction of aircraft—boasting that we would "darken the skies over Europe with United States aircraft." They promised that 263 American squadrons equipped with 22,625 U.S. aircraft would be in action by June 1918. However, when the war ended in November 1918, there were only 45 American squadrons in action, all flying British and French aircraft. Not a single American-designed combat aircraft saw action during World War I. The United States was limited to building British-designed DH-4 aircraft, which saw extensive action in World War I from September 1918 until the end of the war in November.

Here we see the first example of the shortsightedness of the United States Congress with regard to aviation. This short sightedness will be repeated over and over. What Congress had overlooked was that the United States did not possess the engineers to design the aircraft, the industry to build them, or the instructors and planes with which to train the pilots. And, without these resources, all the money in the world would not put the aircraft into the air.

WORLD WAR I

MILITARY ROLE OF THE AIRPLANE

Throughout the history of aviation, the greatest progress in flight has been made during times when either war or threat of war is present. In 1914, when the war started, the average airplane had a speed of 70-80 mph and a ceiling of about 10,000 feet. By the time World War I ended, the speed had increased to 140-150 mph and the ceiling to 24,000 feet.

It is not surprising that few of the military leaders on either side could see the importance of the airplane when World War I started. It had only been in existence for ten years while for centuries the foot soldier and cavalry had been the primary weapons of war. Even trucks, tanks, and machine guns were just beginning to be used in warfare. Military tactics stressed invasion, conquering the defending army, and capturing the enemy's government. National security and defense lay in either natural barriers (mountains, deserts, oceans, etc.) or in man-made barriers (walls, fortresses, strong navies, etc.) to stop the invading armies. The army generals and navy admirals, steeped in centuries of tradition, could not see that the airplane knew no barriers and would revolutionize warfare.

The airplane was first used in the same role as balloons had been in earlier wars—for observation. This role required aircraft which were slow and stable from which the pilot or observer could study and photograph the ground. Aircraft such as the British BE-2 and Avro 504, the French *Morane* and *Farman,* and the German *Taube* and *Albatross* were excellent observation aircraft. These airplanes usually carried no guns and if an Allied observer met an enemy aircraft, the pilots would probably wave at each other (see fig. 23).

As war progressed, there were a few attempts at bombing. The "bombers" were observation aircraft with the pilot or an observer carrying small bombs on his lap. These bombs were released by hand with very poor accuracy.

The first long-range strategic raid during the war was made by three British Avro 504s against the German Zeppelin sheds at Lake Constance in southern Germany. There was little damage done, but the raid did cause the Germans to form their first bombing squadron. Early in 1915, the Germans were raiding behind the British lines in France and later began bombing London, using both dirigibles and airplanes.

EUROPE IN WORLD WAR I

Bombers. At the beginning of the war, the German Army had 20 large dirigibles, nine built by Zeppelin and eleven by other German manufacturers. During the war an additional 88 Zeppelins were produced. Germany's plans were to use these airships as strategic bombers against the French and English cities. On August 9, 1915, they made their first raids

Figure 23. The French Morane

Figure 24.

over London. They were very accurate with their bombing, but because the airships were filled with highly flammable hydrogen, the slightest damage caused them to burst into flames. Because of their vulnerability to anti-aircraft fire from the ground and the air, they began flying only at night.

By 1916 it was clear that a replacement was necessary, and it came in the form of a large twin-engine bomber—the *Gotha IV* (see fig. 24). Beginning in April of 1917, these bombers dropped many tons of bombs on English cities and factories. Although these raids caused considerable damage and some death, the important outcome was that the English had to recall some of their fighter squadrons from France to protect the homeland.

Another outcome of the German air raids was the formation of the Independent Bombing Force within the British Royal Flying Corps. This was the first and only Allied flying force during World War I which was not under the command of a general who was primarily trained in infantry tactics. This organization went on later to become the Royal Air Force (RAF), which was independent from and equal to the British Army and Navy.

By the time the war ended, strategic bombing (bombing enemy territory) had grown from a few observation planes with the pilots dropping small hand-held bombs to large specially designed bombers capable of carrying up to 6,000 pounds of bombs.

Fighters. As more and more bombing raids took place, it was inevitable that other aircraft would be sent aloft to drive off the bombers. At first the armament of these "fighters" consisted of the pilot shooting at the enemy with a pistol or rifle. In 1915, a French pilot, Roland Garros, mounted an automatic rifle on his aircraft so that it could be fired forward through the propeller. To keep from shooting off his own propeller, the rear of the prop was armored with steel plates to deflect the bullets. As primitive as this device was, it was quite effective because, for the first time, the pilot could aim his guns by flying directly at the enemy.

In April 1915, Garros was shot down behind the German lines and his aircraft captured. After examining his armored propeller, the Germans gave a Dutch airplane designer, Anthony Fokker, the task of improving this device. Fokker designed an interrupting gear which connected a machine gun to the aircraft engine and prevented the gun from firing when a propeller blade was lined up with the gun's muzzle. This allowed the machine gun to be fired through the spinning propeller. For nearly a year, this invention gave the Germans almost total control of the air. The Allies tried mounting their machine guns on top of the wing to fire over the propeller. This was not successful because it slowed the aircraft due to the increased drag. In April 1916, a German aircraft equipped with this device was captured and the Allies soon copied it. It was at this point that the great "dog fight" aerial battles between large numbers of fighter aircraft began.

This use of aircraft in a "fighter" role also required development of a specialized aircraft. The fighter needed to be light, fast, and very maneuverable. Some of the famous fighters developed during World War I included the Sopwith *Camel* and the SE-5a by the British, the Spad VII and Nieuport 17 by the French, and the German Fokker Dr-I and D-VII (see fig. 25).

One of the greatest technical accomplishments of World War I occurred too late to affect the outcome of the war. In May of 1918, the German designer Hugo Junkers built the world's first all-metal, low-wing monoplane fighter—the Junkers D-1. Only 45 were manufactured before the war ended and few people realized they were seeing the fighter of the future.

As aerial combat increased, the French developed a method of recognizing pilots who shot down many enemy aircraft. They coined the term "Ace" for a pilot who had shot down five enemy aircraft. This same number was adopted by the British and Americans. The Germans, however, required that ten enemy aircraft be downed before recognizing the pilot as an "Ace."

The term "Ace of Aces" was a designation given to the pilot from each nation with the most "kills." Included as "Ace of Aces" during World War I were Edward V. Rickenbacker, American (26 victories); Rene Fonck, French (75 victories); Edward Mannock, British (73 victories); and Manfred von Richthofen, German (80 victories).

THE UNITED STATES IN WORLD WAR I

Lafayette Escadrille. World War I began in Europe in 1914, but the United States did not enter the war until 1917. Quite a few American pilots did not wait for their own country to declare war, though. Instead, they found ways to get into the flying services of other nations already engaged in combat. Most nations had some legal difficulties in accepting the services of these American "foreigners," but France

Figure 25. World War I aircraft

1. *Nieuport 17*
2. *Fokker D-VII*
3. *Sopwith Camel*

Figure 26.

did not. The famous French Foreign Legion was willing and able to accept volunteers from other nations.

When the war broke out, seven wealthy young Americans living in Paris volunteered to fly for France. These Americans worked as a group and named themselves the Lafayette Escadrille (see fig. 26), in honor of the French nobleman who had lent his services to the Americans during the Revolutionary War. Additional American volunteers soon increased the strength of the unit.

By March 1917, the month before the United States formally entered World War I, only one of the original members of the Lafayette Escadrille was still living. By the time the war ended, 40 of the gallant Americans responsible for the Escadrille's fighting fame had given their lives for the French and Allied cause. Six of these Americans achieved "Ace" status while flying for the French Air Service by shooting down five or more enemy airplanes.

The Lafayette Escadrille was viewed by the French at first largely as a propaganda device for winning American support for the war effort. Soon, however, the young Americans proved their value as fighting men. Before it was incorporated into the United States Army Air Service in February 1918, the Escadrille scored 199 confirmed victories.

Raoul Lufbery. One of the most widely known and most popular of the American flyers was Raoul Lufbery, a native Frenchman who had become an American citizen. He was one of several Americans serving with the French Air Service who later joined the all-American Lafayette Escadrille. Lufbery scored 17 victories during the war. He always advised his pilots to stay with their planes, even if they began to burn—one of the most dangerous possibilities in those days of fabric-covered aircraft. On May 19, 1918, however, he ignored his own advice and paid the full price. Lufbery's machine was hit by enemy bullets and began to burn. Two hundred feet above the ground, he jumped, apparently aiming at a nearby stream. Instead, he landed on a picket fence and was killed.

Black Aviators. Very few black Americans served in the Lafayette Escadrille. However, black Americans did fly for the French in the Lafayette Flying Corps during World War I. Black aviators are little known historically in the development of aviation due to opposition they encountered from government, trade unions, and individuals acting out of their own prejudices. Black development in aviation went through four distinct eras: 1903-1939, 1939-1950, 1950-1967, and 1967-present. While blacks were not to make a significant mark in aviation until after Lindbergh's 1927 transatlantic flight (through centers of black aviation in the form of flying clubs), some did manage to contribute to the United States World War I efforts, usually in the service of an Allied nation.

Lt. Julian, the "Black Eagle of Harlem," claimed that the first black pilots learned to fly in Canada or in France during World War I. Julian got his own training in France. Little is known of these pilots except for Eugene Bullard.

Bullard represented a breakthrough for blacks in aviation, setting the stage for other blacks to enter the field. He first served in the French Foreign Legion, and then he transferred to the French Air Service on November 15, 1916. There he learned to fly, becoming the first black man to earn a flying license. He was then assigned to a French Fighter Squadron as a pilot (flying Spad fighters) and was eventually awarded the coveted French Croix de Guerre with a star for his achievements in combat during World War I.

Figure 27.

Eddie Rickenbacker. Eddie Rickenbacker (see fig. 27), a former racing car driver, learned from Lufbery the value of watching the sky all around for enemy planes. He also learned that a flight patrol leader's main duty is to take care of his men. The American 94th and 95th Squadrons were flying unarmed Nieuports which had been cast aside by the French. When French authorities learned that the Americans' planes were not armed, they supplied machine guns.

The Americans began to shoot down German planes and Rickenbacker soon accumulated five victories. After his fourth victory, Rickenbacker was named Commander of the 94th Squadron. He equipped his men with parachutes, solved a troublesome problem of jamming guns, then kept his squadron atop the list of effectiveness against the enemy. His 26 kills came in the space of only five months of flying. Rickenbacker mastered aerial combat tactics just as he had mastered automobile driving tactics on dirt tracks and, later, on the speedway at Indianapolis.

Rickenbacker was the only living American airman to receive the Congressional Medal of Honor during World War I. Three other Americans, however, received the same medal posthumously.

Lieutenants Harold Goettler and Erwin Bleckley were awarded the medal for their heroic action of 6 October 1918 in locating an American battalion trapped behind enemy lines—an action that cost them their lives. The other airman who posthumously received the Medal of Honor was Frank Luke.

Frank Luke. If Rickenbacker and Lufbery knew the value of discipline and planning, Frank Luke was their opposite. Luke has been described as "an undisciplined, carefree maverick, . . . absolutely impervious to any squadron regulations." However, he was extremely confident of his abilities, and he accomplished one of the most amazing feats of the war by destroying 15 enemy balloons and three planes within 17 days. The balloons were heavily guarded by German planes and antiaircraft guns and were regarded by most pilots as the most dangerous and difficult targets of all.

Luke became a loner, but after one last spree in which he downed three balloons and two planes on the same raid, he did not return to his base. It was later learned that, after his raid in the air, Luke was wounded but strafed and killed six Germans on the ground and wounded an equal number. He then landed his plane to get a drink of water from a

Figure 28.

He was the youngest student ever to have entered George Washington University when he enrolled in 1895. He became a Second Lieutenant in the Wisconsin Volunteers at age 18 and was promoted to First Lieutenant a year later. By 1903, at age 23, he had become the youngest Captain in the Army. In 1909, he completed the Army Staff College as a distinguished graduate. When he was 32 years old, he was ordered to Washington to serve on the War Department general staff—the youngest officer ever given this assignment.

Mitchell's interest in aviation started after the beginning of World War I in 1914. He spent much of his time on the general staff in Washington urging a separate and independent air service. On his own time, he studied flying at the Curtiss Company's school at Newport News, Virginia. He became a pilot at 36, which in those days was considered quite old for flying.

As the war progressed in Europe, Mitchell steadily climbed in rank and responsibilites, finally becoming Chief of the Air Service for the American forces in Europe. He did his best to get first rate aircraft and mechanics for American pilots. As a trained pilot himself, he tested British and French planes before he would accept them for his fliers. He rejected the Sopwith *Camel,* for instance, because its rotary engine gave it a tendency to whip into a right-hand spin, and his pilots were not sufficiently experienced to control it. Later, United States pilots did fly *Camels.*

Mitchell had studied air power theorists and had met the leading ones personally. From his friend General Hugh Trenchard, Commander of the British Royal Flying Corps, Mitchell learned to think of the airplane as an offensive weapon best used in giant fleets of bombers striking against the enemy's homeland.

Mitchell had the title of Head of the Air Services, but control of the air wing was still in the hands of ground-oriented officers. Mitchell saw aviation as a military effort, helping the ground forces but not subservient to them. Most ground officers, however, thought of the Air Service as an auxiliary to the land troops, useful mainly to keep an eye on enemy infantry movements and to keep enemy airplanes out of sight of friendly troops. All Army officers of

stream but was discovered by a German foot patrol. He drew his revolver to defend himself, but was killed by the soldiers.

Billy Mitchell. There were a great number of aviators who earned fame through combat in World War I. One man who was influential in aviation in that war and who was to make a giant contribution to aviation tactics later was not a famous fighter pilot at all, but a student of airpower and its use. His name was Billy Mitchell (see fig. 28).

Mitchell, son of a United States senator, grew up in Milwaukee, Wisconsin. One of his boyhood friends was Douglas MacArthur, who during World War II and the Korean War won worldwide fame for outstanding service in the United States Army. By applying his considerable intelligence and abilities, Mitchell started breaking records at an early age.

that time, of course, had been trained for ground warfare, and it was often difficult to make a case for a strong and independent Air Service.

Billy Mitchell slowly gained favor in certain quarters, but his outspokenness made him some enemies, too. His influence was great on the American flying squadrons, some of whose members were to rise to later prominence. Those men carried Mitchell's teachings forward to a point of great impact on the conduct of air warfare in World War II.

In September 1918, Mitchell commanded the first mass use of aircraft for bombing attacks on enemy supply routes and for support of the ground troops. This attack involved nearly 1,500 Allied war planes and was important in deciding the outcome of the war. However, it was not until after the war that

Mitchell was able to demonstrate the effectiveness of the air weapon against naval vessels. Although Mitchell was forced to sacrifice his military career for an ideal, he unquestionably had a large influence on aviation's golden age.

Airpower. Because World War I was fought in Europe, the American public was isolated from the actual battlefield. Except for the American troops serving in Europe, Americans were unaware of the increasing importance of air power during World War I. Therefore, when the war ended, the United States was the only nation involved in the war that had not learned the most important lesson taught by World War I—*if you control the air, you cannot be beaten; if you lose the air, you cannot win.*

MITCHELL'S AIRPOWER DOCTRINE: SEPT.- NOV., 1918

PREMISE 1
"AIR SUPERIORITY OVER THE BATTLEFIELD MUST BE COMPLETELY ASSURED."

PREMISE 2
"AIRPOWER MAY THEN BE EMPLOYED OFFENSIVELY AGAINST THE ENEMY'S GROUND TROOPS."

"THE AIRPLANE IS FIRST AND FOREMOST AN OFFENSIVE WEAPON"

PREMISE 3
"FINALLY, AERIAL BOMBARDMENT MAY BE DIRECTED AGAINST THE ENEMY'S SUPPLIES, RAILROADS, COMMUNICATIONS, AND AIRDROMES."

DOOLITTLE

MITCHELL

EARHART   LINDBERGH

Chapter 1-3

THE GOLDEN AGE: 1919-1939

The twenty year period between the end of World War I and the beginning of World War II has been called the "Golden Age of Aviation." During this time period, there were many exciting and dramatic exploits by daring aviators from many lands. New speed and altitude records were set, only to be broken and reset over and over again. There were oceans and continents to cross, and each accomplishment led to someone who wanted to do it better or faster. During this time period, the airplane changed from a slow, wood-and-wire, fabric biplane to a fast, sleek, all-metal monoplane.

During the "Golden Age of Aviation," the airplane "grew up." It had proved itself during the war and now it began to show its value in civilian life. There were many daring feats performed during this time period as more and more aviation records were broken. During this same 20 year period, others were perfecting the airplane as the "ultimate" weapon of war.

The general learning objective of this chapter is for you to know aviation developments during the Golden Age: 1919-1939. To reach this objective, you must pattern your study of the material according to the *specific learning objectives* listed in the Appendix of this textbook.

FLYING THE ATLANTIC

The greatest challenge faced by aviation immediately after World War I was to demonstrate to the non-flying public the capabilities of the airplane. This meant flying higher, faster, or further than anyone had flown before. In some cases it meant challenging a natural barrier like an ocean, a mountain range, or the Earth's poles. Some of these record-breaking flights were made for prizes. Others were flown by the military to show off or test a new airplane. Most, however, were done by daredevil pilots simply for the love of flying.

TRANSATLANTIC CROSSING

The first natural barrier to be challenged was the Atlantic Ocean and it was conquered in 1919. The first attempt to cross the Atlantic was made by the United States Navy flying three new Curtiss flying boats. The flight was to be made in four stages: From Rockaway, New York to Trepassey, Newfoundland; to the Azores; to Lisbon, Portugal; to Plymouth, England.

The NC-1, NC-3, and NC-4, commanded by

Lieutenant Commander R.N.L. Bellinger, Commander J.H. Towers, and Lieutenant Commander Albert B. Read, respectively, left Rockaway on May 8, 1919, and all arrived safely at Trepassey. The next stage was, of course, the critical one. It was the long hop to the Azores, 1,200 miles over water. As a safeguard, a succession of naval vessels, 50 miles apart, stretched along the proposed route. If the planes remained on their course, an emergency landing would find them no more than 25 miles from help.

On May 16, 1919, the three great planes took off from Trepassey. Over the Atlantic that night, they occasionally saw each other's lights and checked their courses by radio or by the rockets and searchlights of the destroyers marking the way. But the next day a thick fog settled in. Both Commander Bellinger in the NC-1 and Commander Towers in the NC-3 landed on the water to take bearings.

In waves as much as 12 feet high, Commander Towers was able to land without serious damage to his craft. The plane was off course, southwest of its destination. The crew found that they could not take off in the heavy seas. By skill and bravery, the crew of the NC-3 were able to keep the plane afloat and take it into the Azores after sailing 205 miles on the water. "Taxiing" the plane to Horta, Azores, took three days on rough seas. The plane was not able to continue the flight.

The NC-1 came down after flying 850 miles. The plane was badly damaged in landing and began to break up in the water. A merchant steamship, the *Ionia,* rescued the crew. The plane was taken in tow by a destroyer, but sank.

Commander Read, in the NC-4 (see fig. 29), had kept to the air, and 15 hours and 18 minutes after leaving Trepassey, came roaring down into the harbor of Horta, Azores. On May 20, 1919, Commander Read and his crew flew on to Ponta Delgada, a one hour and 44 minute hop. On May 27th they flew on to Lisbon, Portugal, reaching there in nine hours and 43 minutes. The total flying time

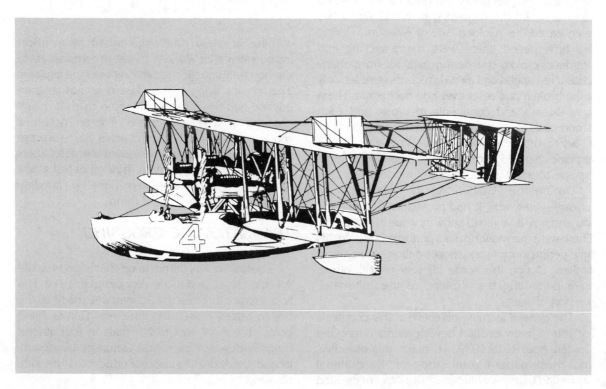

Figure 29.

for the Atlantic crossing, Newfoundland to Portugal, was 26-3/4 hours.

On May 30th the NC-4 proceeded up the coast with stops at the Mondego River and at Ferrol, Spain. The next morning she landed at Plymouth near the spot where the *Mayflower* had moored 300 years before. The total airline distance from Rockaway was 3,936 miles. The total flying time was 52 hours and 31 minutes. This was the first transatlantic crossing. Just two weeks later the first nonstop crossing of the Atlantic was made.

NONSTOP TRANSATLANTIC CROSSING

In 1913, the *London Daily Mail* made a standing offer of $50,000.00 to the crew of the first airplane that made a nonstop crossing of the Atlantic, starting from either side, and lasting no longer than 72 hours. Because of the war, no one attempted to win the prize until the spring of 1919. The first team to make the attempt was Harry Hawker, an Austrian war hero, and his navigator, Lieutenant Commander Kenneth McKenzie-Grieve of the Royal Navy. Their attempt ended in failure.

The second pair of hopefuls were Captain John Alcock and Lieutenant Arthur Whitten Brown. While Hawker and McKenzie-Grieve were leaving Trepassey, John Alcock and Arthur Whitten Brown, with their Vickers-Vimy converted bomber, were on a

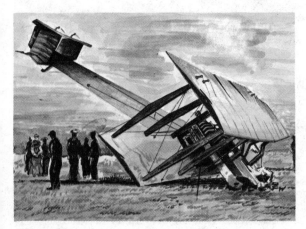

Figure 30.

steamship headed for Newfoundland. Brown, who was born in America, was a veteran of the Royal Air Force, as was Captain John Alcock. Both had outstanding war records. They reached St. John's, Newfoundland, on May 24th—the day before it became known that Hawker and McKenzie-Grieve had been rescued, and three days before the NC-4 reached Lisbon. It looked as if they still had a chance to win the *London Daily Mail* prize and also to be the first to cross the Atlantic. But they were grounded for several days. The first delay was caused by bad weather, and the second by needed radio repairs.

They took off at 4:28 P.M. on July 14, 1919. With 856 gallons of gasoline aboard, their plane weighed 13,500 pounds, and the two 350 horsepower Rolls Royce engines were barely able to lift it over a fence at the end of the runway. With the help of a 30 mph tail wind, the plane was soon headed for Ireland at a speed of 120 mph. When the aviators were scarcely out of sight of land, they ran into heavy fog. During the first seven hours they had only occasional glimpses of sea or sky. Later the visibility became even worse. Once, at 4,000 feet, the plane went into a spin, and Alcock had difficulty in pulling it out in time to prevent a crash.

As they flew on, the weather seemed to get worse. Snow and sleet clogged the radiator, and icing threatened to overload the plane. The radio had quit early in the flight, and it was impossible for them to get bearings from ships as they had planned. When Brown was finally able to determine their position, he was delighted to find that they were on course and nearing Ireland. Soon they saw the islands of Turbot and Eashal, off the Irish coast. Next they recognized the masts of the radio station at Clifden. They circled over the station, but no one appeared to see them.

Soon they discovered what appeared to be a meadow suitable for a landing place. It turned out to be a bog. When they landed, the front wheels disappeared and the nose of the plane plowed into the ground. Fortunately, neither Alcock nor Brown was injured, and they managed to extricate themselves from the muck without too much difficulty (see fig. 30).

It was then 8:40 A.M. on June 15th—16 hours and 12 minutes since they had left St. John's. They had traveled 1,880 miles at an average speed of almost two miles a minute to make the first nonstop crossing of the Atlantic and win the $50,000.00. This accomplishment of 1919 was a remarkable advance over the achievements of 1903.

APATHY IN AMERICA

During World War I, all of the nations involved built up a large number of aircraft, pilots and a great aviation industry. During the war, France built 67,982 aircraft, Germany produced 47,637 and Italy about 20,000. Even the United States produced 15,000 airplanes during the 21 months it was involved in the war. The British production had increased from an average of about 20 per month at the beginning of the war to 3,500 per month when the war ended.

When the armistice was signed on November 11, 1918, there were over 177,000 aircraft in service in Europe. Despite our slow start, America's front line strength consisted of 750 combat aircraft and 800 pilots. We had an additional 3,000 training aircraft and about 9,500 men in the Air Service. Almost overnight this changed.

Three days after the armistice, $100 million dollars in airplane contracts were cancelled by the United States Government. Within three months 175,000 factory workers were laid off and aircraft production dropped by 85 percent. Surplus war planes were dumped on the market causing the aviation industries to lose what small market they did have. These industries, which had built up slowly during the war, now closed at an alarming rate.

Military aviation was cut back by 95 percent, and

Figure 31.

the pilots and other aviation personnel who had taken so long to train were unemployed. Military airfields were closed, which created a shortage of landing fields for those airplanes which were flying. In fact, aviation in the United States might have died completely except for two groups—the "barnstormers" and the Army aviators led by the outspoken General Billy Mitchell.

THE BARNSTORMERS

The barnstormers were, for the most part, ex-military aviators who flew war-surplus aircraft such as the Curtiss JN-4 *Jenny.* They would fly around the countryside, circle over a village or small town to attract attention, and land on some farm nearby. When the curious townspeople began to gather to get a good look at the plane, the pilot would offer rides to individuals. The charge was usually three to five dollars.

The barnstormers also put on flying exhibitions at county fairs, carnivals, and anywhere else that crowds gathered. Sometimes several of the pilots would work together as a team, calling themselves a "flying circus." Those who did not work as part of a large group learned that they could offer the crowds more thrills if they teamed up with a stunt man.

"Wing walking" (see fig. 31) was one of the tricks that always pleased the crowds. While the pilot flew the biplane in a circle, the stunt man would walk out on the edge of the lower wing, climb to the upper wing, and walk in toward the cockpit. Some of the wing walkers would give the viewers an extra thrill by standing on their heads.

"Breakaway" was a daring variation on wing walking. The stunt man would walk the length of the wings, appear to lose his balance, and fall. During a frantic looking struggle, he would manage to hang on, and finally to pull himself back onto the wing. From the ground, the excited onlookers could not see that the stunt man was wearing a harness anchored to the plane by a cable. But even with these trappings, the stunt was difficult and dangerous.

Another favorite with the crowds was "plane change." It required two planes with pilots and a stunt man. After the planes were both in the air, the stunt man would climb to the upper wing of his plane and wait for the second plane to fly over with a rope ladder dangling from a wing. After catching the ladder and scrambling up to the second plane, the stunt man would frequently parachute to the ground.

One barnstormer who would later become world famous was Charles Lindbergh. He performed a stunt that the audiences could hardly believe. He would stand on the upper wing of a plane while the pilot flew a series of loops. The trick would not have been possible without some aids that the viewers could not see. Lindbergh's feet were strapped to the wing, and he was steadied by wires running from his belt and firmly attached to the wing. But as helpful as these devices were, they offered no guarantee of safety. Lindbergh did not win fame by barnstorming, however, but by making the first transatlantic solo flight.

Besides ex-military aviators, there were a number of women aviators who attracted the public's attention during this barnstorming period. Less famous than Lindbergh, but a pioneer in her own right, was a female barnstormer named Phoebe Fairgrave Omlie. She not only ran her own "flying circus" but went on to become the first female licensed transport pilot in the United States. Another stunt pilot was the first licensed black female pilot, Bessie Coleman. Just as Bullard represented the first breakthrough for black males in aviation, Coleman (who had to go to France to get her license) represented the first breakthrough for black women in aviation, and she would serve as a model for other black women to enter aviation. "Bessie" died in a crash in Florida at the early age of 27. Her tombstone states that she "fell 5,300 feet while flying at Jacksonville, Florida 30 April 1926." She was one of the first American women to pilot a plane and her goal was to inspire black youth to fly.

Barnstorming was a risky way to make a living. The planes, even when newly purchased, were frail. They were made of wood and canvas and strung together with wire. Forced landings were commonplace, and accidents cost the lives of many of the performers.

But these daring young men and women were

happy because they were doing what they liked—flying. And they were proud to be earning a living. Perhaps without realizing it, the barnstormers performed a service for aviation and for the public. With their exciting exhibitions, these "flying gypsies" publicized aviation.

When World War I ended, many people had never seen an airplane, and if they thought of aviation at all, it was probably with fear and disapproval. Then, along came the barnstormers with air shows that may not have done away with the fears but certainly did create interest in fliers and flying. These colorful daredevils ushered in two decades that were to see improvement after improvement in aircraft design and achievement after achievement by the men who took to the air. Unfortunately, their days became numbered after Congress enacted the Air Commerce Act of 1926.

ARMY AVIATION

MITCHELL AND AIR POWER

General William "Billy" Mitchell returned home after World War I convinced that, in any future war, military air power would decide the winner. He strongly supported using the airplane for strategic warfare, that is, for bombing important military and industrial targets deep inside the enemy's homeland.

In the early 1920s, Mitchell was appointed Assistant Chief of the Army Air Service, which was then struggling to survive. The government support for the military was very small, and the two major branches of the military—Army and Navy—were competing for what little money was available. Since the Air Service was merely a branch of the Army, it received little money to buy new aircraft.

General Mitchell was a very vocal advocate of an Air Service separate from but equal to the Army and Navy. He also spoke of the superiority of the airplane as a military weapon. Mitchell decided that the only way to overcome the official indifference toward aviation, both within the Army and the Congress, was to demonstrate the capability of the airplane as a military weapon. Since it was widely agreed that

America's first line of defense was the Navy with its battleships, Mitchell chose to prove that the airplane could sink a battleship.

By 1921, Mitchell had created such an uproar that the Navy agreed to allow him to perform his demonstration. Confident that he could not succeed, the Navy provided several captured German ships as targets, including the battleship *Ostfriesland*. The *Ostfriesland* was a huge ship which had been called "unsinkable" by naval experts. In the first attempts, using light bombs, Mitchell's pilots did little damage to the giant battleship.

The next day the Army fliers returned carrying 1,000-pound bombs, and again the battleship survived. On the afternoon of July 21, 1921, the Army pilots were back, this time carrying 2,000-pound bombs which Mitchell had ordered specifically made for these tests. Eight of these bombs were dropped (see fig. 32), and 25 minutes later, the "unsinkable" pride of the German Navy slipped beneath the waves.

The lesson to be learned from this demonstration, unfortunately, was lost on the Army generals. It was also rejected by Congress, who controlled the purse strings. Mitchell did not get additional money for aircraft. Several Navy admirals, however, did learn the lesson. They could see that in future wars the airplane would play a dominant role in naval warfare. Within eight months the Navy had its first aircraft carrier.

Mitchell decided that if he could not convince the Congress or the Army leaders, he would try to convince the American public. Determined to gain public recognition for the Army Air Service, Mitchell planned many spectacular flights.

TRANSCONTINENTAL FLIGHT

In 1922, Lieutenant Oakley G. Kelly and Lieutenant John A. Macready of the United States Army Air Service made two attempts to fly nonstop from San Diego to New York. The first time they had to turn back because of bad weather; the second time a leaky radiator forced them down at Indianapolis, Indiana, after flying almost three-fourths of the way to their goal. Then they decided to

Figure 32.

reverse their direction and fly from New York to San Diego. They believed that the advantage of having a light gas tank when crossing the Rocky Mountains would outweigh the advantage of the tail wind they would probably have traveling east.

At 12:30 P.M. on May 2, 1923, they took off from Roosevelt Field on their third attempt. Their plane was a Fokker T2 with a 400 horsepower Liberty engine (see fig. 33). The heavily loaded plane barely

cleared some obstacles at the end of the runway. Kelly and Macready flew over Indianapolis after nightfall and entered the mountains near Tucumcari, New Mexico, early the next morning. Luck provided them with a tail wind most of the way. In spite of their heavy fuel load, they flew much of the way at 100 mph. Shortly after noon on May 3rd, they landed at San Diego after flying 2,520 miles in 26 hours and 50 minutes.

Figure 33.

Figure 34.

ROUND-THE-WORLD FLIGHT

The greatest demonstration of the ability of the airplane was the first round-the-world flight. The Army performed this amazing flight in 1924 using aircraft built by Douglas Aircraft (see fig. 34). The four airplanes—the *Boston, Chicago, Seattle* and *New Orleans*—were named for the cities that sponsored each of them. The flight originated in Seattle, Washington, proceeded to Alaska, Japan, China, Indochina, Burma, India, Syria, Austria, France, England, Iceland, Greenland, Labrador, Newfoundland, Nova Scotia, and across the United States back to Seattle.

The entire flight took 175 days and only two of the aircraft *(Chicago* and *New Orleans)* completed the entire flight. The *Seattle* crashed in Alaska soon after the journey began, and the *Boston* was forced down in the Atlantic between England and Iceland. A replacement aircraft named the *Boston II* was taken to Nova Scotia and the crew of the *Boston* flew it on to Seattle. The total distance flown was 26,345 miles and the actual flying time was 363 hours and

seven minutes.

OTHER ARMY ACCOMPLISHMENTS

In August 1923, the Army performed the first refueling of an airplane while in flight. Lieutenants Lowell H. Smith and J.P. Richter remained airborne for 37 hours and 15 minutes by refueling their aircraft through a 50-foot hose from another airplane. The refueling operation was done 16 times with about 50 gallons of fuel being transferred each time. This feat would be repeated again in 1929, not by military aviators but by two civilian females—Elinor Smith and Bobbi Trout. These two plucky women were the first women pilots to refuel a plane in mid-air.

On June 23, 1924, Army Lieutenant Russell H. Maughan flew a Curtiss PW-8 pursuit aircraft from coast-to-coast in a dawn-to-dusk flight. The 2,850 mile trip was completed in 21 hours and 47 minutes at an average speed of 156 mph. Although he had to land five times to refuel, Lieutenant Maughan left New York at dawn and landed in San Francisco

Figure 35.

before dark. This flight demonstrated that Army aircraft located anywhere in the United States could be alerted and flown to any other location in the country in less than one day.

The Army also experimented with dropping troops from airplanes. The first test of the feasibility of using paratroops was in September of 1929 at Brooks Field in Texas. Sergeant Edwin H. Nickles and a squad of 17 men jumped from nine DH-4s and landed safely on the ground 3,000 feet below (see fig. 35). At the same time, three bundles of

machine guns and ammunition were dropped from three Douglas transports, and within four minutes after the jump, the machine guns were in action.

MITCHELL'S FAILURE AND SUCCESS

These flights gained wide national and world acclaim, but still did not result in the outcome Mitchell sought—a separate Air Service and more money for military aviation. Following a world tour of foreign military aviation, Mitchell criticized the defenses of the United States, particularly at the Navy base in Pearl Harbor, Hawaii. He stated that a surprise air attack on Pearl Harbor would destroy our Pacific Fleet. Mitchell's verbal attacks on our defense systems led to his being relieved of his command and reduced in rank to colonel.

Later, his continued attacks on the military hierarchy led to his court-martial and subsequent retirement. His court-martial, however, did lead to some of the things he sought. The Army Air Service was changed to the Army Air Corps, the post of Assistant Secretary of War for Aeronautics was created, and additional funds for military aviation were provided. However, less than 15 years later, on December 7, 1941, the military was finally to see that Mitchell was right about the importance of aviation in the military.

NATIONAL AIR RACES

Almost from the beginning of aviation, air shows and air races became very popular. Not only did these air races create great interest in flight but they also provided the incentive for manufacturers to build better and faster aircraft.

PULITZER

Air racing got its start in the United States when a newspaperman, Ralph Pulitzer, offered a trophy to promote high-speed flight. He did this because American aircraft were making such a poor showing in the European air races.

The first Pulitzer Trophy Race was held at Mitchel Field, Long Island, New York, on Thanksgiving Day, November 27, 1920. There were 37 entries who flew four laps around the 29 mile course. The winner was United States Army Captain Corliss Mosley flying a Verville-Packard aircraft, with an average speed of 156.6 mph.

NATIONAL AIR RACES

By 1924, the Pultizer Trophy Race had grown into ten separate events, six limited to civilian aircraft and four restricted to military aircraft. Because the

air races had grown so large, the name was changed to the National Air Races. In 1926, the military withdrew from competition for the Pulitzer Trophy. Therefore, the 1925 National Air Races was the last time that the Pulitzer Trophy was awarded. It was won by United States Army Lieutenant Cy Bellis in a Curtiss R3C-1 racer at 248 mph. Although the Pulitzer Trophy Race was conducted for only six years, the winning speed had increased by nearly 100 mph.

Thompson Race. In 1930, Charles E. Thompson, President of Thompson Products, Inc., established a trophy to encourage faster land-based aircraft. The Thompson Trophy Race became the feature event of the National Air Races. It was an open event with no limit on fuel, number, or type of engines, and it was open to civilian and military aircraft. Like the Pulitzer Trophy Race, this was a pylon race, meaning that it was flown around a closed circuit marked by towers (pylons). The Thompson Trophy was awarded annually until the outbreak of World War II (1939).

Bendix Race. In 1931, The Bendix Trophy Race, a transcontinental speed race, was added to the National Air Races; it was open to both sexes. Rather than fly around a closed course, the Bendix Race was flown from the West Coast to Cleveland, Ohio. Jimmy Doolittle was a winner of the Bendix Trophy (see fig. 36). This race was also suspended in 1939, and neither the Thompson nor the Bendix Races were restarted after World War II.

SCHNEIDER TROPHY RACE

Another air race which must be mentioned, even though it was not a part of the National Air Races, is the Schneider Trophy Race (see fig. 37). This race was started in 1913 by Jacques Schneider, a wealthy French aviation enthusiast. Schneider felt that water aircraft were not developing fast enough so he offered a trophy for an annual race over open water by seaplanes. The 1913 race had four entries and only one finished. His average speed was 45.8 mph.

By 1931, when the Schneider Trophy was retired, the speed had increased to over 340 mph.

Figure 36.

The Schneider Trophy Races led to the development of seaplanes like the English Supermarine S.6B and the Italian Macchi MC-72. Both of these aircraft were faster than any land aircraft of the 1930s. In October 1934, the MC-72 established a world record for seaplanes of 440.68 mph. This speed is still a record for propeller driven seaplanes and will probably never be beaten.

Figure 37.

WOMEN'S AIR DERBY

In 1929, the National Air Races were opened to women for the first time. The *Women's Air Derby*, the first cross-country competition for women, was the major opening event of the 1929 races and signaled the start of women competing in air races. The first race went from Santa Monica, California, to Cleveland, Ohio. The race was won by Louise Thaden who flew a Travel Air J-5. Second place went to Gladys O'Donnell, and Amelia Earhart finished third.

In 1930, a pylon race was added; Gladys O'Donnell won both the cross-country and the pylon race. Although the Bendix Trophy Race was open to women, none entered this race until 1933. Amelia Earhart finished fifth in the 1935 Bendix Trophy Race, and in 1936 women finished first and second in this formerly male-dominated event. Louise Thaden and Blanche Noyes won the race in a Staggerwing Beech while Laura Ingalls finished second in a Lockheed Orion. The only other woman to win the Bendix Trophy Race was Jacqueline Cochran in 1938, who flew a modified Seversky P-35. For Jacqueline Cochran, this was just a beginning of a career which would eventually lead to "Jackie" being called the "greatest woman aviator of all time."

The Women's Air Derby lead to the formation of an association of women fliers called the "Ninety-nines" (named after the 99 original charter members). Amelia Earhart was the "99s" first president. This organization, dedicated to the improvement of women's opportunities in aviation, included the leading female pilots from all nations and still exists today.

AIR RACING TODAY

During the late 1920s and 1930s, the National Air Races were the prime sporting event in the nation. In fact, there has never been an event, even today, that could rival them as far as numbers of spectators. The National Air Races grew into a ten-day event and crowds of over a million people were commonplace. The names of pilots became household words, even more famous than today's baseball and football superstars. Today the National

Figure 38.

Air Races are held annually at Reno, Nevada, but they do not compare with those of the 1920s and 1930s.

COMMERCIAL AVIATION

Immediately after World War I ended, many countries in Europe began to look at the airplane for its commercial value. Less than three months after the armistice was signed, Germany started the world's first passenger airline service using heavier-than-air aircraft between Berlin, Leipzig, and Wheimar. The British and the French both began passenger service in 1919, using modified military bombers to carry passengers between London and Paris.

AIRMAIL

While Mitchell was creating such controversy in military aviation, progress was being made in commercial aviation in the United States but not as fast as in Europe. The Post Office Department started airmail service in the United States on May 15, 1918, using aircraft and pilots borrowed from the Army. Three months later the Post Office Department took over the operation completely, hiring its own pilots and buying its own aircraft. The first airmail route was between Washington, D.C. and New York City. In 1919, airmail service was extended from New York to Chicago via Cleveland; and, in 1920, from Chicago to San Francisco. However, true airmail service on a regular basis did not begin until July 1, 1924.

The history of these early airmail flights is among the most dramatic in all of aviation. The airmail pilots were true pioneers, flying their own small open cockpit aircraft along uncharted air routes. They flew in all types of weather, night and day, with no radios and very primitive instruments. It is no wonder that during the first three years there were 25 flyers killed along these routes.

During the early years, the airmail routes were marked at night by bonfires on the ground lighted by local citizens (see fig. 38). In 1926, the first electric beacon lights were installed along the airways.

These powerful rotating lights, atop 50-foot towers, were erected about 15 miles apart. Emergency landing fields, with rotating beacons and landing lights, were built at intervals between the towers. Landing and navigational lights were installed on the aircraft. The first radio receivers were also installed, allowing the pilots to listen to weather forecasts.

Many were opposed to the development of an airmail service, especially the railroads. They viewed government subsidizing mail service as unfair competition. The Post Office Department justified the airmail service as experimental in nature, therefore, requiring federal funds. By 1925, the airmail service had developed to the point that it was no longer considered experimental, and the Post Office was ready to turn it over to private enterprise.

AIR MAIL ACT OF 1925

The legislation which made possible the private carrying of mail was the Air Mail (Kelly) Act of 1925, a law which essentially dealt with the economic regulation of the Federal air system. This act authorized the Post Office Department to contract for airmail service. Among other provisions in the act was one which allowed the contractor to be paid 80 percent of the airmail revenue for carrying it.

This was the incentive needed to get big business into the aviation field, and really marked the beginning of commercial aviation in America. This was also a "shot-in-the-arm" for the aviation industries, since the awarding of these airmail contracts created a demand for newer and larger aircraft. As the airmail contracts were let, and as airmail service spread out across the country, a few commercial passengers were carried by the mail planes. However, it was much more profitable to carry mail than passengers. Except for some foreign-built aircraft, such as the Fokker trimotor, most mail planes were small and could carry only two or three passengers.

AIR COMMERCE ACT OF 1926

The first attempt to standardize and regulate commercial aviation was made on May 20, 1926, when Congress passed the Air Commerce Act, which established the Aeronautics Branch within the Department of Commerce. This act provided for the first Federal *safety regulation* of aviation—both of pilots and aircraft. The Aeronautics Branch was authorized to license all planes and pilots, establish and enforce air traffic rules, develop navigational facilities, map airways, furnish flight information, investigate accidents, and provide aviation safety through assistance and guidance to civil aviation.

The act was significant because it aided in the continuing development of the commercial airlines. At this point in time, civil aviation was regulated in the safety area by the Aeronautics Branch and in the economic area by the United States Post Office Department. This arrangement lasted for eight years, when it was changed by a new airmail act.

AIR MAIL ACT OF 1934

On June 12, 1934, Congress passed a new Air Mail Act which changed the economic and safety regulation arrangement of commercial air transportation. Commercial air carriers became responsible to three United States government agencies. The Post Office Department awarded airmail contracts and determined routes and structures. The Aeronautics Branch of the Department of Commerce (renamed the Bureau of Air Commerce on July 1) was responsible for operating airways and regulating the licensing of aircraft and pilots. And the Interstate Commerce Commision's (ICC) Bureau of Air Mail fixed rates of airmail payments to the commercial air carriers.

This act was significant because it separated air transport companies and aircraft manufacturers, and the payments it provided for carrying airmail developed a sound and well-organized air transport system. Also, the act authorized a thorough study of commercial aviation which would lead to the independent Civil Aeronautics Authority in 1938 (and, in 1940, to two new organizations—the Civil Aeronautics Board and the Civil Aeronautics Administration).

AIR MAIL ACT OF 1938

Established air carriers felt threatened by the 1934 Air Mail Act, not only because of the subsidized competition of new independent carriers, but also by the prospect of losing business to the independents. They appealed to Congress for help and on June 23, 1938, President Roosevelt signed into law the Civil Aeronautics Act of 1938. This law combined both *economic* and *safety* regulation into one independent agency called the Civil Aeronautics Authority (CAA). The CAA had a complex structure—it contained a five-man board, an administrator, and a three-member air safety board.

The new structure of the CAA was designed to keep its functions as the agent of Congress distinct from its function as agent of the President, but at the same time, function as a unified regulatory body. The new law did keep competition within bounds and protected the routes of the established carriers. But more important, it unified the economic and safety regulation of the entire field of aviation (independently of the Department of Commerce) and increased the breadth and depth of government control over aviation activities and operations.

THE LONE EAGLE

Progress in aviation in American was being made, but very slowly. What was needed was something that would excite the American people and unite them in support of aviation—and, it wasn't long in coming. Many of the accomplishments in flight following World War I were made because of prizes. These accomplishments included most of the long-range flights, flights over the Poles, and many of the flights leading to speed and altitude records. By 1927, only one of these prizes remained to be claimed—the $25,000.00 prize offered in 1919 by Raymond Ortieg to the "first aviator to cross the Atlantic nonstop from New York to Paris." Many famous pilots had attempted this crossing, but all had failed.

In 1927, a twenty-four year old ex-barnstormer, airmail pilot, and captain in the Missouri National Guard, Charles A. Lindbergh, approached a group of businessmen in St. Louis seeking sponsorship for an attempt at flying the Atlantic. With the $13,000.00

which they provided and $2,000.00 of his own money, Lindbergh engaged Ryan Aircraft, Inc., in San Diego, to build him an aircraft. What Lindbergh wanted was a highwing monoplane powered by a single 220 horsepower, air-cooled, Wright Whirlwind engine.

Just sixty days after signing the contract, Ryan delivered the aircraft which Lindbergh named the "Spirit of St. Louis." One month later, on May 20, 1927, Lindbergh took off from Roosevelt Field in New York and headed east. Flying alone, through bad weather with no radio and only a simple compass to guide him, Lindbergh crossed the Atlantic. Thirty-three and one-half hours after take-off, he landed at Le Bourget Airport in Paris.

Lindbergh instantly became a world hero. Never before had so many people throughout the world given so much admiration and affection to a single individual. The response from the American public was explosive! Here was a symbol the public could identify with and respond to, and Lindbergh was equal to this "hero role." Following his return to the United States, he became a promoter of civil aviation, traveling to every state in the Union. He, more than any other individual, was responsible for thousands of people entering pilot training and for hundreds of cities building airports.

AMELIA EARHART

Another individual who would rival the fame of Lindbergh was Amelia Earhart. This active aviatrix earned her pilots license in 1923, and on June 17, 1928, she became the first woman passenger to fly across the Atlantic. She accompanied Wilmer Stultz and Louis Gordon in an airplane called the "Friendship."

Earhart gained fame as the world's greatest woman flyer before her disappearance in 1937 on a round-the-world flight. In May of 1932, she became the first woman to make a solo transatlantic flight. In her Vega monoplane, she landed near Londonderry, Ireland, instead of at Paris, her planned destination. The flight took 20 hours and 40 minutes and greatly promoted women's interest in flight—serving as a mark for other women to surpass. In August of the same year, she set a new long distance record for women. She was also active in the women's Air Derby and first president of the "Ninety-Nines," an international organization of women pilots.

Charles A. Lindbergh

Amelia Earhart

GENERAL AVIATION— A BEGINNING

It was also during the "golden years" that General Aviation came into being. It was easy for an individual to learn to fly during the years following World War I. He could buy a war surplus DH-4, or "Jenny," and either teach himself to fly or find an ex-Army aviator to teach him. Remember, back then there were no licenses or government regulations, and aircraft did not have fancy instruments or electronic equipment.

In the 1920s, new companies were formed to build small, private aircraft for a growing market of pilots. Among the earliest of these was a company called Travel Air Manufacturing Company, which was formed in 1925 in Wichita, Kansas. This company was formed by three men who would become giants in the light aircraft field—Lloyd Stearman, Clyde V. Cessna, and Walter Beech. They built small bi-wing sport planes which were very successful, but Cessna was convinced that a small private monoplane would be even more successful.

The other two partners did not agree with Cessna; so in 1927, he left Travel Air and started his own company—Cessna Aircraft Company. The other two also broke away from Travel Air and formed their own companies—Beech Aircraft in 1932 and Stearman Aircraft Company in 1933. All three remained in Wichita, and even today, this city is the light aircraft capital of the world.

In 1929, another partnership was formed which would also lead to some world famous aircraft. The two men were G.C. Taylor and William T. Piper. Mr. Taylor was building aircraft on a very small scale in Bradford, Pennsylvania. In 1929, the stock market crash bankrupted him, and Piper, a wealthy oilman, bought the company for $600.00. He reorganized the Taylor Aircraft Company, keeping Taylor as president. In 1935, Piper bought out Taylor's share of the company and renamed it Piper Aircraft Corporation. Taylor moved to Ohio and started the Taylorcraft Company. Both men would produce fine aircraft, but none as famous as the Piper J-3 "Cub."

The spark which really ignited public interest in private flying was, of course, Charles Lindbergh. By

"Amelia" would probably have been the most outstanding woman in aviation, but, as so often happens with record-setters, she was killed at the peak of her aviation career. On March 17, 1937, Amelia and her crew, Fred Noonan, Paul Mantz and Captain Harry Manning, took off from Oakland, California, in her Lockheed *Electra* for the first leg of the flight to Hawaii. Unfortunately, her plane ground looped in Honolulu and had to be returned to Lockheed in California for repair, delaying the flight until 1 June 1937.

This time, Amelia and Fred Noonan climbed aboard the *Electra* at the municipal airport in Miami, Florida—going east to west rather than west to east as originally planned. All went well, but as she approached her scheduled stop at Howland Island in the Pacific, she developed trouble in getting her bearing (direction). She could not hear the signals being sent her by the Coast Guard Cutter *Itasca* and apparently was lost somewhere in the vast Pacific, never to be seen or heard from again. Women's aviation had lost its greatest advocate!

1939, the United States had 39,264 licensed pilots—most of whom had learned to fly either in a Cessna, a Beechcraft, a Piper "Cub," or a Taylorcraft.

AERONAUTICS

RESEARCH CENTERS AND PROGRESS

The late 1920s also saw the science of aeronautics take its place as a true and recognized science. In 1915, President Woodrow Wilson formed an organization named the National Advisory Committee for Aeronautics (NACA). Its purpose was to "supervise and direct the scientific study of the problems of flight, with a view of their practical solution." During the 1920s, this federal agency performed valuable basic research in aeronautics and solved many of the problems that plagued early aircraft.

In 1926, Daniel Guggenheim, an air-minded New York philanthropist, founded the School of Aeronautics at New York University (NYU). He also established a two and a half million dollar "Daniel Guggenheim Fund for the Promotion of Aeronautics" (grants from this fund spread a program of aviation education across the country, and provided many colleges and universities with money for private flying clubs). This insured a supply of trained people in the aeronautics field.

The results were many improvements and changes in the aircraft built during the late 1920s and the 1930s. In efforts to reduce drag, the bi-winged aircraft finally gave way to the more efficient monoplane. More efficient wing shapes and cowlings (covers) to enclose the engines were developed by NACA scientists, and the retractable* landing gear came into existence. Pressurized cabins permitted higher altitude flights, and air-cooled radial engines replaced the heavier water-cooled ones. Other refinements included the development of wing flaps to increase lift and allow

slower takeoff and landing speeds and deicing equipment for safer all-weather flying.

James H. Doolittle (see fig. 39), a young Army lieutenant, did a lot of research on aircraft instruments to make flying at night and in bad weather safer. On September 24, 1929, Doolittle made the first successful "blind" takeoff and landing

Figure 39.

*Capable of being drawn in or pulled up.

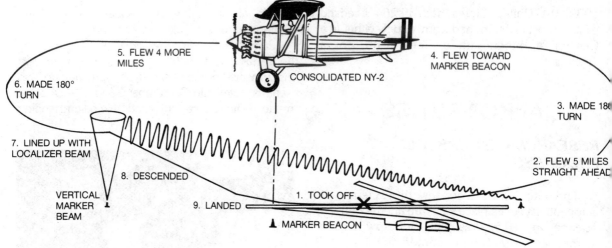

5. FLEW 4 MORE MILES

6. MADE 180° TURN

CONSOLIDATED NY-2

4. FLEW TOWARD MARKER BEACON

3. MADE 180 TURN

7. LINED UP WITH LOCALIZER BEAM

2. FLEW 5 MILES STRAIGHT AHEAD

8. DESCENDED

VERTICAL MARKER BEAM

9. LANDED

1. TOOK OFF

MARKER BEACON

Figure 40. Doolittle's "blind flight" route

(see fig.40). He took off, flew five miles, made a 180° turn, and then came down for a safe landing—all without looking outside the airplane. As a result of this research, instruments for flight and navigation and two-way radios were installed in aircraft.

With the development of an all-metal aircraft by Hugo Junkers, a German aircraft builder, and the stressed-skin principle by another German, Adolph Rohrbach, the airplane began to resemble our modern day aircraft.

Figure 41. Sikorsky VS-300

ROTARY-WING PROGRESS

The helicopter also became a successful aircraft during this period. Little progress had been made during WWI and it wasn't until 1923 that significant rotary-wing advances were achieved. In that year, Juan de la Cierva (Spanish) built the first successful autogiro. Lift was produced by rotor blades which turned independently in flight—the craft was propelled in flight by a regular engine and propeller. But the craft could not move in every direction as the helicopter could. During the 1920s and 1930s, many autogiros were made which led to the helicopter design—a design which was eventually to signal the death of the autogiro.

Progress in rotary-winged aircraft was made by Spain, France, and Germany during the 1930s. Cierva's earlier work on the autogiro (hinged rotor-blade and autorotation feature) contributed to the first helicopter with complete controllability—the Focke-Achgelis, FA-61, built in Germany in 1937 by Dr. Heinrich Focke. It had two rotors mounted side-by-side on outriggers that extended from the fuselage. The world's first female helicopter pilot, Hanna Reitsch, demonstrated the FA-61 inside the Sportzplatz in Berlin in 1938. She "hovered" and performed 360° turns as well as backward, sideward, and forward flight.

However, it was a Russian-born American, named Igor Sikorsky, who finally developed the first practical helicopter. This aircraft, called the VS-300, accomplished vertical takeoff and landing (tethered flight) in September of 1939, and could carry a useful load, perform productive work, and be controlled in flight (see fig. 41). Its first free flight was May 13, 1940. (The VS-300 led to the R-4, the first military helicopter in the world, which was used in World War II.) From this small 1,150 pound, 50 mph craft, the helicopter has grown to the successful "workhorse" aircraft we know today. The name of Sikorsky still stands for excellence in helicopters throughout the world.

ROCKET AND JET RESEARCH

During this period, another great development was made in aerospace—this time in the field of rocketry. Doctor Robert H. Goddard, a Physics Professor at Clark University in Massachusetts, was conducting experiments in rocketry—particularly in the use of liquid fuels. His work not only included the research, but he also actually built the hardware. On March 16, 1926, he launched the world's first liquid fuel rocket. For the next 20 years he did most of the pioneering research on liquid fuel rockets. He developed methods for steering the rockets, ways to pump the propellants, and combustion chamber and nozzle designs. Doctor Goddard has been called the "Father of Modern Rocketry," and rightfully so. His work laid the foundation upon which the Space Age was built.

Two other rocket pioneers of this period who also deserve mention were Konstantin Tsiolkovsky, a Russian school teacher, and Herman Oberth, a German rocket expert. Tsiolkovsky wrote many articles about liquid fuel rockets and did a great deal of theoretical study. Although he never put any of his ideas into practical use, his writings had a strong influence on later Russian rocketry and space flight.

Herman Oberth, on the other hand, led the German liquid fuel rocket program in the 1920s and early 1930s. This research led directly to the German rocket program of World War II and the development of the liquid fuel V-2 rocket.

The first rocket-propelled flight took place June 11, 1928, in Germany. Friedrich Stamer flew a glider powered by rockets for one mile—however, it was a ground-towed launch. It was not until September 30, 1929 that the first rocket-propelled, man-carrying

airplane (taking off under its own power) became a reality. It was the German Opel rocket aircraft (see fig. 42) flown by Fritz von Opel. It flew for about two miles for ten minutes and reached a maximum speed of 100 mph before it crashed. Meanwhile, Frank Whittle was working on the gas-turbine in England, and the Bayerische-Motorenwerke and Junkers in Germany were working along similar lines. It was a Heinkel 178 which first took off with a gas-turbine engine on August 27, 1939. It would be mid-1941 before Whittle would produce a successful gas-turbine aircraft.

Figure 42.

COMMERCIAL AVIATION MATURES

All of the technology was present in the 1930s to develop "modern" commercial airliners. What was needed was a reason. This was provided by President Herbert Hoover's new Postmaster General—Walter F. Brown. In 1930, at Brown's urging, Congress passed the McNary-Watres Act as an amendment to the Kelly Act of 1925.

Under the Kelly Act the airmail carriers were paid according to the weight of the mail carried. The new law changed this so the contractors would be paid according to the available cargo space (using a space-mile formula). In addition, a bonus would be paid to operators flying multi-engine aircraft equipped with the latest instruments. This was clearly an incentive for the operators to fly larger aircraft. It was also an attempt to provide a subsidy*

*A monetary government grant to a person or company to assist an enterprise advantageous to the public.

Figure 43.

to the airlines for carrying passengers as well as mail.

The McNary-Watres Act also authorized the Postmaster General to extend or combine airmail routes. When Brown entered office, all transcontinental airmail was carried by United Airlines on the northern route (New York-Chicago-San Francisco). Brown opened two additional transcontinental routes—a central route from New York-Kansas City-Los Angeles and a southern route from Atlanta-Los Angeles. Transcontinental and Western Airlines (TWA) was given the central route, and American Airways won the southern route.

NEW AIRLINERS

The effect of the McNary-Watres Act on aviation wasn't long in coming. United Airlines contracted with Boeing Aircraft in Seattle to build a "modern" two-engine aircraft. In February 1933, Boeing brought out the 247, a twin-engine, all-metal, low-wing monoplane (see fig. 43). It was constructed with stressed-skin and retractable landing gear and could carry ten passengers and 400 pounds of mail. The 247 had a cruising speed of 189 mph and made

possible the first "same day service" between New York and San Francisco.

Transcontinental and Western Airlines soon responded by contracting with Douglas Aircraft of Santa Monica, California, (September 20, 1932) to build them an airplane better than the Boeing 247. In July of 1933, Douglas began tests in this new aircraft which they called the Douglas Commercial One (DC-1). Only one DC-1 was built for test flights and was delivered to TWA in September. When the production aircraft came out, it was called the DC-2 (May 11, 1934). It had a cruising speed of 192 mph, carried 14 passengers, and several thousand pounds of mail. Douglas built and sold about 200 of the DC-2 aircraft, including many in Europe.

While United Airlines was flying its Boeing 247s and TWA its DC-2s, American Airways was losing money flying foreign-built aircraft. Again Douglas Aircraft was approached; this time to build an aircraft bigger than its own DC-2. Douglas already had more orders for DC-2s than it could handle; but American Airlines agreed to buy 20 of the new aircraft, with an option for 20 more, so Douglas agreed to build it. On December 17, 1935, the first of these new aircraft, called the DC-3, was finished. American Airways was first to put the DC-3 into

Figure 44.

service (June, 1936). The DC-3 was larger than the DC-2, carrying 24 passengers or 5,000 pounds of cargo a distance of 1,200 miles.

This aircraft became the standard commercial airliner for all airlines. It also was one of the most successful aircraft ever built (see fig. 44). By 1938, DC-3s were carrying 95 percent of all commercial traffic in the United States, and by 1939, they were carrying 90 percent of the commercial traffic in the world. A total of 800 DC-3s were built for the commercial airlines between 1935 and 1942. During World War II, 10,000 more (designated C-47) were built for the Army Air Corps.

SEAPLANES

We cannot leave our discussion on commercial aviation without mentioning the Pan American Clippers. In 1927, Pan American Airways was formed to fly the first airmail route between Key West, Florida and Havana, Cuba. This route was extended from island to island throughout the Caribbean. It was eventually extended into Central America and down the Atlantic coast of South America.

Since most of this route was over water, and because seaplane bases were easier to build in remote areas than airports, Pan American Airways wanted a large advanced seaplane. Igor Sikorsky built a large four-engine flying boat called the S-40. It could fly at 125 mph and carry 40 passengers. Sikorsky also developed a larger flying boat, the S-42, which had a range of 3,200 miles. This airplane became known as the Pan American Clipper and made the first airline crossing of both the Pacific and Atlantic oceans.

In 1934, Pan Am took delivery of an even larger

Figure 45. China Clipper

Figure 46.

flying boat, the Martin 130, which they called the China Clipper (see fig. 45). On November 22, 1935, the China Clipper took off from California for the first transpacific flight. After stops in Hawaii, Wake Island, and Guam, the Clipper arrived at Manila in the Philippines. By 1937, this route was extended to Hong Kong, and Pan Am made one round trip flight across the Pacific every seven days.

The ultimate in the flying boats was the Boeing 314, which was delivered to Pan Am in 1938. A total of six of these "Yankee Clippers" were built and they opened up transatlantic passenger service on June 28, 1938. In the six and one-half years they were flown, they made 596 Atlantic crossings and carried 42,042 passengers a total of 4,238,867 miles—all without a fatal accident.

During World War II, the Clippers continued to fly across both oceans for the government. However,

they would never return to airline service. The day of the Clippers was over. They were replaced by the large, four-engined land planes developed during the war.

THE RISE AND FALL OF THE RIGID AIRSHIPS

The time between World War I and World War II saw rigid airships rise to the peak of their success and then completely disappear from the field of aviation.

Following World War I, the Germans were forced to surrender all of their Zeppelins to the Allies. The LZ-126 came to the United States and was named the *Los Angeles*. It served for eight years with the United States Navy, then it was retired and scrapped.

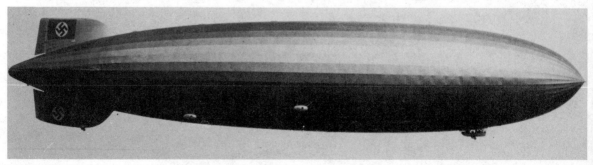

Figure 47.

In 1926, the Treaty of Versailles allowed the Germans to construct Zeppelins again and they built three giant rigid airships. These new Zeppelins were the LZ-127 *Graf Zeppelin,* the LZ-129 *Hindenburg,* and the LZ-130 *Graf Zeppelin II.*

The *Graf Zeppelin* (see fig. 46) was very successful. It was launched in 1928; the following year it made a successful round-the-world flight. During the ten years it flew, the *Graf Zeppelin* made 590 flights including 144 ocean crossings. It flew more than one million miles and carried 13,110 passengers. In 1939, the *Graf Zeppelin* was retired.

The *Hindenburg* (see fig. 47) became the most famous of all Zeppelins, not because of its success but because of its spectacular failure. The *Hindenburg* was launched in 1936 and made ten successful round trips between Germany and the United States. On May 6, 1937, as the *Hindenburg* was preparing for landing at Lakehurst, New Jersey, it exploded. It crashed to the ground and burned, killing 36 of the passengers. These were the first fatalities in the history of scheduled airship operations.

The *Graf Zeppelin II* was commissioned in 1938. Before it could go into commercial service, World War II began, and it was scrapped during the war.

The United States also had its problems with rigid airships. In 1923, the United States Navy built a large airship, the ZR-1 *Shenandoah.* On September 3, 1925, the *Shenandoah* broke up during a storm over Ohio. Fourteen of the 43-man crew were killed.

In 1924, the Goodyear Tire and Rubber Company was granted patent rights by Germany to build Zeppelins in the United States. They built two of these airships for the Navy and both met with disaster. In 1931, the *Akron* went into service flying out of Lakehurst, New Jersey. On April 4, 1933, after only 1,200 hours of flying service for the Navy, the *Akron* crashed in a storm off the New Jersey coast. Seventy-three crewmen were killed.

The other Navy airship, the *Macon,* was built in 1933. It flew out of Moffett Field, California, and patrolled the Pacific coast. On February 12, 1935, the *Macon* suffered a structural failure of the upper fin. Gas leakage and structural collapse caused the *Macon* to crash into the sea off the California coast.

Two crew members were killed in this crash.

Investigations by both the Navy and Congress endorsed the continued use of dirigibles for the Navy. However, due to the outbreak of World War II, construction was never started.

Today, the only dirigibles flying in the United States are the three non-rigid Goodyear "blimps." They are used mainly for publicity and filming sporting events.

MILITARY ADVANCEMENT

The developments made in commercial aviation during the 1930s provided the business necessary to maintain a healthy aviation industry. These same industries were also making advances in military aircraft, although not as rapidly as in the commercial field. During the 1920s and 1930s, despite what General "Billy" Mitchell had done, our national policy regarding military aviation was that the airplane was primarily a defensive weapon used to protect our homeland.

Many of our Army Air Corps officers understood the offensive potential of the airplane, and it was only because of their efforts that some progress was made in the development of fighters and bombers during the 1930s. A prime example of this was the development of the B-17—a bomber which would gain great fame during World War II.

When Douglas Aircraft built the DC-2 and DC-3 commercial airliners, the 247 which Boeing had built became obsolete. This was a blessing in disguise for the Boeing Company, because it allowed them to respond to an Army design competition for a new multi-engine bomber for use in coastal patrol. The term "multi-engine" had always meant two engines, but several Air Corps officers encouraged Boeing to enter the competition with a four-engine aircraft. These officers were all dedicated to Mitchell's doctrine of air power. They envisioned a large four-engine bomber that could be used not only for defensive coastal patrol, but also for long-range strategic bombing.

On July 28, 1935, the four-engine giant,

Figure 48a.

designated the Boeing 299, made its first flight test (see fig. 48a). The 299 was flown to Wright Field in Dayton, Ohio, for competition against two competitors, both twin-engine aircraft. Not only did the 299 (Army designation XB-17) win the competition, but it could outfly any pursuit (fighter) airplane flying during this period. The Army Air Corps made an initial order for 13 of these B-17s (see fig. 48b) and, soon after these were delivered, ordered 39 more.

The Army Air Corps now possessed its first long-range bomber, but during its trials, the XB-17 proved that we were lacking in fighter aircraft. Contracts were let for the Seversky P-35 and the Curtiss P-36, both "modern," low-wing monoplanes, and believed by our Army Air Corps leaders to be equal to any fighter in the world. However, as the United States made these small advances in military aviation, other countries of the world were testing their aircraft in the arena of aerial combat and developing aircraft which they would use during World War II.

Even though the military made modest gains in military aircraft during the 1930s, they were woefully behind in producing pilots to fly them in the event of war. By the time Germany invaded Austria in 1938,

and then Czechoslovakia and Poland in 1939, certain military planners could see that the Army Air Forces alone would not be able to train enough pilots to engage in combat should the United States enter the European war.

MILITARY PILOT TRAINING

The presidential message to Congress of January 12, 1939, marked the beginning of Army Air Forces (AAF) expansion before World War II. The President called for a build-up of our existing forces, which he described as "utterly inadequate." Within three months of this address, the United States Congress would pass a bill authorizing an increase to 3,203 officers from the prior limit of 1,200 officers. Under the impact of even darker threats from abroad, the military planners could foresee that this officer strength would not be enough, and that, even if Congress were to appropriate money for more men and aircraft, the military establishment would be pressed for time to train pilots to be ready for our possible entry into the war in Europe.

Figure 48b.

Despite the lack of training capability, pilot training goals were successively raised by these planners to keep pace with the anticipated progress of other defense programs.* These goals also called for the training of a proportionate number of other aircrew members and ground technicians. The Air Corps had neither the instructors nor facilities for training men and women in such numbers—nor did it have the experience.

Its training program at the beginning of 1939 was based on an annual graduating class of approximately 500 pilots. To step that up in three years to a rate of 50,000 pilots was as difficult a problem as increasing aircraft production from 2,000 to 50,000. To build all the additional facilities required by the new objectives would have required the outlay of vast sums of money. But most importantly, building new facilities to train pilots would have delayed the training program by two precious, vital years.

*From an objective in early 1939 calling for the training of 1,200 pilots annually, the figure was raised in 1940 to 7,000, then to 12,000, and in February of 1941 to 30,000. By the fall of 1941, the AAFs contemplated a training rate of 50,000 pilots a year by mid-1942.

CONTRACT SCHOOLS

Arnold Speaks Out. Turning to civilian flying schools, the AAFs Air Corps discovered that there was a limited reservoir of instructors, aircraft, flying fields, trained maintenance personnel, and experienced administrative officials. Consideration of the possibility of using civilian training facilities had begun in the fall of 1938. At that time, there were twenty-three privately owned flying schools which held an approved rating from the Civil Aeronautics Authority (CAA). However, it would take a person of decisive action to act on the Air Corps discovery.

General "Hap" Arnold was such a person. He had sized up the situation early in 1939—"To build another Randolph Field (Army's only pilot training base) to handle 500 pilots a year would take another five years," he said. And Arnold decided to remedy the situation. In a forthright statement to the House Military Affairs Committee—and making no secret of his intention—on January 18, 1939 (four months before he would call eight private operators to his office), Arnold said:

"Our present system is training all our military pilots at our training center at San Antonio. The capacity . . . is somewhere around 550 a year.

That is approximately what we are turning out now. That is not sufficient . . . The output of pilots must be materially increased. If we are to continue our present policy it means that we will have to increase the facilities at San Antonio . . . I think the War Department decided that is not the proper way to do it. We should . . . build up a war reserve . . . for pilots . . . the War Department policy contemplates the utilization of civilian schools for all our dual instruction."

Arnold then explained his plan for civilian-operated, Army-supervised primary flight schools. Volunteers for the Air Forces would be given physical and mental examinations by the Army. Those who were qualified would be sent to designated civilian schools in their immediate localities to receive dual instruction. Regular Army flyers would examine graduates and give them "checkrides." Cadets would then go to Army bases for basic and advanced training. General Arnold also required civilian instructors to get standard training at Randolph so all cadets would "speak the same language." Among advocates of Arnold's plan were Lt. General Yount, Maj. General Stratemeyer, and Col. McNaughton.

Congress at that time didn't think very much of Arnold's plan, so Arnold went outside the Army for help. He asked eight WWI pilots and non-military aviators who ran private flying schools to help train combat pilots for the Army—with or without pay. Fortunately for Arnold, all agreed to his request.

Civilian—AAF Pilot Training Program. With CAA approval in May of 1939, preparations were made for nine of the schools (through eight contractors) to give primary flying training for the Air Corps—although no contracts could be offered until July 1, 1939. The program was actually in the nature of an experiment, but it would prove very successful and gain wider use as the Air Corps expanded.

The Army sent flying cadets to these "contract" schools July 1, 1939—50 at first, then by the thousands, following Arnold's original blueprint. That first blueprint would be revised and refined as experience showed up its many flaws. Also, the program, which looked so simple on paper, would be full of headaches and near-heartbreaks. In a short

time, these "civilian bases" mushroomed throughout the nation, doing for the AAFs what it could not do by itself—produce combat pilots ready to go to war.

The schools were a gamble for the contractors, since there was no official congressional authorization to pay them. But the program was begun. Originally, the schools intended to train 2,400 pilots annually, but later raised the goal to 12,000, and finally to 30,000 and above. In the end, they were turning out 110,000 cadets each year. The schools even trained Allied pilots at their facilities. After working for nothing for many months, Congress finally authorized their program officially (by *two* votes) and the money to go along with it.

CIVILIAN PILOT TRAINING PROGRAM

Another source of potential aid for the Air Corps pilot shortage existed in the Civilian Pilot Training Program (CPTP) authorized in mid-1939 by the CAA. This program created a great reserve supply of pilots which could be used in a serious national emergency—which was the objective of the program. The Civilian Pilot Training Act of 1939 was signed into law by President Roosevelt. The act authorized the CAA to conduct a program for the training of civilian pilots through existing educational institutions and to prescribe pertinent regulations. The objective was to provide sufficient training to prepare a student for a private-pilot certificate of competence.

The act authorized $5,675,000 to be appropriated for the program during fiscal years 1939 and 1940 and specified that thereafter the appropriations should not exceed $7 million for any one fiscal year. The act was to expire on July 1, 1944. The program called for the training of 11,000 civilian pilots; however, considerably fewer were actually trained the first year.

The name of the program would be changed to the CAA War Training Service (WTS) in 1942, and training would be limited to inactive reserve personnel. The War Training Service could eventually produce 300,000 pilots by 1944.

The CPT programs were set up in educational institutions throughout the country, offering an extensive program of flight training. For blacks, the CPT program marked the beginning of the second era of black aviation progress, and it was to dispel doubts as to the black man's ability to perform in all areas of aviation. Although participation in CPTP was on a segregated basis, the program provided a rapid increase in black pilots and aircraft technicians on the eve of WWII. Many famous black airmen were to emerge from the CPTP and take their place of honor in American history.

Black CPT programs started at a number of schools. West Virginia Institute in Virginia was one of the first black colleges to engage in the program. Another, the Coffey School of Aeronautics in Chicago, which was operated by Willa Beatrice Brown, was to become the hub of black Civil Air Patrol activity in 1941. Instructors at Coffey included famous blacks such as Henri Fletcher, Charles Smallwood, and Edward Gibbs, the founder of Negro Airman International. But the real start of black participation in the CPTP, and in the Air Corps, came as a result of a chance meeting.

On May 9, 1939, Dale L. White and Chauncy E. Spencer set out on a 3,000-mile roundtrip demonstration flight (cross-country) to promote black aviation within the public and to urge Congress to allow more opportunities for blacks in the field of aviation. On a stopover in Washington, D.C., the dashing duo accidentally met Senator Truman, who was unaware that not only were blacks excluded from the Air Corps but that they also did not figure in the proposed CPT Program. This chance meeting led directly to the intervention of Congress on behalf of black Americans regarding aviation opportunities. From it came the activation of the 99th Pursuit Squadron—an all-black unit—on 22 March 1941 at Tuskegee Sub Depot, Tuskegee, Alabama. This was the first CPT program for blacks, was probably the most well-known program, and produced the most distinguished black aviators. Eleanor Roosevelt did much to promote equal opportunity for blacks in aviation and worked ceaselessly to make the Tuskegee program a success.

The Tuskegee program was run by Major James Ellison, base commander, and Charles Alfred "Chief" Anderson, who was the principal flight instructor. The program produced the first black Air Force general, Benjamin O. Davis, Jr. (whose father was an Army general). Davis earned the Distinguished Flying Cross and the Silver Star in World War II. He commanded the all-black 99th Pursuit Squadron in March of 1941 and served in combat in North Africa in 1943. He later became commader of the 332nd Fighter Group ("Red Tails"), which flew more than 15,000 combat sorties and destroying 260 enemy aircraft. Davis was to become the Assistant Secretary of Transportation for Environment, Safety, and Commerce after his retirement from the United States Air Force.

The White-Spencer effort to get blacks into aviation worked well for military aviation, but when the war was over, black aviators were not in great demand by private industry. Thus, some blacks maintain that the CPTP was a chance for the black man to fail.

EFFECT OF CIVILIAN SCHOOLS ON AVIATION

The civilian schools, in hindsight, were vital for the United States to win the war in Europe and Japan. Had it not been for these private pilot trainers, the AAF would not have had the pilots nor technicians available to fly and maintain the planes they would get by the time we entered World War II. These programs represented the military's first formal preparation to enter the war; it was also an official, indirect acknowledgement that the military was unprepared to fight a war—any war in fact.

The pilots and technicians produced by these civilian schools were to provide aviation after the war with a pool of trained, experienced professionals. Many of these same professionals were to advance the cause of aviation greatly after World War II.

RISE OF MINORITIES IN AVIATION

The 1930s represented a fruitful decade for minorities in aviation—a decade which saw the rise of female, black, and other minority group aviators. Although non-minority groups were still predominant in aviation activities, receiving most of the publicity, minority groups began to offer serious competition—showing that they also could do what others had done, and even better in some cases.

BLACK PERSONALITIES

Many blacks were mentioned in connection with the CPT program above. There were others, however, who became famous earlier. Black aviators showed the greatest fame in the first half of this decade with the 1932 flight of the aircraft "Alexander Eagle Rock," which flew from Los Angeles, California, to New York in 41 hours and 27 minutes. The flight was made by James Herman Banning and Thomas Allen (a passenger). This duo was known as the "Flying Hoboes." Their flight was the first west-to-east, transcontinental flight by blacks. Banning was also the first black pilot licensed in the United States.

The year 1934 produced a few more well-known black aviators. Another of the first licensed black pilots in the United States was William J. Powell. Powell actively promoted black aviation as president of the Bessie Coleman Aero Club. In his unique book of 1934, Black Wings, he urged black youth to become pilots, aircraft designers, and business leaders in aviation.

The first east-to-west, roundtrip transcontinental flight by blacks was made by Charles "Chief" Anderson and Dr. Albert E. Forsythe in 1932. Anderson had a reputation for long-distance flying with his doctor friend in the 1930s. On this New York-to-Los Angeles flight, they flew a Fairchild 24— without parachutes, landing lights, radio, or blind-flying instruments. Their most remarkable feat, however, took place in 1934. In that year they became the first aviators to fly a land plane from Miami, Florida, to Nassau in the Bahamas, the Virgin Islands, and the West Indies—this was the "Pan Am Goodwill Flight of 1934." Using a 90 horsepower Monocoupe, with only a ball and needle instrument, this pair flew a plane into a region where no person—white or black—had ever flown before. The route they blazed on this trip is the same route that commercial airlines follow today—but with

sophisticated instruments. Anderson was also instrumental in forming the CPT program at Howard University (1939) and was an instructor in the Tuskegee CPT program (1940).

Other blacks in aviation during the last part of the 1930s were John C. Robinson, President of Chicago's Challenger Air Pilots Association, Grover Nash, and Willie Jones. Robinson aroused considerable interest in the black community by advising Ethiopia's Emperor Haile Selassie on how to build up his air force in 1935. Before he could succeed, however, Italy invaded Ethiopia and Robinson barely escaped capture by the Italians. During "National Airmail Week" in 1938, Grover C. Nash became the first black to fly the U.S. airmail. Blacks also engaged in barnstorming. Probably the most famous was Willie "Suicide" Jones, who was a wing walker and parachutist in the 1939 "Mammoth Air Show" at Chicago.

FEMALE PERSONALITIES

A number of women made significant contributions to aviation in the 1930s. Beginning in 1930, there was Amy Johnson, who, on May 5th, became the first woman to make a solo flight from England to Australia. Amy also served in the British Air Transport Auxiliary and lost her life on a mission ferrying an airplane during World War II. Another record-setter was Ruth Nichols. By 1931 she had flown higher and faster than any other woman in the world. On March 6, 1931, she set a new women's altitude record of 28,743 feet. The remarkable feature of this flight was that Nichols used only an oxygen tank and a rubber hose for breathing.

The barnstormer Phoebe Omlie made a real contribution to aerial navigation for all pilots in 1935. She conceived a plan to paint the names of towns on roofs of buildings all across the United States. The Bureau of Air Commerce liked her idea and had the system implemented; eventually, there was a marker every 15 miles on every air route in America. Omlie was also to be the first woman appointed to a Federal Government job in aviation (Special Assistant for Air Intelligence for NACA). She later opened a flying school in Memphis, Tennessee, and also became the Assistant Chairperson of the

Tennessee Aviation Commission.

We have previously mentioned the beginning of Jacqueline Cochran's aviation career in the section on air races. Cochran had such a long aviation career that she is discussed in several chapters in Part One, primarily because she set more speed, altitude, and distance records than any other pilot in aviation history. She won 14 Harmon Trophies—Eleanor Roosevelt awarded her the first one on April 4, 1938, for being the most outstanding female pilot of 1937. She also received awards for setting the women's national speed record, the women's world speed record, and the New York-to-Miami speed record.

"Jackie" soloed in 1932, in only three days, and got her license in less than three weeks—even though she had not finished grammar school. She later moved to California and got her commercial license. By 1934, she had entered air races and was the only American female entrant in the McRobertson Race (London to Melbourne)—but she was forced down in Rumania. She tried again in the 1935 Bendix Trophy Race but again was forced down, this time in Arizona. She began winning in 1937, taking third place in the Bendix Race and, in 1938, first place in the Bendix, flying a new plane which she had never flown before (P-35). Winding up the 1930s, she made the first blind landing by a woman pilot in 1939, and in the same year, also set the women's national altitude record over Palm Springs, California, and set the international record for the 1,000-kilometer straight course. Later, in 1940, she set a new world speed record on a 2,000-kilometer course, which exceeded the German pilot Ernst Seibert's previous record by 20 mph. Without a doubt, no other woman had achieved so much in this decade, except perhaps Earhart.

The year 1934 brought many firsts for women aviators in a number of aviation areas. Most people think that until very recently only men were hired as commercial airline pilots. In fact, the first woman airline pilot was Helen Richey. Richey was hired by Central Airlines in 1934 to fly between Detroit and Washington, D.C. As you would expect, her reception by male pilots was less than enthusiastic. Because of this, and pressure by the Bureau of Air Commerce (which would allow her to fly only in good weather), she resigned after only three months. Nevertheless, she had penetrated the then male-dominated profession—but it would be more than 30 years before women airline pilots were accepted in the United States. In the balloon area, Jeannette Picard of Minneapolis, Minnesota, set an altitude record in the same year (1934) of 57,559 feet. In 1935 the "99'er Magazine" featured an article on Mary Riddle—the only female American Indian pilot in this period.

In 1937, Willa Beatrice Brown earned her pilot license and became an active promoter of black aviation. She became the operator of her husband's flying school, the Coffey School of Aeronautics, and took an active part in the CPT program. She was an officer in the Civil Air Patrol and in 1971 became an FAA Women's Advisory Board member. 1937 also produced the first female combat pilot in the world—Sabiha Gokcen (gurk-chen), adopted daughter of Turkey's president, Kemal Ataturk. This little "Amazon of the Air" was the first Turkish female pilot (and army pilot) and was probably the first female combat pilot in the world. She blazed to fame in 1937 when she joined a nine-plane force that helped quell a Kurdish revolt, bombing and strafing the rebels for a month.

Many of the minority aviators of these formative years were to open the doors for future would-be minority avaitors—they made it possible for others to get into aviation, breaking down the social barriers which had for so long prevented them from making real, worthwhile contributions to the development of aviation. Future minority groups would achieve perhaps even greater aviation feats, but none would do so under the horrible adverse social conditions which faced the minority aviators of the 1920s and 1930s.

Chapter 1-4

WORLD WAR II

This chapter deals with aviation during World War II. This conflict has often been called the *Air War* because it started with an airplane and ended, five years later, with an airplane. During these five years, the airplane developed faster than during any other five year period in its history.

The general learning objective of this chapter is for you to know aviation developments during World War II. To reach this objective, you must pattern your study of the material according to the *specific learning objectives* listed in the Appendix of this textbook.

PRELUDE TO CONFLICT

AXIS POWERS

There were seven nations which made up the Axis powers during World War II. Of these seven nations, Germany, Italy, and Japan were the three major powers. In addition, Bulgaria, Finland, Hungary, and Rumania also fought on the side of the Axis. We will limit our discussion to the three major Axis nations.

Germany. The Treaty of Versailles, which ended World War I, strictly forbade Germany from developing any type of military aircraft. However, except for a brief six-month period, the treaty did not prohibit German manufacture of commercial aircraft. The German aircraft industry began to revive in the early 1920s, building aircraft which could be very quickly converted from civilian to military use. Many German aircraft manufacturers also established subsidiary companies in such foreign countries as Russia, Sweden, Denmark, Italy and Switzerland. Also, many German pilots were trained in foreign countries, especially in South America.

It was therefore under the guise of commercial aviation that the German Air Force was revived. By 1932, the German Air Force (officially nonexistent) consisted of three bomber squadrons, four fighter squadrons, and eight observation squadrons. There were also 1,500 trained pilots and another 3,000 in training in 1932. When Hitler assumed power in 1933, the buildup became more obvious; by 1935 all pretense ended, and the Luftwaffe was officially formed.

In July of 1936, the Spanish Nationalists (led by General Francisco Franco) launched a revolution against the Spanish Loyalist Government. Both Germany and Italy provided aid to the Nationalists and used this Civil War to test their armament and military tactics. This war provided a proving ground for the pilots of the Luftwaffe and many German aircraft that would be used in World War II.

Italy. The Italian Air Force had become obsolete following World War I. When Mussolini came into power in 1922, it had only about 100 aircraft. Mussolini was an advocate of air power, and he started building up Italy's Air Force.

In 1935-1936 Italy invaded Ethiopia with her Air Force providing air support for the Army. Later, Italy also provided assistance to the Spanish Nationalists. By the time World War II began, the Italian Air Force had about 2,600 first line aircraft and pilots who had received combat experience.

Japan. The Japanese Air Force received its early training from a group of sixty French airmen who arrived in 1919 to provide assistance to the Japanese Army. The Japanese actually had two separate air arms, the Army Air Force and the Navy Air Force. Each had a separate mission; the Army Air Force was designed solely to support the Japanese Army, and the Navy Air Force was responsible for convoy protection, coastal patrol, and antisubmarine patrol. In 1920 the Japanese Navy built its first aircraft carrier, and in 1921 a group of retired Royal Air Force officers from Britain provided training in carrier operations.

In 1931 Japan invaded Manchuria and then drove into China in 1937. These wars provided combat training for pilots of both the army and navy air forces. The Japanese pilots also received combat experience during the Russian-Japanese border clashes from 1936 to 1939.

ALLIED PREPAREDNESS

The term Allies refers to twenty-four nations which signed the Declaration of United Nations on January 1, 1942. The principal Allied powers included the United States, Great Britain*, France, the USSR, and China. Our discussions here will deal mainly with these five.

At the end of World War I, the Allied Nations (England, France, and the United States) had the most powerful air forces in the world. However, without exception, once the war was over they began

*Great Britain includes England, Canada, Australia, New Zealand, South Africa and India.

cutting back until by the early 1920s their air forces were very weak. While the Axis powers were building up their air forces prior to World War II, the Allies maintained an attitude that war could be prevented by diplomatic negotiations. This attitude prevailed until the mid-1930s, when the Axis powers began fighting in Ethiopia, Spain and China. Only then did the British and French begin rebuilding their air forces. The United States did not really begin until after World War II actually started.

Britain. As we mentioned earlier, England emerged from World War I with an independent Air Force, the Royal Air Force (RAF). Between the world wars they emphasized large, strategic bombers and fighters to defend their shores from enemy bombers. Their pilot training was excellent and they stressed quality rather than quantity. In 1935, the British aviation industry began increasing its production, and money was provided to expand and enlarge the industry. When England entered World War II, she had a small but well-trained Air Force and an industry which was capable of producing large numbers of very fine aircraft. The first task of the RAF, therefore, was to hold off the German Luftwaffe until the new aircraft were available.

France. The nation which best understood the important lessons of air power taught by World War I found itself completely unprepared for World War II. The French expended enormous sums of money in the development of ground defenses like the Maginot Line. They believed that this fortification would turn back an invading army.

It was not until 1936 that the French Air Force was born. That same year the aviation industries were nationalized and forced to build military aircraft. The result was a small, poorly trained Air Force and an industry which, because of labor disputes and low morale, produced very few first-line aircraft. When World War II began, the French had about 400 first-line fighters, fewer than 100 modern observation aircraft, and 400 obsolete bombers.

United States. As was mentioned earlier (Chapter 1-3) the United States was almost completely disarmed following World War I. General William

"Billy" Mitchell's failure to get an Air Force separate from but equal to the Army and Navy resulted in the Army Air Service receiving last priority for a budget to build up and modernize our air arm. The mood of the United States was one of isolationism* and this, coupled with the severe depression of the 1930s, resulted in very little money available for the military.

It was not until after World War II actually started that the United States began to see that they could not isolate themselves from events taking place in the rest of the world. Even when France fell in 1940, a majority of Americans still believed that we should not become directly involved in the war but we should provide additional assistance to Britain. The President and Congress did, however, begin to listen to the Army and Navy about improving our defenses and providing money for strengthening them.

In 1940 and 1941, great strides were taken toward gearing up United States industry for war. Orders from Britain and France—and from our own military services—began pouring into our aircraft industries. In 1939, the aviation manufacturers in the United States produced only 2,100 military aircraft for the entire year. By July of 1940, this production had increased to 560 planes per month and, in September of 1941, 1,900 aircraft were produced.

Again, as had been the case before World War I, even though our Allies gave us time, it was a matter of too little, too late. When Pearl Harbor was bombed, two years after Hitler invaded Poland, the United States military was still largely equipped with obsolete equipment and there was a shortage of active-duty pilots ready for combat in Europe.

THE WAR IN EUROPE

HOW THE WAR BEGAN

World War II in Europe started as a result of Germany's desire to reunite those portions of Germany which were separated at the end of World War I. Hitler's ambition was to bring all Germans living in Austria, Czechoslovakia, and Poland back into the "Fatherland." He planned to accomplish this with a short, limited war.

Hitler was convinced that he could threaten most of the smaller countries of Europe into submission. He also believed that the British and French would not try to stop him because they wanted "peace at any price."

Since Germany's plan was to make the European countries they conquered a part of Germany, their military strategy was to do as little damage to the country as possible. Based on this philosophy, Hitler made the decision to produce only those types of aircraft useable for supporting the ground troops and for defending the homeland. He could not foresee a need for large, long-range strategic bombers* and therefore did not produce any. Rather, he ordered Germany's aviation industries to concentrate on short-range, twin-engine bombers and single- and twin-engine fighters. These aircraft were very suitable for the type of war which Germany fought in Europe, but later this decision would lead to Germany's downfall.

German aircraft were generally satisfactory and some possessed outstanding qualities. The Messerschmitt 109 was the backbone of the fighter aircraft, although a few squadrons had been equipped with the longer-range and speedier twin-engine Me-110 (see fig. 49). There were no four-engine bombers comparable to the American B-17 or the British *Sterling*. German bombers were two-engine mediums, chiefly the Heinkel 111 and the Dornier 17. Added to these was the Junkers 87—the highly publicized *Stuka* dive bomber (see fig. 50).

Austria was the first victim of German aggression. Hitler took Austria without warfare by propaganda and assassination. German troops marched into Austria and occupied it on March 11, 1938.

On March 14, 1939, Germany took over Czechoslovakia in much the same manner. Hitler was so much stronger militarily than these smaller countries that they could not possibly defend themselves against a Nazi invasion. When the British

---

*A political policy in which a nation believes they are removed from any relations with other countries.

*Strategic bombers—bombers designed to destroy an enemy's ability to wage war by bombing military, industrial, and political targets.

Figure 49. ME-110

and French refused to help them, they would surrender rather than be crushed.

An exception to this was Poland. Hitler tried the same tactics on Poland that had worked on Austria and Czechoslovakia. However, Poland had a fairly strong modern army and she also had a formal treaty with England and France which promised armed support if the Axis attacked. Hitler, however, was convinced that England and France would not intervene, and when Poland refused to surrender, Germany invaded her. The date was September 1, 1939, and this date marks the beginning of armed conflict in World War II.

BLITZKRIEG

The German invasion of Poland was the first example of a tactic called blitzkrieg (lightning war), a tactic which would be used throughout the war in Europe. Blitzkrieg was a closely coordinated effort between the Luftwaffe and the German Army to crush all opposition. The Luffwaffe first destroyed any opposing air force, generally by catching them on the ground with a surprise strike. Once this was accomplished, the German Air Force would strike at railroads, ammunition dumps, and troop concentration without opposition. The German Army used armored divisions consisting of tanks, motorized infantry, and artillery to strike rapidly at the defenders. Any attempt to reinforce the defenders or to retreat was immediately crushed by the Luftwaffe.

Blitzkrieg was so successful that Poland's Army, which was the fifth largest in Europe, was defeated in only twenty days.

When Germany invaded Poland, Britain and France did declare war on the Axis. But, they were unable to provide any relief for Poland. Neither England nor France had sufficient military strength to attack Germany so they started a defensive war. France mobilized its forces behind the Maginot Line

Figure 50. JU-87 "Stuka"

and England sent a small expeditionary force to take up defensive positions in France. They established a naval blockade of Germany and tried to produce enough planes and tanks to fight Hitler wherever he attacked next. This defensive action continued until April of 1940.

THE CONQUEST OF EUROPE

When Britain and France declared war on Germany, it placed Hitler in a strange position. He believed so strongly that the Allies would not oppose his taking over of Poland that he really did not know what to do next. He was prepared only for a short war and realized that the longer the war lasted, the less chance Germany had of winning. Finally, when the naval blockade was instituted by the English and French, Germany was forced to expand the war. Hitler still hoped that the war could be limited to Europe and the United States could be kept out.

To break the naval blockade, in April of 1940, Hitler invaded Norway and Denmark, using the tactic of blitzkrieg together with the first airborne infantry landings of the war. This campaign was as successful as the invasion of Poland. Denmark was overrun in one day and the Norwegian Army was never really able to mobilize. The German airborne infantry was landed at the Oslo airfield and soon captured the Norwegian capital. Other airborne landings were made at strategic locations. In one day Germany had captured Norway's capital and its principal harbors.

British troops landed to reinforce the Norwegians

but, lacking air cover and antiaircraft artillery, they were soon beaten back. Norway surrendered in June of 1940, and now the Netherlands, Belgium, the Balkans, and France were all that remained of mainland Europe to be captured.

This campaign began on May 19, 1940, and saw the continued success of the German forces as they sped across the Low Countries and France. Two air fleets of the Luftwaffe, comprising some 3,000 planes, were more than sufficient to wipe out the weak air opposition of the invaded countries and to provide support for German Army forces.

For the first time, German parachute troops were successfully employed when the Nazi forces invaded Holland. The Netherlands Army ceased formal resistance within four days. Leading the rapidly advancing German divisions through the Low Countries, the *Stukas* bombed troop concentrations and installations of the defending forces. German transport aircraft evacuated many of the wounded and carried supplies to air force units which quickly moved into bases in southern Belgium and northern France.

The French had concentrated their defenses along the Maginot Line between France and Germany. The German blitzkrieg, however, struck from the north through Holland and Belgium.

Lacking the defensive air force to stop the German aerial offensive, and with no air support for their army, France fell in only six weeks. When France surrendered on June 22, 1940, only Britain and the RAF stood between Hitler and final success.

The success of the Luftwaffe during 1939 and

early 1940 seemed to indicate that they were invincible. However, these successes were scored against weak opposition—England was far from being weak.

THE BATTLE OF BRITAIN

After their successes in France, the German Luftwaffe commanders urged an immediate invasion of England. However, the German Navy was no match for the British Royal Navy and could not guarantee the security of the supply line across the English Channel. The German Army also required time for preparation for the invasion.

Hitler decided not to invade England immediately, but to use the Luftwaffe as a strategic bombing force

moderate scale. During the next ten days, mass formations of German bombers (accompanied by similar formations of fighters) made daylight assaults on shipping and southern ports. The effective opposition of *Hurricanes* (see fig. 51) and *Spitfires,* assisted by ground defenses, caused the Germans to call a brief halt after August 18. On that day they sustained losses of 71 planes destroyed and 23 damaged. For the period extending from August 8th to August 23rd, total Luftwaffe losses were 403 destroyed and 127 damaged. In contrast the RAF announced the loss of only 153 planes.

In the second phase of the campaign, from August 24th through September 6th, the Luftwaffe revised its tactics. Bomber formations were reduced

Figure 51.

against the British Isles. This was the most serious mistake Hitler ever made because, as we mentioned earlier, the bombers and fighters of the Luftwaffe had not been designed for strategic use. They were small, fast aircraft meant to bomb at low altitudes and carried a small bomb load.

The Germans made sporadic raids during July and the first week of August 1940 in order to feel out British defenses. For their bombing of England, the Germans used four main types of bombers: the Junkers 87, the Junkers 88, several models of the Heinkel 111, and the Dornier 17 (sometimes known as the Dornier 215). Fighter escort was provided by Messerschmitt 109's and 110's. The entire strength of the Luftwaffe was not thrown into the campaign at once.

On August 8, 1940, the attacks began on a

in size, while fighter escorts were increased. The attacks were directed mainly against airdromes and aircraft factories instead of shipping and harbors in an apparent attempt to knock out the RAF. As in the first phase, German losses were so heavy that the direction of the assault was again changed.

The third phase (from September 7th to October 1st) saw the peak of the German air effort, which was directed toward industrial areas in general and London in particular. By the end of September, the RAF had asserted its control of the air over the British Isles. During the third phase the British destroyed 435 planes and damaged 161. Total German losses since July 10th now amounted to 1,408 planes destroyed. Unable to sustain such losses, the Germans instituted still further changes in their tactics.

Nearly all the so-called long-range bombers were withdrawn, while fighters and fighter-bombers continued the campaign with a decreasing number of daylight attacks and an increasing number of attacks at night. London was still the principal target. The British suffered heavy casualties and extensive material damage, particularly during the night assaults when their fighter protection was not so effective as it was during the daylight hours.

Nevertheless, the Luftwaffe had failed to achieve its objectives, and the aerial blitz was gradually reduced to intermittent attacks which continued throughout the spring of 1941. The Luftwaffe had sustained its first major defeat and Britain had been saved, for an invasion was contingent first of all on defeat of the RAF.

During the Battle of Britain, the Nazis dropped 190,000 tons of bombs on Britain, killing more than 43,000 civilians and seriously wounding another 56,000. This figure represented more casualties than British troops had suffered in battle.

BRITISH MILITARY PROBLEM

Once the war had started, Britain began to get new aircraft. However, these new planes presented a problem which would face them all during the war— ferrying the aircraft to the places and people who would use them. "Manpower" shortage was the problem, so they turned to "womanpower." At the outset of the war the British had not reacted favorably to requests from women to join the RAF. But one determined Englishwoman had an influential friend in the British military establishment. With this friend's help, she managed to get women involved in the flying area of the war. In 1940 this woman, Pauline Gower, was granted the "privilege" of forming a women's section (British Air Transport Auxiliary) of the British Air Transport Command's (BATC) ferrying division.

Gower started out with eight women pilots, ferrying aircraft right along with the "Englishmen." Since the women were only an "auxiliary" of the BATC (they were not considered military personnel), her ferry pilots had to fend for themselves every inch of the way—from food to lodging.

By the end of WWII there were more than 100 of these courageous women flying 120 different aircraft in and out of combat zones, often without a checkride. Many (such as Amy Johnson, who we mentioned in the last chapter) died in the performance of their duties.

An American group of ferry pilots—organized in 1941 by Jacqueline Cochran— was later added to Gower's BATC Auxiliary. Cochran was refused entry into the American AAFs, so she did the next best thing by joining the English ferry auxiliary as a ferry pilot. This gave her the experience—and precedence—for the group she was to eventually organize and direct in the United States Army Air Corps.

THE WAR FRONTS

Italy Joins Germany. When France surrendered to Germany in 1940, Italy joined with Germany and declared war on Great Britain. The immediate goals of the Italians were to capture the oil rich Middle East and the Suez Canal. They also invaded Greece to secure their invasion of Egypt.

There were two Italian armies, one in Ethiopia and one in Libya. They were to invade Egypt at the same time and destroy the British defenders in a pincer action. This was to be the first of several Italian defeats and the first of many times that Germany would have to come to their rescue.

A small force of British troops from Australia, New Zealand, South Africa, and India opposed the two Italian armies in Egypt and defeated them. They took 133,000 Italian prisoners. This British force went on to liberate Ethiopia from the Italians, where they defeated a force of 200,000 Italian troops. This defeat brought Germany to the aid of the Italians in the Mediterranean.

Mediterranean Attacks. By January of 1941, the Luftwaffe had moved approximately 330 aircraft into Italy and Sicily, and, on January 18th, the Germans inaugurated the first of a long series of heavy air attacks on the island of Malta (a strategically located base for British operations in the Mediterranean). Before the end of the year, the island had experienced its one-thousandth air alert but continued to withstand the aerial pounding from the Axis. By using advanced bases in North Africa, the Luftwaffe also began to strike at British forces in the Suez Canal area and to participate more actively in the Western Desert campaign.

Eastern Europe. Early in April 1941, German bombers were moved into the Balkans in preparation for the next blitzkrieg. From bases in Hungary, Bulgaria, and southern Germany, the Luftwaffe on April 6th began extensive operations in support of German ground forces against Yugoslavia and Greece. The British expeditionary forces, though fully occupied in North Africa, came to the aid of Greece. However, the German onslaught overpowered all opposition, and Axis victories followed in rapid-fire succession. By the end of April, most of the British forces had been evacuated from Greece, and the Germans had entered Athens.

Luftwaffe units quickly moved forward to prepare for an airborne attack against Crete. That attack came on May 20th with a spectacular and successful demonstration of glider-borne and parachute troop operations. After seizing key airdromes, the advance German forces were supplied and reinforced by *Junkers* 52 troop carriers (see fig. 52), while Luftwaffe bombers attacked the British who were attempting to evacuate the island.

Figure 52.

By the first of June the British had been forced to yield Crete to the invaders. With new bases in Greece and Crete, the German Air Force was able to bring more strength to bear against British forces in the Western Desert, and the Luftwaffe, for a brief period, increased its support of German ground forces in North Africa.

By this time, Germany had occupied all of south and southeastern Europe and was heavily engaged in Africa against the British. They also had successfully blockaded the British Isles through combined submarine and aircraft operations. Hitler now made his second big mistake. On June 22, 1941, Germany invaded Russia.

Russian Front. Because Hitler was convinced that the Russian campaign would be concluded within a very short time, he was opposed to the destruction of Russian factories by bombing. Upon his insistence, the Luftwaffe was used primarily as an extended form of artillery in support of ground forces.

In its initial assault against Russia, the German Army was supported by 3,300 aircraft out of a total strength of approximately 5,900 operational and non-operational aircraft. In the drive toward Moscow, in the autumn of 1941, the Luftwaffe deployed almost 60 percent of its strength along the eastern front and suffered extremely heavy losses.

Russia met the Luftwaffe with everything it had, including women pilots. Russian women flew combat missions almost from the beginning of the war (the only country among the major powers to use women in combat sorties). In 1941 Major Marina Raskova formed three regiments of women fliers who flew fighters and bombers. These were all-female squadrons, but women also flew in male squadrons. Lilya Litvyak was a top woman ace who destroyed 12 German planes. In 1943, at age 22, she was shot down and received the Soviet Union's highest award for aviators.

Attacks on Britain Dwindle. The Russian operations caused no immediate increase in German aircraft production. The German High Command, apparently still convinced that the hostilities could be concluded in short order, seemed to feel that no great expansion in the Luftwaffe was necessary. The operations in eastern Europe, the Mediterranean, and North Africa necessitated the use of so large a proportion of German air strength that air attacks against England and British shipping in the west dwindled almost to the point of cessation.

During the last six months of 1941, no night attack against Britain exceeded 15 percent of the maximum scale of effort made during the autumn of 1940. The Luftwaffe was assuming a defensive attitude in the west. Hitler was said to have promised Luftwaffe leaders that the air offensive against Britain might be resumed after the defeat of Russia. But the opportunity had come and gone in 1940, and the future held for the Luftwaffe in the west only a defensive mission.

What Hitler had hoped would be a short-duration war was now settled down to a long struggle of large land armies. In this type of a struggle, Germany was bound to lose, especially when she was committed to fighting on three different fronts—British, Russian, and African. As the year 1941 drew to a close, Germany was still a powerful nation and the Allies (British and Russians) were still on the defensive. It was at this point that two new nations entered the war, one on the side of the Axis and one on the side of the Allies. The war which had been limited to Europe and the Middle East, would become a World War. On December 7, 1941, the Japanese bombed Pearl Harbor and the United States entered World War II.

THE UNITED STATES ENTERS THE WAR

ALLIED STRATEGIC PLANS

Even before the United States entered World War II there had been several conferences between the Allied leaders to discuss the conduct of the war if the United States were to be forced into it. The overall strategy worked out by the leaders was to give priority to the war in Europe and defeat Germany first.

Their belief that Japan might also go to war against the Allies required that the Allies contain Japan and hold her until Germany was defeated. There were several reasons for this. First, Germany was viewed as a more immediate threat and her industrial ability was more feared than was Japan's. Secondly, the Allies in Europe had already been involved in the war for over two years and they needed more immediate relief. Third, the Allies did not believe that their capacity, even including the United States, would be sufficient to allow a

maximum war both in Europe and the Pacific if the latter became a reality. This strategy was followed during the war, although by 1944 the third reason was proved wrong and from that time on we did fight a maximum war in both theaters.

JAPANESE TERRITORIAL STRATEGY

The Japanese attack on Pearl Harbor was not a sudden irrational act. It actually began as early as 1931. The island nation of Japan had always depended on imports for her survival. As Japan's population increased in the early 1930s, she began to develop plans to expand her territory into China and Indochina to gain the raw materials she needed to become an industrial nation.

Japan moved into Manchuria and China in 1931 and expanded into French Indochina after the French surrender in 1940. Alarmed by these movements, the United States and Britain embargoed all trade with Japan. This embargo forced Japan to either give up her thoughts of expansion or to resort to war. Japan chose the latter.

The Japanese strategy was to strike swiftly in several directions, capturing the East Indies, Philippines, New Guinea, and the Marshall, Caroline, and Mariana Islands. They would then use these as a defense perimeter by fortifying them and building air bases (see fig. 53).

The only weakness in the Japanese strategy lay in her Navy and Merchant Marine. She needed to import large quantities of raw materials to manufacture the war goods necessary to sustain her military operations. Her fleet was also vital to support her Army and Air Forces, which were spread across more than six million square miles of the Pacific. She realized that, in order to succeed, she must keep her losses in ships to a minimum. Therefore, the first phase of her war plan was to destroy the United States Pacific Fleet at Pearl Harbor.

PEARL HARBOR

The Japanese attack on Pearl Harbor early in the morning of December 7, 1941, was well planned and skillfully executed. The Japanese task force of six aircraft carriers and 25 support vessels left Japan

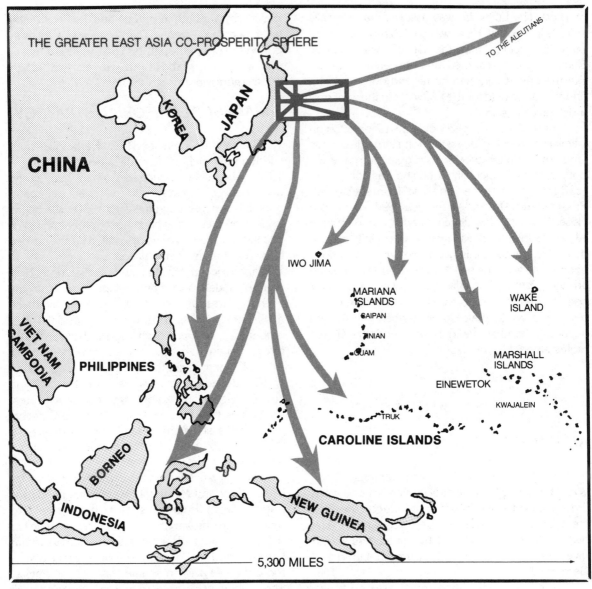

THE GREATER EAST ASIA CO-PROSPERITY SPHERE

TO THE ALEUTIANS

KOREA

JAPAN

CHINA

IWO JIMA

MARIANA
ISLANDS
SAIPAN
TINIAN
GUAM

WAKE
ISLAND

VIET NAM
CAMBODIA

PHILIPPINES

MARSHALL
ISLANDS

EINEWETOK

KWAJALEIN

TRUK

CAROLINE ISLANDS

BORNEO

NEW GUINEA

INDONESIA

5,300 MILES

Figure 53. Japanese strategic plans for the first phase of the war

on November 28th. They were directed to be at a spot two hundred miles north of Hawaii before dawn on December 7th.

At 5:00 a.m. on December 7th, two Japanese Zero reconnaissance planes surveyed Pearl Harbor and reported that the fleet was in. One hour later, takeoff orders were issued to combat aircraft pilots. Soon, 50 fighters, 50 horizontal bombers, 40 torpedo bombers, and 50 dive-bombers were in the air. Forty-five minutes later, a second wave composed of 50 horizontal bombers, 80 dive-bombers, and 40 fighters followed.

The primary purpose of the Japanese attack was to cripple the American Fleet at Pearl Harbor. To do this, the Japanese had to eliminate the threat of Army and Navy interception by destroying their planes on the ground. The enemy planned his strategy accordingly. At 7:55 A.M., the Japanese launched their attack by blasting American airfields on the island of Oahu.

Every advantage lay with the enemy. One of these advantages—surprise—was a result of careful Japanese planning. Another advantage was a result of American fear of sabotage. On November 27, 1941, American Air Force and Navy airplanes had been taken out of hangars and parked closely together on runways as a precautionary measure.

Both advantages proved to be disastrous. The Japanese destroyed 96 Army and 92 Navy planes and damaged 159 more. During the attack only six Army fighters and 36 Navy aircraft got into the air.

Meanwhile, as the Japanese were wiping out our air strength on Oahu, other Japanese pilots were taking advantage of an attractive target at Pearl Harbor—eight battleships, seven cruisers, 28 destroyers, five submarines, and 32 other ships. For 30 minutes, starting at 8:00 a.m., this helpless fleet, moored and wholly unprepared for an attack, was pounded by wave after wave of dive, torpedo, and horizontal bombers. After a 15-minute lull, the Japanese renewed the attack with vigor.

One hour later, the Navy suffered a staggering blow. The battleships *Arizona, California,* and *West Virginia* were sunk, the battleship *Oklahoma* capsized, the battleship *Nevada* and three other battleships were severely damaged. Three cruisers, three destroyers, and a seaplane tender also were damaged.

The Japanese inflicted one of the worst defeats in American military history upon our forces in Hawaii. In addition to heavy losses of airplanes and ships, the attack cost the Navy and Marine Corps a total of 2,117 killed, 960 missing, and 876 wounded. Two hundred and twenty-six Army and Army Air Force personnel were killed and 396 wounded. The Japanese lost 28 planes and a total of 64 men in the entire operation.

The only bright spot in the bombing of Pearl Harbor was that the Japanese had also hoped to destroy the four aircraft carriers of the Pacific Fleet. Fortunately, they were on maneuvers and not present when the attack occurred. Because of the

treaties between Japan, Germany, and Italy, the attack against Pearl Harbor brought the United States into war against all three of the Axis powers. On December 8th, the United States declared war on Japan; on December 11th, she declared war on Germany and Italy. England and the other Allies followed suit and declared war on Japan. Now, all the major powers were engaged in world warfare.

U.S. MILITARY BUILD-UP

The aircraft production of 1940 and 1941 was increased dramatically after we declared war on the Axis Powers in December of 1941. However, the AAFs still had pilot training and strength problems. In the last chapter we discussed the initial efforts of the United States military to build up a pilot reserve for our potential entry into the war. Without these early moves, our increased aircraft production would have been of little value.

After Pearl Harbor, the "contract" schools increased their production of pilots, and on December 7, 1942, the CAA's Civilian Pilot Training Program became the CAA War Training Service. This change in name gave official recognition to changes that had already occurred in the armed services. Beginning July 1, 1942, and lasting until the following December, training under this program was given only to members of the inactive reserve of either the Army Air Forces or the Naval Reserve. On December 15, 1942, the Navy placed its trainees under the program on active duty. The Army took this step in the summer of 1943. In all, some 300,000 pilots were trained in the War Training Service program, which lasted until June 30, 1944, for the Army and until August 4, 1944, for the Navy.

Like the British, the American AAFs did not trust women as combat pilots. They also had a problem getting new aircraft to England and/or to the battlefield—especially in view of the shortage of pilots for combat planes as we entered the war. This problem was solved in the Autumn of 1942 with the establishment of the Women's Auxiliary Ferrying Squadron (WAFS), which was set up within the AAF's Air Transport Command.

The WAFS personnel were civil service

employees and not military members of the AAF—they did not wear the AAF uniform. Nancy Love was the WAFS first director and her group had the duty of ferrying aircraft. To prepare women for these ferrying duties in the WAFS, Jacqueline Cochran formed the Women's Flying Training Detachment (WFTD). On August 5, 1943, the WAFS and the WFTD were merged to form the Women's Air Force Service Pilots (WASP). With Cochran as the first WASP director, the group increased their efforts at delivering planes to England and other locations. The WASPs were still not considered "military" and wore no uniforms (later in the war, the women pilots created their own unofficial uniform). They also received no veterans benefits until Congress enacted a law in the late 1970s to give them all veterans rights.

The women ferry pilots served the nation from September 1942 through December 1944, flying all types of aircraft. Approximately 1,830 women were accepted in the program but only 1,074 graduated and actually ferried aircraft. At the program's end about 900 were still active pilots. Their primary purpose was to release men for combat by ferrying aircraft. However, they also towed targets, instructed, flew drones, and did engineering test flying. They logged in excess of 60,000,000 miles and the aircraft they flew included B-17s, B-25s, P-47s, and B-29s (77 types in all). The first female B-29 pilots were Dorothea Johnson and Dora Daugherty.

The WASP record stands up well against the record of male ferry pilots; they also lost less time for ill health than their male counterparts. Some 38 WASP personnel lost their lives in the service of their country (such as Virginia Moffatt, whose plane crashed and burned on October 5, 1943). Following America's official entry into the war on December 8, 1941, the WASPs helped offset our poor initial preparation for World War II by freeing the men who had been trained by "contract" schools and the CPTP/WTS to be used in combat roles rather than in noncombat, ferrying duties. The American preparation for WWII was weak, and stop-gap measures had to be taken after we entered the war.

For the remainder of this chapter we will separate the war into the European/Mediterranean campaign and the Pacific campaign and discuss them separately. It is important to remember that both campaigns were going on at the same time and that what was happening in one area affected the campaign in the other.

EUROPEAN/ MEDITERRANEAN CAMPAIGN

BASIC ALLIED STRATEGY

The basic Allied strategy once the United States entered the war was to change from the defensive to the offensive, to invade and recapture territory occupied by Germany, and finally to defeat Germany. The army and air force leaders had different ideas on how to accomplish this.

The Army leaders saw this being accomplished by invading France and then having the ground forces fight their way across France into Germany. The Allied Army would crush the Axis forces and force the enemy to surrender. They viewed the use of air power as consisting of those air operations which the ground commanders determined necessary to support their ground operations.

The air force commanders viewed the use of air power as being twofold: First, as strategic operations using large bombers under the control of air force commanders to attack deep within an enemy's homeland for the purpose of destroying his will and ability to continue the war; and, secondly, as tactical operations using fighters and light bombers against targets such as enemy forces, or geographic positions, in support of Allied armies. Control over these tactical air forces would be shared by ground commanders and air force commanders.

STRATEGIC BOMBING

To perform the strategic bombing of Germany, the Eighth Air Force was formed in January, 1942. The Eighth Air Force was moved to England and conducted its first strategic bombing mission on August 17, 1942. The strategic bombers used by the Eighth Air Force were B-17 *Flying Fortresses*

Figure 54.

Figure 55.

(see fig. 54).

The United States Army Air Forces strategy called for precision daytime bombing which differed from the RAF strategy which stressed night blanket bombing operations. The United States claimed better accuracy with their daytime bombing. The British claimed their losses from German fighters and anti-aircraft fire were less at night. Both claims were true and both strategies had merit. Throughout the war each continued using their own strategy and they proved to complement each other very well. With the Americans bombing during the day and the British bombing at night, the pressure on Germany never let up.

At the beginning of the strategic bombing of Germany, the first priority targets were submarine factories, sheds, docks, and ports. The German submarines were doing tremendous damage to Allied naval convoys. In order to carry the war into Germany, both in the air and on the ground, the supplies had to get through. Second priority were aircraft factories and munitions plants and third priority went to communications and transportation systems.

Throughout 1942 and 1943 the Eighth Air Force's B-17s and B-24 *Liberators* bombed targets mostly in France (see fig. 55). The reason for this was that during this time they were still in a building phase, trying to get aircraft to England from the

United States and training the crew members. Also, the Eighth Air Force was hampered by a lack of long-range fighters for escort purposes. The majority of the fighter escorts at this time were the British *Spitfires* and *Hurricanes* and the American P-38 *Lightnings,* and the P-40 *Warhawks* (see fig. 56). The P-47 *Thunderbolt* was just arriving in Europe, but even it did not have enough range to escort the bombers deep into Germany.

During the late summer and early fall of 1943, the Eighth Air Force made its first big effort at bombing deep inside Germany. There were no long-range fighters available so they flew without escorts. The results were disastrous. In six missions from July 24th to July 30th they lost 88 bombers. On August 17th, in a raid against Schweinfurt and Regensburg, 60 bombers were lost. During the second week in October, there were 148 bombers lost, mainly to the FW-190, ME-109, ME-110, and ME-210 fighters of the Luftwaffe. These heavy losses resulted in a cessation of air raids into Germany until long-range fighter escorts like the P-51 *Mustang* became available. They also elevated German fighter manufacturing facilities to the top of the target priority list.

By the spring of 1944, the fighter escorts were available and the Eighth Air Force increased its bombing activities against Germany. On March 4, 1944, the first raid against Berlin was flown. The priority targets were still fighter manufacturing facilities as well as oil refineries (which produced fuel for the Luftwaffe), engine manufacturers, and ball bearing manufacturers (if the supply of ball bearings was cut off, aircraft engine production would stop and so would the building of aircraft). In addition, the invasion of Europe was planned for June 1944, and more and more raids were flown to pave the way for the invasion.

TACTICAL OPERATIONS

The United States Ninth Air Force was established in Egypt in May of 1942 to provide aerial assistance to the British in Egypt. The Ninth Air Force was equipped with medium bombers (B-25 *Mitchells* and B-26 *Marauders*—as well as P-38, and P-40 fighters. The Ninth Air Force was used to attack Axis supply lines, docks, shipping pipelines, munition dumps, airfields, and supply

Figure 56. P-38 "Lightning" (top), and P-40 "Warhawk"

dumps. This was a new use of air power by the Americans, although the RAF had used it for years. The German Afrika-Korps (led by Field Marshal Rommel) began to feel the effects of these efforts as supplies of food, water, fuel, ammunition, and replacements ran short. In October 1942, Rommel began retreating but even his retreat was harassed by the Ninth Air Force and the RAF.

In October 1942, the American and British troops invaded French West Africa. This landing represented a pincer movement with the Allies now in both the east and the west and the Axis between them.

To support the British and American troops in West Africa, the Twelfth Air Force was formed. This was both a strategic and a tactical air force with the heavy bombers (B-17s and B-24s) being used to bomb ports and airfields, and the medium bombers (B-25s and B-26s) and the fighters (P-38s, P-39s, and P-40s) being used to destroy tactical targets.

By May of 1943, the Axis forces were defeated in Africa, and the United States Army Air Force had perfected the concept of tactical air warfare which would be used throughout World War II and even today. This tactic is made up of three parts:

1. *Air superiority*—The first requirement is to attack enemy airfields, repair shops, and fuel supplies as well as to destroy enemy aircraft. This insures that air operations can be conducted without meeting enemy resistance.

2. *Interdiction*—Step two consists of crippling enemy supply lines, railroads, bridges, highways, supply dumps, troop

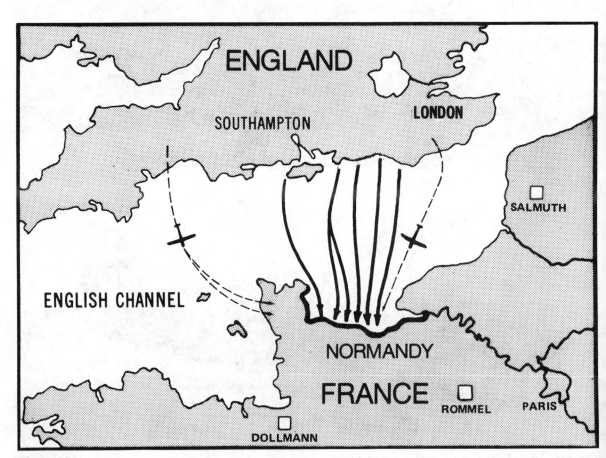

Figure 57.

concentrations, and communications so as to isolate the battle area and prevent the enemy from entering or leaving the battlefield.

3. *Close Ground Support*—Once the first two are accomplished, air power is used to bomb and strafe enemy troops and gun positions and provide aerial cover for Allied troop movements.

Once the war was completed in Africa, the Ninth and Twelfth Air Forces began a strategic bombing operation against Italy and southern Germany. They also provided tactical support for the invasion of Sicily in July, 1943 and Italy in September, 1943.

Following the surrender and occupation of Italy, the Ninth Air Force was removed to England to support the invasion of France. The Twelfth Air Force was split into two parts—the Fifteenth Air Force, which was a strategic air force, and the Twelfth Air Force, which was a tactical air force. Now the Luftwaffe had another thorn in its side. They had to defend against the Eighth Air Force from England and the Fifteenth Air Force from Italy.

THE INVASION OF EUROPE

On June 6, 1944, the Allies landed in Normandy, France for the invasion of Europe (see fig. 57). The invasion was supported by both the tactical and strategic air arms of the Army Air Forces and the Royal Air Force. The pre-invasion air strikes had been going on for two months before the landings. These strikes were made against the Luftwaffe, railroad centers, coastal batteries, and all airfields within a 130-mile radius of the landing beaches. They were so successful that the invasion was completely unopposed by the Luftwaffe. The United States and British forces, with their tactical air cover, fought across France and Belgium and entered Germany in September of 1944.

The strategic bombing of Germany resumed after the Normandy invasion with priority given to aircraft factories, oil refineries, and transportation facilities. By 1945, the Luftwaffe had been beaten and was no longer a serious threat to the British and American bombers. The Eighth and Fifteenth Air Forces had by now built up to the point that it was

not unusual for 1,000 to 1,500 bombers to be in the air every day. On April 15th, the strategic bombing of Germany ended because there were no targets left to bomb.

On May 7, 1945, Germany surrendered and the war in Europe ended. Without exception, the German leaders (military and civilian) who were captured stated that air power had won the war in Europe. During the air war in Europe, British and American planes dropped nearly two and one-half million tons of bombs. The Army Air Force and RAF lost 8,000 bombers and 7,000 fighters. Luftwaffe losses were nearly 33,000 aircraft destroyed.

THE PACIFIC CAMPAIGN

JAPANESE/ALLIED STRENGTH

From a military standpoint, Japan was stronger than either the British or the Americans. The British were fully engaged with the Germans in Africa and in defense of their homeland, so they would not be an immediate threat to the Japanese in the Pacific. At the time Japan entered the war, she had an army of 2,400,000 well-trained men and 3,000,000 reserves. Her air arm consisted of 7,500 aircraft and her industry was producing over 400 new aircraft per month.

In the Far East, the Allies opposed this force with an army of about 350,000 poorly equipped troops, less than 1,000 aircraft (mostly obsolete), and about 90 war ships.

JAPANESE ADVANCES

By the summer of 1942, the Allies had been pushed back all the way to Australia in a series of Japanese victories. At the same time as the attack on Pearl Harbor, the Japanese launched their offensive against the American bases on Midway Island, Wake Island, Guam, Hong Kong, Thailand, Burma, and the Dutch East Indies. By March of 1942, the Japanese occupied the entire area of the Southwest/Central Pacific which they had outlined in their original war plan.

The Japanese tactics in all of these campaigns

were the same. Their air power would first gain air superiority; this was followed by invasion. The Allies were unable to resupply their troops because the Japanese controlled the air, and it became only a matter of a short time before the defenders had to surrender.

As these battles in the Pacific were being fought and lost by the Allies, they were gradually being forced back toward Australia. By March 1942, what remained of the Allied Air Forces and Navies had already been evacuated to Australia.

STOPPING THE ADVANCE

The advance of the Japanese in the Pacific was stopped in the spring and summer of 1942 by two battles which were fought entirely by air power. These were the Battle of the Coral Sea and the Battle of Midway. Both of these battles were naval battles, and for the first time in history, these battles were conducted without the surface ships ever seeing each other or firing a shot—they were fought entirely by aircraft.

These two battles established the strategy for all subsequent naval battles of the war and the aircraft carrier (rather than the battleship) as the primary naval weapon.

Task forces from the United States and Japan met in the Battle of the Coral Sea off the east coast of Australia on May 7 and 8, 1942. Aircraft from carriers of both fleets were launched. Their primary targets were the enemy aircraft carriers. After a two-day battle involving hundreds of dive bombers, torpedo bombers and fighters the losses were: two Japanese aircraft carriers, three heavy cruisers, one light cruiser, and two destroyers sunk and 100 aircraft destroyed; one United States carrier (Lexington), one destroyer, and one tanker sunk and 50 aircraft destroyed.

Almost exactly one month later, the United States and Japanese navies met again in the Battle of Midway in the North Central Pacific. The tactics were virtually the same and the results were even more disastrous for the Japanese. When the battle was over, the Japanese losses were: four aircraft carriers, a heavy cruiser, and three destroyers sunk; three battleships, three heavy cruisers, one light

cruiser, and several destroyers damaged; and 275 aircraft destroyed. United States losses were one aircraft carrier (Yorktown) and one destroyer sunk, and 150 planes lost.

These two naval victories stopped the advance of the Japanese in the Pacific and changed the strategy of the Allies from the defensive to the offensive posture.

ISLAND HOPPING

In terms of tactics, the war in the Pacific was an entirely different war from the European campaign. While the entire war in Europe was fought on a single land mass about one-third the size of the United States, the Pacific campaign involved hundreds of separate islands scattered over millions of square miles. The Pacific campaign could best be described as a relentless struggle for island air bases.

This island hopping campaign required that each island be invaded and that the invasions be supported by the Navy. The Pacific war, therefore, required much more Navy involvement than had the European war. There were few strategic targets on these small islands, so most of the bombing was tactical in nature and was carried out by medium bombers of the AAF and by fighters of the AAF and the Navy.

As each island or group of islands was conquered, one of the first things the U.S. would do was build new airfields. These airfields were then used as bases from which to fly close-air-support missions in support of the next landing. Some of these battles became legends and names like Tarawa, Rabaul, Bougainville, Kwajalein, Iwo Jima, and Okinawa became household words.

The ultimate goal of this island hopping campaign was to acquire air bases close enough to allow the strategic bombing of the Japanese Islands. The islands selected for these bases were Guam, Saipan, and Tinian in the Mariana group. The Japanese realized the strategic importance of the Marianas and the fighting there was particularly fierce. The U.S. casualties in the battle for the Marianas totaled 7,200 killed and 18,000 wounded. The Japanese lost 40,000 troops.

It was at this time (late 1944) that the Japanese unveiled their last desperate weapon—the Kamikaze (see fig. 58). During the last ten months of the war, more than 5,000 Japanese airmen gave their lives in these suicide planes. The tactic was to make a suicidal crash in an aircraft loaded with bombs on a Navy vessel (preferably an aircraft carrier), explode the bombs, and sink the ship. The Kamikaze raids wreaked havoc on the U.S. Navy, producing heavy damage and many casualties, but they did not achieve their goal of stopping the progress of the war.

THE BOMBING OF JAPAN

The only bright spot for the Allies in the Pacific was the first bombing of Japan which took place on April 18, 1942.

Lt. Colonel James H. Doolittle led this first bombing raid which consisted of sixteen Army Air Force B-25 bombers. The bombers were launched from the United States Navy aircraft carrier *Hornet* (see fig. 59). The cities of Tokyo, Yokohama, Yokosuka, Kobe, Osaka, and Nagoya were bombed without a single B-25 being lost to the enemy. The bombers continued across the sea of Japan and crash landed in China. Only six crew members were

lost due to this raid and four of these died in Japanese prisons.

The next strategic bombing of Japan began on June 15, 1944. The first raids were flown from air bases in China. The bombing of Japan was carried out using a new strategic bomber which had been developed specifically for these missions—the B-29 (see fig. 60). By November 1944, the airbases on the Marianas were in operation and the strategic operations shifted from China to the Marianas.

The tactics followed in bombing Japan differed from those used in Germany. Japanese industries were scattered within the populated areas of the cities instead of being concentrated in industrialized zones. Also, much of Japan's industry was of the small "home" operation type. This made pinpoint bombing operations useless; the job had to be accomplished by blanket bombing. It was inevitable that many civilian casualties would occur because of the location of these industrial targets.

In February of 1945, the use of explosive bombs was discontinued and the U.S. began using incendiary bombs. These fire raids were very destructive against the wood and paper houses of the Japanese, and many of their larger cities were literally burned off the map.

The bases in the Marianas were about 1,500

Figure 58.

miles from Japan, which meant that the B-29s had to fly without the protection of fighter escort. The results were the same as over Germany. Losses from enemy fighters were quite large. We needed a base closer to Japan. This resulted in the invasion and capture of Iwo Jima. This island was only 750 miles from Japan and served two important roles— a base for fighter escorts and an emergency landing field for damaged B-29s. By the end of the war, 2,400 B-29s had made emergency landings on Iwo Jima.

The plan to conquer Japan included invasion of the Japanese Islands. This plan would have resulted in hundreds of thousands of casualties for both the Japanese and the Americans. For this reason, President Harry Truman made the decision to use the new "ultimate" weapon which had just been developed in the United States—the atom bomb. On August 6, 1945, a B-29 dropped an atom bomb on the city of Hiroshima, and on August 9th another was dropped on Nagasaki (see fig. 61). Five days later, on August 14, 1945, Japan surrendered and World War II was over.

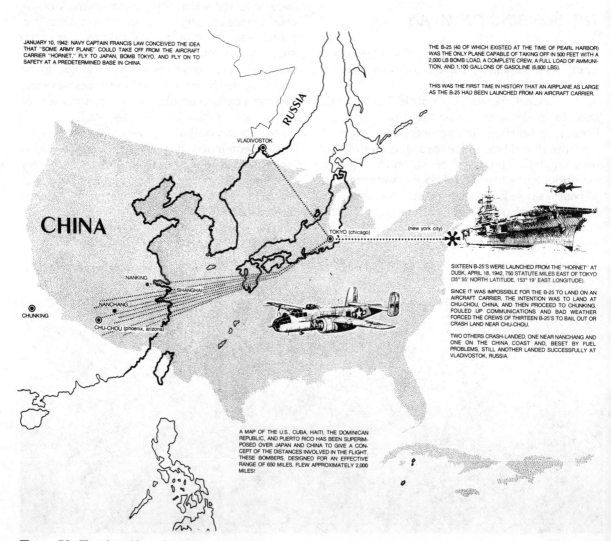

JANUARY 10, 1942: NAVY CAPTAIN FRANCIS LAW CONCEIVED THE IDEA THAT "SOME ARMY PLANE" COULD TAKE OFF FROM THE AIRCRAFT CARRIER "HORNET," FLY TO JAPAN, BOMB TOKYO, AND FLY ON TO SAFETY AT A PREDETERMINED BASE IN CHINA.

THE B-25 (40 OF WHICH EXISTED AT THE TIME OF PEARL HARBOR) WAS THE ONLY PLANE CAPABLE OF TAKING OFF IN 500 FEET WITH A 2,000 LB BOMB LOAD, A COMPLETE CREW, A FULL LOAD OF AMMUNITION, AND 1,100 GALLONS OF GASOLINE (6,600 LBS).

THIS WAS THE FIRST TIME IN HISTORY THAT AN AIRPLANE AS LARGE AS THE B-25 HAD BEEN LAUNCHED FROM AN AIRCRAFT CARRIER.

RUSSIA

VLADIVOSTOK

CHINA

TOKYO (chicago)   (new york city)

NANKING

SHANGHAI

NANCHANG

CHUNKING

CHU-CHOU (phoenix, arizona)

SIXTEEN B-25'S WERE LAUNCHED FROM THE "HORNET" AT DUSK, APRIL 18, 1942, 750 STATUTE MILES EAST OF TOKYO (35° 55' NORTH LATITUDE, 153° 19' EAST LONGITUDE).

SINCE IT WAS IMPOSSIBLE FOR THE B-25 TO LAND ON AN AIRCRAFT CARRIER, THE INTENTION WAS TO LAND AT CHU-CHOU, CHINA, AND THEN PROCEED TO CHUNKING. FOULED UP COMMUNICATIONS AND BAD WEATHER FORCED THE CREWS OF THIRTEEN B-25'S TO BAIL OUT OR CRASH LAND NEAR CHU-CHOU.

TWO OTHERS CRASH-LANDED, ONE NEAR NANCHANG AND ONE ON THE CHINA COAST AND, BESET BY FUEL PROBLEMS, STILL ANOTHER LANDED SUCCESSFULLY AT VLADIVOSTOK, RUSSIA.

A MAP OF THE U.S., CUBA, HAITI, THE DOMINICAN REPUBLIC, AND PUERTO RICO HAS BEEN SUPERIMPOSED OVER JAPAN AND CHINA TO GIVE A CONCEPT OF THE DISTANCES INVOLVED IN THE FLIGHT. THESE BOMBERS, DESIGNED FOR AN EFFECTIVE RANGE OF 650 MILES, FLEW APPROXIMATELY 2,000 MILES!

Figure 59. First bombing of Japanese mainland

Figure 60. B-29 Strategic Bombers

Figure 61. Nuclear devastation in Nagasaki

THE LESSONS LEARNED

World War II ended the same way it began, with an awesome display of air power. The German blitzkrieg in Poland was no less awesome a display of military air power to the people of Europe at that time than the atomic bombings were to the Japanese six years later. During those six years the entire nature of war, as it had been practiced for over 6,000 years, changed. The airplane became the dominant weapon of war and the aircraft carrier became the primary naval weapon. While no claims are made that the war was won by air power alone, neither can it be argued that control of the air was not essential to the success of every major military operation of World War II.

In the final analysis, the war was won by the technological and wartime production capabilities of the Allied Powers. Of all the Allied nations, it was the United States that combined the manpower and materials into the greatest manufacturing effort in history.

In the area of aviation, the United States produced 300,000 aircraft in the 62 months between July 1940 and August 1945. The cost of this production was 45 billion dollars. This amounts to an average of 4,838 aircraft per month or 161 per day produced during the war. Breaking the cost figure down, it averages an amazing 24 million dollars per day for aircraft—every day of the war. This is an amazing figure even in today's world and completely unheard of in the 1940s. However, these average figures do not tell the entire story because they include the low production years at the beginning of the war as well as the high ones at the close of the war. The highest monthly production occurred in March of 1944 when 9,113 planes were produced. This remarkable production figure equaled the combined production of England, Russia, Germany, and Japan during that month.

The final lesson which World War II hopefully taught us is the utter futility of war in a modern society. Twenty million people were killed during the war. Four million of these were civilians. At least three times this many were injured and many were severely and permanently disabled. Warfare had finally reached a point where no one could win or lose, and the only sensible solution was to prevent wars rather than to fight them.

Chapter 1-5

THE POSTWAR YEARS: 1945-1958

The postwar years were the time of the Cold War. Russia was trying to increase her influence in the world and the United States was trying to decrease Russia's influence without going to war. There were some magnificent flying machines built during this time period, many of which are still in use today. It was also a time when the world was approaching the ultimate flight experience—spaceflight.

The general learning objective for this chapter is for you to know aviation developments in the postwar years: 1945-1958. To each this objective, you must pattern your study of the material according to the *specific learning objectives* listed in the Appendix of this textbook.

WARTIME ADVANCES

While no one can question that the airplane caused great changes in World War II (WW II), it is equally true that World War II caused great changes in the airplane. Advances in instrumentation, navigation aids, electronics systems, and armor protection were just as great. By the end of WW II the aircraft, powered by a piston engine and driven by a propeller, had advanced to the ultimate. Better ones were never built.

The advances in aerospace and aerospace power that would be achieved after WW II would not have been possible without the groundwork that was laid during the war. WW II conventional aircraft, helicopters, and jets as well as air-delivered weapons were developed out of necessity and proved under actual combat conditions. It was from these advances in aircraft and weapons that the postwar developments would come. We will briefly look at what these advances were before going on to our discussion of the postwar years.

CONVENTIONAL AIRCRAFT

Bombers had grown in size, speed, and bomb load, showing little similarity to their prewar ancestors. The B-29 carried three times the bomb load and had three times the range of the B-17. In addition, the B-29 was the first bomber to have a pressurized crew compartment, which allowed it to fly at much higher altitudes. It also had a central fire control system, which allowed its guns to be aimed and fired by remote control.

Figure 62. He-178

Figure 63. XP-59

Figure 64. P-80A

The P-51 *Mustang* has often been called the best fighter of WW II. A comparison of the P-51D and the Curtiss P-40 shows the advancements made in fighter aircraft during the war.

	P-51D	P-40
Maximum weight	11,600 lbs.	7600 lbs.
Maximum speed	437 mph @ 25,000 ft	352 mph @ 15,000 ft
Maximum range	2300 miles	1200 miles
Service ceiling	41,000 feet	32,000 feet
Rate of climb	3500 ft/min	3000 ft/min

Warfare has a habit of producing revolutionary new developments to replace things that have developed to the ultimate. In this case, it was the jet aircraft; this development would rapidly make piston engine aircraft obsolete.

JET PROPULSION

Frank Whittle, an Englishman, designed the world's first turbojet engine for use in an airplane and this engine was tested for the first time in April of 1937. However, it was not until May 15, 1941, that England flew her first jet aircraft. By this time Germany had flown several. The first German jet (also the first in the world to fly) was the Heinkel He-178 (see fig. 62), which was first flown on August 22, 1939.

The United States flew its first jet aircraft, the Bell XP-59 *Airacomet* (see fig. 63), on October 1, 1942. However, the P-59 was no better than the piston engined P-51 *Mustang* and was never put into production. The first production U.S. jet fighter was the Lockheed F-80 (originally designated the P-80A) *Shooting Star* (see fig. 64) which flew for the first time in January 1944. The *Shooting Star* was far superior to any fighter aircraft in the world (jet or propeller driven) but it came too late to be used in WW II.

Both the British and the Germans produced jets which saw combat in World War II. In fact, before WW II ended, Germany had produced 22 models of jet aircraft, including some with sweptback wings, delta wings, afterburners, ramjets, and even variable-sweep wings. England produced two aircraft, the Gloster *Meteor I* and the DeHavilland *Vampire*, which were operational before the war ended.

The most famous jet of WW II, and probably the best, was the Messerschmitt Me-262A (see fig. 65). It could have possibly changed the outcome of the war if it had come a little earlier and in greater numbers. Fourteen hundred of these twin-engine German jets were produced during the war but only about 100 ever saw operation as fighters. An additional 200 were used as tactical fighter-bombers. The Me-262 was a formidable aircraft, carrying four 30mm cannons and capable of a speed of 550 mph.

"VENGEANCE" WEAPONS

The last twelve months of WW II in Europe saw the use of two new German "vengeance" weapons. The first was a small, 26-foot long, unmanned flying bomb called the *V-1*. The V-1 weighed 4,800 pounds, of which 1,800 pounds represented high explosives. It was powered by a pulse-jet engine mounted in a "stove pipe" above the fuselage (see fig. 66). This simple engine drew air into the combustion chamber through a flap valve in front of the stove pipe. The valve closed and the fuel was injected into the combustion chamber and ignited. The exhaust through the tail pipe provided the thrust.

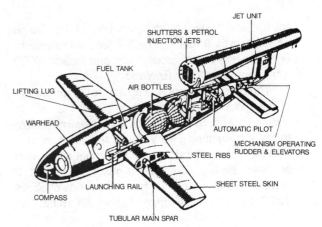

Figure 66. Diagram of V-1

This type of engine produced a unique sound which gave the V-1 its nickname, "buzz bomb." Between June, 1944, and March, 1945, 10,500 "buzz bombs" were launched against England and 12,000 more against targets in Europe. Most of the V-1s were launched from ground ramps, but about 1,900 of those launched against England were air launched from He-111 bombers.

Flying at about 400 mph, the V-1 had a range of about 200 miles. When the predetermined target area was reached, the V-1 nosed down, which cut off

Figure 65. Me-262A

the fuel and the engine stopped. The V-1 then fell on whatever was under it. The V-1 was vulnerable to fighter aircraft and ground fire and nearly 4,000 were shot down over England.

The other vengeance weapon was the forerunner of the space age—the rocket-propelled V-2 ballistic missile (see fig. 67). Unlike the V-1, it was impossible to defend against. The V-2 was the product of a brilliant rocket scientist named Wernher von Braun and was the first liquid-fueled missile ever built. It carried a 2,000-pound warhead at speeds of about 3,600 mph and had a range of about 220 miles. The high, arching flight of the V-2 carried it to an altitude of about 100 miles from which it fell at speeds faster than the speed of sound, landing before any warning could be given. Altogether about 4,300 V-2s were launched between September 1944 and March 1945—1,120 of them against London. Records show that 1,050 actually fell on England. Again it was fortunate for the allies that this effort occurred late in the war. If Germany had been able to develop and launch great numbers of V-2s, the tide of the war might have been changed.

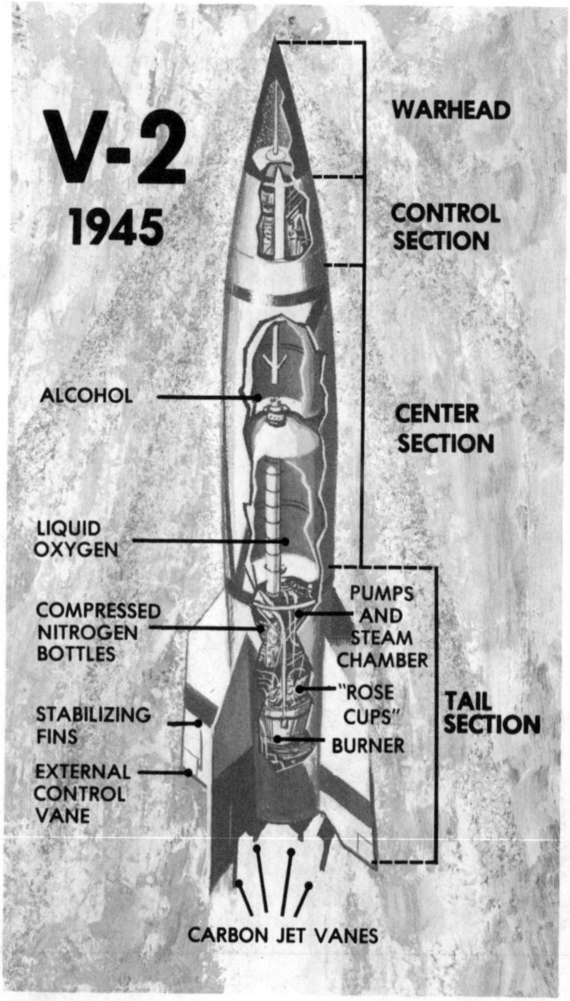

HELICOPTERS

The final WW II aviation development which we will mention is the use of the first successful military helicopter—the Sikorsky R-4 (see fig. 68). Earlier we mentioned the pioneering work Sikorsky had done on rotary-wing aircraft. After 30 years of building large bombers and flying boats, Sikorsky built and flew (in untethered flight) the first successful single-rotor helicopter (VS-300) in May of 1940. In 1942, a military version (renamed the R-4) went into service with the AAFs. Before the war ended, 400 of them were being used in Europe, the Pacific and the United States. On April 23, 1944, an R-4 made the first successful rescue of a downed pilot from behind enemy lines. The helicopter became part of the AAFs during WW II, but it was in the Korean War, 5 years later, that it really demonstrated its value.

THE POLITICAL SITUATION

At the end of World War II, the world was left with two major political forces—Soviet Communism and Western Democracy. Because of the radical change in warfare brought about by aviation during the war, it was apparent that the smaller countries of the world could not maintain the armed forces necessary to defend themselves. This same situation faced countries such as Britain, France, Germany, Japan, etc., who had historically been world powers. The true leader for Western Democracy was the United States.

The Russians made it clear almost immediately

V-2

1945

WARHEAD

CONTROL SECTION

CENTER SECTION

ALCOHOL

LIQUID OXYGEN

COMPRESSED NITROGEN BOTTLES

STABILIZING FINS

EXTERNAL CONTROL VANE

PUMPS AND STEAM CHAMBER

"ROSE CUPS"

BURNER

TAIL SECTION

CARBON JET VANES

Figure 67.

Figure 68.

after the war that they were not going to allow the nations they had occupied during the war to determine their own form of government. Russia forced the countries of Austria, Hungary, Czechoslovakia, Rumania, Yugoslavia, Poland, East Germany, etc., into communism as satellite countries of the USSR.

On the Western side, many international alliances, such as the North Atlantic Treaty Organization (NATO) and the Southeast Asia Treaty Organization (SEATO), were formed to insure the security of the "free world." This was the beginning of the Cold War in which we have been engaged ever since.

MILITARY DEVELOPMENTS

True to form, immediately after the end of fighting in the Pacific, there was a rush in the United States to return to "normal." The Army Air Forces had 2,125,000 men in uniform in September, 1945; by January, 1946, there were less than 900,000, and by 1947, this figure had been cut to 300,000. The United States political leaders were certain that the monopoly we had on the atomic bomb provided us with all the security we would ever need. No one would dare attack us or our allies for fear of massive

retaliation; therefore, there was no need to maintain large military forces.

A SEPARATE AIR FORCE

Following V-J Day*, the military leaders and the political leaders started moving toward the creation of a unified national military establishment organized under a Secretary of Defense. This would give the Army Air Forces equal status with the Army and Navy and would finally fulfill General "Billy" Mitchell's dream. On July 26, 1947, with the passage of the National Security Act, the Army Air Forces of World War II became the United States Air Force (USAF). The first Secretary of Defense was James Forrestal, the first Secretary of the Air Force was Stuart Symington, and General Carl Spaatz became the first Chief of Staff, United States Air Force.

The newly formed United States Air Force's primary mission was that of nuclear deterrence** — and this mission was given to the Strategic Air Command (SAC). At that time, SAC had nothing but a handful of B-29s and a few atom bombs. Even though funds were limited, SAC developed into a capable force by 1948. SAC's strategic bombers included the World War II B-29s and an improved offshoot, the B-50.

The new, giant B-36 (see fig. 69) was also beginning to enter the inventory in 1948. This bomber was the largest bomber ever built. It was designed in 1941 when it appeared that England might be lost to the Germans and therefore would be unavailable as a base for the bombing of Germany. The B-36 was designed to carry 10,000 pounds of bombs 10,000 miles. This huge plane weighed six times as much as the B-17 and was powered by six pusher propellers (later four jet engines were added).

THE BERLIN AIRLIFT

In June 1948, the Soviet Union decided to test

---

*V-J Day—Victory in Japan Day—August 14, 1945.
**Nuclear deterrence—prevention of war by convincing an enemy that if you are attacked, you will destroy him with your nuclear weapons.

Figure 69. B-36 "Peacemaker"

the will of the West by initiating the Berlin Blockade, preventing any surface transportation into or out of the city. The peace treaty ending World War II divided the city of Berlin into four sectors, each controlled by one of the Allied Nations (United States, Britain, France, and USSR). In addition, the nation of Germany was divided into two parts—West Germany, controlled by Britain, France, and the United States, and East Germany, controlled by Russia.

It so happened that Berlin was located in East Germany, and all supplies for the sectors of Berlin controlled by Britain, France, and the United States had to travel through East Germany. The Berlin Blockade was an attempt by Russia to take over all of Berlin, and unless the blockade could be broken, the strategy would succeed. Our answer to the blockade was the Berlin Airlift.

This was a massive undertaking. It was estimated that Berlin would require 4,500 tons of supplies a day just to survive. Initially there were only one hundred and five C-47 aircraft, each capable of carrying three and one-half tons, and fifty-four C-54 aircraft with a ten-ton payload available. By November the airfleet had grown to three hundred and nineteen C-54 aircraft (the C-47s had been phased out) and one hundred and fifty British planes of various sizes. During the winter the airlift also had to include heating fuel (mostly coal) as well as the other supplies. By April 1949, the airlift had grown to

Figure 70.

the point that a one-day record of 12,940 tons were delivered by 1,398 flights.

In all, 1,750,000 tons of supplies were carried in the world's greatest demonstration of carrying cargo by air (see fig. 70). In May 1949, the Russians conceded that they could not isolate Berlin and lifted the blockade.

THE KOREAN WAR

Failing to conquer Berlin with their blockade, the Soviet Union turned to the other side of the globe. On June 25, 1950, communist North Korea invaded

South Korea. This was to become a favorite tactic of the Soviet Union—to supply and support a communist nation in the takeover of another nation—without becoming directly involved in the fighting themselves.

This act of aggression would be the first test of the United Nations (U.N.), which was formed after World War II to insure world peace. On June 27, 1950, the United Nations resolved that its members would provide assistance to South Korea. Sixteen nations provided armed forces and five more provided medical assistance. However, it still fell to the United States to do most of the fighting.

On the same day the United Nations resolution was made, President Truman authorized the use of United States air and naval forces and on June 30th he authorized General Douglas MacArthur to use United States ground troops.

The first priority was to stop the advance of the much stronger North Korean Army. This was accomplished on August 5th, but by then the United Nations' forces had been driven back to where they occupied only a very small perimeter around the port city of Pusan.

From the beginning, the Korean War was also an air war. Korea is only slightly larger than the state of Minnesota, which meant that all of Korea was within range of naval aircraft operating off the carriers of the Seventh Fleet or United States Air Force aircraft operating from bases in Japan and Korea. There were very few strategic targets in Korea, and though B-29s based in Japan did make raids throughout the war, they were mainly tactical in nature. Most of the tactical warfare consisted of U.N. fighter aircraft bombing and strafing enemy troops, supply lines, transportation systems, and communications—almost at will.

To accomplish this the Air Force used the F-80 *Shooting Star*, the World War II P-51, and the F-84 *Thunderjet* (see fig. 71). The Navy carriers were equipped with the F9F *Panther* jet fighter and the AD *Skyraider* propeller-driven attack aircraft. Early in the war these were sufficient because the North Korean Air Force was equipped with only 120 obsolete Russian aircraft and these were soon destroyed.

In September 1950, the U.N. forces landed at Inchon. This amphibious operation placed the U.N. forces behind the enemy lines and was timed to coincide with the Eighth Army breakout of the Pusan perimeter. So successful was their operation that within 45 days the North Koreans had been pushed back 600 miles to the Manchurian border. Most people believed the war had been won.

In November 1950, the war changed completely when the Communist Chinese entered the war with 850,000 troops and the best fighter aircraft in the world—the Russian-built MIG-15 jet (see fig. 72). The

Figure 71. F-84

Figure 72. MIG-15

relatively small helicopters available. The helicopter also proved to be a unique vehicle for reinforcing battle positions by rapid transportation of combat teams to the battlefield.

The first all-jet air battle in history took place during the Korean War on November 8, 1950, when an F-80 piloted by Lieutenant Russell J. Brown shot down a MIG-15.

The Chinese had about 1,000 MIG-15s when they entered the Korean War. This aircraft was smaller, faster, more maneuverable, could climb faster and higher, and possessed more firepower than the F-80, F-84, or the Navy F9F fighters. In fact the MIG-15 even had the edge, at high altitude, over the F-86 *Sabrejets* (see fig. 73) which were the best aircraft the United States had during the Korean War.

The big advantage held by the United States was that of pilot skill, and because of this there were nine MIGs shot down for every United States aircraft lost during the war.

Once the Chinese advance was stopped, and the U.N. troops had advanced to approximately the 38th parallel, the war settled down to a war of attrition*. For two years the United States and the Chinese continued the war. The Chinese were unable to advance because of United States airpower and the United States was unable to advance because of the sheer numbers of Chinese troops.

The Korean War was also a political war—the first of several we would be involved in. The overall controlling strategy of the war was to ensure that it did not enlarge into World War III. This meant that political leaders were in charge of the strategy rather than military leaders. There were certain targets which were off limits. For example, the Chinese airfields were located north of the Korean border in Manchuria. United States planes were prohibited from bombing targets north of the Yalu River, which marked the Korean-Manchurian border. In fact, our aircraft could not even pursue the communist aircraft across the border. This meant that the communists could take off from their secure airports, cross the Yalu River to engage in combat,

Chinese pushed the U.N. troops back across the 38th parallel* and the South Korean capital of Seoul was again captured.

United Nations aircraft provided air cover for the retreat and kept the U.N. forces from being completely overwhelmed. They used two weapons which proved to be the best new weapons used in Korea—aerial rockets and napalm. The rockets carried the destructive force of a 105mm cannon shell and could be delivered with great accuracy by the fighter bombers. Napalm bombs were 110-gallon tanks of jelled gasoline which exploded when dropped and burned an area some 250 feet long and 80 feet wide. Postwar interviews showed that Korean and Chinese troops had great fear of these weapons.

Although helicopters were used late in World War II, it was during the Korean War that they proved their effectiveness. Less than a month after the war started, Air Force and Marine helicopters were on duty in Korea. They were initially used for reconnaissance but they also showed their value at transporting the wounded to emergency aid stations. By the end of the war, more than 15,000 men had been evacuated to safety by the few and

---

*This line marked the original boundary between North Korea and South Korea.

*A gradual wearing away of the ability to fight without gaining or losing any territory.

Figure 73. F-86

and then retreat across the Yalu to safety.

By the middle of 1953, United States close air support for the ground troops developed into a very precise art. Thousands of enemy troops were killed by aircraft, and our airpower hampered the communists' ability to supply their troops. It became clear they could not win the war but neither could we. On July 27, 1953, an armistice was signed, another war was over, and Korea was almost precisely where it had been in 1950. However, although neither side finished the war as an outright victor, the objectives of the United Nations were accomplished. The War in Korea was halted and South Korea remained an independent nation.

Once again, as in WW II, black pilots proved their skill and ability as combat aviators. Unlike WW II, black pilots in the Korean War were integrated and flew right along with other aviators in the same units. One black pilot who became famous was Ensign Jesse L. Brown—the first black naval aviator. Brown was awarded the Distinguished Flying Cross, the Air Medal, and the Purple Heart in Korea; unfortunately, he crashed and lost his life before the war was over. Another black who was to rise to the rank of Major

General was 1st Lt. William E. Brown, Jr. 1st Lt. Brown had 126 combat missions in Korea and later, in the Vietnam War, was to have 100 more missions.

The Korean War did teach us a lesson: Our atomic arsenal alone is not enough to prevent our involvement in war. We learned that there are various levels of conflict and we need the military strength and flexibility to participate in any or all of them. The United States Air Force manpower increased by 300 percent during the Korean War and it never again decreased to pre-war levels.

OTHER MILITARY DEVELOPMENTS

Strategic Bombers. In 1944, the Air Force requested bids for a high-performance, all-jet bomber. There were three prototypes built: the North American XB-45, the Convair XB-46, and the Boeing XB-47. All three of these prototypes had straight wings. However, the Boeing engineers were not satisfied. They had studied some German reports on sweptback wings and decided to try them on their aircraft. The XB-47 (see fig. 74) became the United States Air Force's first all-jet strategic

Figure 74. B-47

bomber. The XB-47 flew for the first time on December 17, 1947, and more than 1,600 of these aircraft eventually entered service with SAC. By 1956, the final B-36 was retired and we had an all-jet Strategic Air Command.

The only shortcoming the B-47 had was in its range. Unrefueled, its range was only about 3,000 miles. Because of this the Air Force decided it needed another bomber which would be larger and have a longer range than the B-47. The result was another Boeing aircraft, the B-52 (see fig. 75). It flew for the first time on April 15, 1952. The B-52 is twice the size of the B-47 and has an unrefueled range of 10,000 miles. There have been eight models of the B-52 built, and the G and H models still make up the majority of our strategic bombers.

Figure 75. B-52

F-105 THUNDERCHIEF

F-106 DELTA DART

Figure 76.

During this time period the first supersonic strategic bomber, the B-58, was designed and built. It was a remarkable technical accomplishment. The B-58 was faster than most fighter aircraft of its time, but it proved very expensive to operate and was not that much better than the B-52; after a few years, the B-58 was retired.

Fighter Developments. Following the Korean War discovery that the Russian MIG-15 was superior to any United States fighter, many new fighter aircraft were built during the 1950s.

In 1953, the F-100 *Super Sabre* flew for the first time at Edwards Air Force Base, California. This aircraft was far superior to any aircraft in the world and was the world's first production supersonic fighter. More than 2,200 F-100s were produced and some are still in service with the USAF Reserve and the Air National Guard.

Other famous United States fighters developed during this time period, and the dates of their first flights are: the F-101 *Voodoo*-1953; F-102 *Delta Dagger*-1953; F-104 *Starfighter*-1954; F-105 *Thunderchief*-1955; and the F-106 *Delta Dart*-1956. Even the F-111 and the F-4 were in the design and prototype production phases during this time period. It is very evident that more new production aircraft were built during the 1953-1958 time period

than have been designed in the 25 years since then (see fig. 76).

CIVIL AVIATION DEVELOPMENTS

One outcome of World War II was that it made all people of the world aviation-conscious. Even here in the United States the citizenry became aware of the decisive part airpower played in winning the war. More than two million Americans had been involved in building aircraft during the war and more than 16 million Americans had served in uniform—most had witnessed airpower firsthand. Hundreds of thousands of service men and women flew for the first time during the war, either as a crew member or as a passenger.

These ex-service people knew what aviation could do, and many who had played important roles in the war continued to publicize the merits of aviation. Some wrote or lectured, while others went on to set new records, especially women. After the war, political leaders and the news media tended to push the women under the rug. The central theme of post WW II was that the women's role was now in the home. But some, such as Jacqueline Cochran, did not want to go "back home." She continued her flying career and maintained the level of progress in aviation that women had reached during the war. In 1946 she finished second in the Bendix Race and in 1948 she was commissioned Lt. Col. in the U.S. Air Force Reserve (as well as Lt. Col. in the Civil Air Patrol). She set a new international record for speed for prop-driven aircraft (P-51) in 1950 at 447.47 mph. After 1953, when she became the first woman to fly faster than sound (May 18 in an F-86E), flying became her principal interest. In later years, Cochran would continue to show the world that women could do anything men could do.

Whether these ex-service men and women wrote, lectured, continued flying, or just went back home, they all recognized the importance of aviation as a transportation system and created an immediate demand for commercial airline travel after the war.

Even those who were not directly involved in the war became conscious of aviation because of hearing almost daily about wartime developments and accomplishments. Thus, the interest was present for the airlines to return to their prewar operations, but at a greatly increased level.

COMMERCIAL AIRLINES

In addition to a citizenry which was ready to accept aviation, there were several other reasons that the airlines boomed after the war. There had been some remarkable developments in aircraft design during the war. This led to better instrumentation, better navigation, longer-range aircraft, more reliable airplanes, and increased safety. There were also larger and better airports available because of wartime requirements. Radar had been developed which improved navigation and safety. There were more and better pilots available than prior to World War II. Weather forecasting and the ability to fly through weather had improved. Another factor which cannot be overlooked is that there were a great many very fine surplus airplanes available after the war at a very good price.

Propeller Aircraft. The aircraft most widely used immediately after the war was the Douglas DC-3. More than 10,000 of these aircraft were built during the war with the Army designation C-47. The C-47s were modified for civilian use to carry 21 passengers. They worked fine for short flights and some are still flying today. For longer routes, and where traffic was heavier, two other aircraft developed for the AAF were available—the four-engine Douglas DC-4 and the Lockheed *Constellation* (see fig. 77). The DC-4 had been built for the military as the C-54 and the *Constellation* as the C-69. The *Constellation* had two advantages over the DC-4; it was pressurized (allowing it to fly higher) and it was about 100 mph faster. However, there were many more DC-4s available; 1,100 DC-4s were built during the war whereas only a few hundred C-69s were built.

The DC-4 won the first round against the *Constellation* as a commercial airliner because of availability; eventually it was in use with nearly every large airline, including foreign carriers. When the supply of "cheap" surplus DC-4s ran out, and the airlines had to start buying new airplanes, the *Constellation* took the lead. This resulted in both Douglas and Lockheed developing several versions of their aircraft, each bigger and better than the last. The DC-4 was followed by the DC-6, DC-6B, DC-7, DC-7B, and DC-7C. Lockheed countered with the *Super Constellation* and the *Starliner*.

During the competition, the Douglas aircraft grew from 44 seats (DC-4) to 105 seats (DC-7C), and the *Constellation* grew from 44 seats to 99 seats *(Starliner)*. Both the DC-7 and the *Starliner* were fast (300 mph) and long-range. Both aircraft offered non-stop transcontinental service in about eight to nine hours and transatlantic service—New York to London. In all, about 800 DC-6—DC-7s were built and about 650 *Constellations*. They were the airliners of the 1940s and 1950s and were the biggest, fastest, safest, and most comfortable piston-engine airliners ever built. They started the dominance of the world market by United States airline aircraft which continues even today.

Another result of the increase in speed and range of the DC-7s and *Super Constellations* was the death of flying boats. The large "Clippers" had been developed in the 1930s when non-stop flight across the oceans was impossible. The flying boats were used briefly after the war, but they were made

Figure 77. Lockheed "Constellation"

obsolete by the much faster Douglas and Lockheed aircraft.

In 1940, the year before we entered World War II, our nation's airlines carried about three million passengers. By the end of the war (1945) this figure was about the same (due to wartime travel restrictions). By 1950, it had increased to 17 million (a 600 percent increase). By 1958, the year the first commercial jets were introduced, this figure had grown to about 30 million.

From these figures it can be seen that the Korean War did not cause the decrease in commercial travel that World War II had. This was true because the national war effort was not as intense during the Korean War and because we had enough large transport planes to serve both the military and civilian needs. Worldwide the figures were similar. Airline traffic increased from three million in 1938 to eighteen million in 1946 and twenty-four million in 1948. The "Aviation Age" was upon us.

In the short- and medium-length route market, the DC-3 was challenged by the Martin 2-0-2 and the Convair 240 in 1947-48. Both were faster, pressurized, and offered the same comfort to the short-haul passenger that the DC-6s and *Constellations* offered the long-haul passenger. The 40 passenger Convair 240 was enlarged to become the 44 seat Convair 340 in 1952, and in 1956, it grew even more into the 56 seat Convair 440. There were more than 1,000 of these Convair aircraft built for civilian and military use and later more than 200 were equipped with turboprop engines. Some of these are still in service today (see fig. 78).

It was right after the war that the first all-cargo airlines came into existence. They also used surplus C-47s and C-69s, but they carried air cargo rather than passengers. There were many of these all-cargo airlines (such as Riddle, Resort, Slick, Flying Tiger, etc.) formed, but only Slick and Flying Tiger survived.

The First Jets. With the military converting to jet fighters and bombers, it was inevitable that jet aircraft would also be developed for airline use. When this did occur, the first jets were British-built, not American, which is rather surprising since United States aircraft had dominated the airlines since World War II.

There are two types of jet propulsion, turboprop and "pure" jet. Both types use a gas turbine engine, the difference being that in a turboprop the gas turbine is fastened to a propeller which is used to propel the aircraft. There is some thrust provided by the jet exhaust, but the propeller provides most of the power. In a "pure" jet, all the thrust is provided by

Figure 78. Convair 440

the jet exhaust.

The British developed both the first turboprop and the first turbojet airliners. The Vickers *Viscount,* powered by four Rolls Royce Dart turboprop engines, was the world's first turboprop airliner. The *Viscount* flew for the first time in July 1948 and went into commercial service in 1953. There were a total of 444 *Viscounts* produced in three series. The first series carried 47 passengers; this was increased to 75 in later models. The *Viscount* had a cruising speed of about 350 mph and a range of about 1,700 miles.

The DeHavilland *Comet 1* (see fig. 79) was the world's first "pure" jet airliner and entered service in May 1952. The *Comet* was a revolutionary aircraft in that it increased the speed of commercial travel to 500 mph. Also, it flew at a higher altitude (25,000-30,000 feet) which put it above most of the weather and made for a much smoother ride.

In 1954, two *Comets* were involved in fatal accidents which were found to be caused by structural failure. Flying at extremely high altitudes, a pressurized aircraft has a tremendous amount of pressure on the inside. In the case of the *Comet,* the aircraft could not withstand the pressure difference, and explosive decompression occurred. This caused the aircraft to disintegrate in flight. This was a serious setback to the British avaition industry, but the results were that all later jets were safer because of the knowledge gained from *Comet 1.*

Blacks Enter The Airlines. This period of aviation history marks the third era (1950-1967) of blacks in aviation. Just before this era began, in 1948, James O. Plinton had established an inter-island air service, flying the Boeing 247-Ds. This air service linked the islands of Jamaica, Port-au-Prince (Haiti), Grand Turk, and Caicos. It was probably the first commercial air service begun and operated by a

Figure 79. DeHavilland "Comet 1"

black pilot.

The established airlines, however, had not hired any blacks, despite the fact that hundreds of ex-WW II military black pilots were eager to fly commercial planes. Refused employment in the airlines, these black pilots had to turn to other occupations (such as a former pilot of the 99th Pursuit Squadron who currently runs a shoe repair shop in Tuskegee, Alabama) and fly in their spare time.

A third breakthrough for blacks came in 1955, when Seaboard World Airlines hired the first black airline pilot—August H. Martin, an ex-WW II military pilot. Martin died July 1, 1968, in a plane crash in Biafra, Africa, helping deliver supplies for the Red Cross.

The following year, Perry H. Young, Jr., was hired by New York Airways. Young had soloed in 1933, been a flight instructor at Coffey School of Aeronautics, and served as an aviation flight instructor at the Tuskegee CPTP school at Tuskegee, Alabama, during WW II. He became the first black helicopter pilot for any airlines and logged 8,000 hours in fixed wing aircraft and 16,000 in helicopters.

GENERAL AVIATION

There were thousands of pilots in America who had flown during World War II. Thousands more earned their pilot licenses using the GI-Bill after the war. The Civil Aeronautics Administration (fore-runner of FAA) predicted that there would be 500,000 aircraft in service by 1950. This prediction failed to materialize, but there was a great demand for general aviation aircraft after the war. Some of this demand was filled by surplus airplanes but the manufacturers also began building new civilian airplanes immediately after the war.

In 1946, Cessna Aircraft brought out its first post-war aircraft—the C-120 and the C-140. Both of them were all metal, high-wing monoplanes; the 120 was a two place aircraft and the 140 a four place. Prior to World War II, all Cessna aircraft were wood and fabric but the new technology which had developed during the war killed fabric aircraft. Both of these aircraft were very successful. The 120 led directly to the present day Cessna 150/152 while the 140 was

the direct ancestor of the Cessna 172. By the end of the 1950s, Cessna had grown to number one in general aviation manufacturing, a spot it still holds today.

Piper Aircraft also resumed production of general aviation aircraft right after the war. Here, too, they initiated a change which has become a Piper trademark through the years. Their first new postwar aircraft was called the *Skysedan*. It was a four-place, all-metal, low-wing monoplane. Prior to World War II, all Piper aircraft were high-wing, fabric-and-wood aircraft. Their immediate switch to a low-wing aircraft set a pattern which they still follow. The *Skysedan* can be considered the direct ancestor of today's *Cherokee* series of Piper aircraft.

Of course, Piper also left World War II with the most famous light aircraft of all time—the J-3 *Cub*. This aircraft had the traditional high wing and was fabric covered. After the war Piper wisely continued production of the *Cub* and even today you can buy a brand new Piper PA-18 *Super Cub* which has a high wing and is fabric covered.

During the war the general aviation manufacturers had been involved in building training, observation, and liaison aircraft for the military. After V-J Day they began immediately to convert over to building aircraft for civilian use. Generally, the initial aircraft they built were the same type they had been manufacturing for the military with whatever changes were required to get them licenses for civil use. On December 7, 1945, just sixteen weeks after the war ended, Beech Aircraft received a certificate for their Beech 18 executive aircraft. Beech had produced more than 5,000 model 18s during the war and now began delivering the civilian model at the rate of two airplanes per day.

In 1947 Beech first offered an airplane which would become a classic, the Model 35 *Bonanza*. This was an all-metal, low-wing, retractable-gear aircraft which could fly at almost 200 miles per hour. It was equipped with a two-way radio and all navigation gear required to fly at night and in all types of weather. This was the closest thing the public could get to a "fighter" and was so attractive that they had 500 on order before it made its first flight. Cessna, Piper, and Beech are the big three of general aviation manufacturers today. Others, such as Mooney, Rockwell, Maule, etc., have come into existence since the war, but some famous names like Waco, Stinson, and Taylorcraft did not survive the postwar transition.

AVIATION RESEARCH AND DEVELOPMENT

It was also during World War II that large scale advances in Research and Development (R & D) took place in aviation. This is not to say that there was no R & D prior to the war. We mentioned earlier that the National Advisory Committee on Aeronautics (NACA*) was founded in 1918 to do government-funded research in aeronautics. NACA's original research facility was established at Langley Field, Virginia, and the wind tunnels and laboratories are still there and still in operation.

RESEARCH CENTERS

During the war NACA opened two other research centers—the Ames Research Center at Moffett Field, California, and the Lewis Research Center in Cleveland, Ohio.

The aviation manufacturers also did a great deal of their own research, and many, such as Boeing and Lockheed, developed research facilities which would rival those of NACA. Industry research, however, was most often done in support of a particular aircraft which that manufacturer was building and was not aimed at answering basic questions about flight.

The basic research was most often carried out by NACA or by a college or university under government contract. Many colleges and universities had departments of aeronautics and possessed wind tunnels to do research to support their graduate programs. Universities such as Purdue, Miami of Ohio, and Auburn are examples of schools that did, and still do, basic research in aeronautics.

During the war, a team effort between the NACA scientists and engineers, and their counterparts in

*NACA became the National Aeronautics and Space Administration (NASA) in 1958.

industry and the universities, led to some great developments. One example of this was the P-51 *Mustang.* A need existed for a fast, long-range fighter escort in Europe. The requirements were known, so a team from North American Aviation, the Royal Air Force (RAF), and the Ames Research Center went to work. The results were the P-51 which was designed, built, and flown in a period of only 120 days. This aircraft was equipped with a revolutionary new wing design called the *laminar flow wing.*

After the war there was a need to continue this type of aviation R & D because there were many problems that needed solving and questions that needed answering. This was particularly true in the realm of high speed flight. The new jet fighters, and some of the most modern propeller driven ones, began to approach the speed of sound. They encountered many strange things like severe vibrations, control reversal (the controls of the aircraft would function opposite to how they were supposed to), and, in some cases, even destruction of the aircraft.

The Air Force formed a new command, Air Research and Development Command (ARDC), in 1950 to lead the Air Force research effort. Part of the mission of ARDC was to do laboratory research and also to do flight testing. These functions are still accomplished by the Air Force through the Air Force Systems Command.

RESEARCH AIRCRAFT

While some of these questions could be solved in the laboratory, eventually research aircraft were going to have to be built to test the laboratory theories. And, also, someone was going to have to fly these research aircraft—the test pilot. A number of experimental research aircraft were built and tested to solve complex aeronautical problems. Research findings from these aircraft were to lead to many future operational supersonic and innovative aircraft.

Bell Aircraft Company led this research effort in 1946, developing the X-1, an aircraft that flew faster than the speed of sound. Two other projects were carried out in 1949. The Americans worked on the Republic XF-91 (which had a combination turbojet and rocket engine); at the same time, the French carried out experimental flights on a ramjet-propelled craft called the Leduc 0.10 (which was a single-seat aircraft carried aloft above a Languedoc 161 transport). The X-5 followed in 1951 to test variable-sweep wings. In 1952 the X-3 was built to study supersonic speeds with a jet rather than a rocket engine, and on March 2, 1953, the Douglas/USN D-558-2 flew at Mach 2.

Besides conventional airplanes, Vertical Takeoff and Landing (VTOL) aircraft also got their start during this period. In the 1950's attempts were made to lift off straight up as soon as the power-weight ratio of the turbojet was sufficient to lift an aircraft vertically on the jet thrust alone. In 1954, the Rolls-Royce "Flying Bedstead" was successfully flown. In the same year, the Convair XFY-1 "Tailsitter" took off vertically by means of a propeller mounted at the tail. VTOL aircraft will be discussed more in depth in another Part.

Experimental craft following 1954 were the X-2 in 1955, the British Saunders-Roe SR-53 and the Nord Griffon in 1957, and the X-15 in 1958 (as well as the XB-70). The X-2 was designed to reach Mach 3 (three times the speed of sound). The SR-53 flew with a combined turbojet and rocket engine, while the Griffon was powered by a combination turbojet/ramjet engine. Flown in 1957, the Griffon exceeded Mach 1 in a climb and later reached Mach 1.85. The X-15 was a hypersonic aircraft that was first launched from a B-52 into rocket-powered, wing-borne flight in June of 1958. Eventually it reached Mach 6.04, or 4,070 mph. The X-15 was outfitted with a device which was developed in the 1950s—an adaptive autopilot (a device which automatically senses the aircraft's response to disturbances and adjusts the control settings). Another aircraft which was in the design and construction phase (but did not fly until the 1960s) was the XB-70. Both the X-15 and XB-70 will be discussed further in Chapter 1-6.

While all these aircraft contributed to aviation knowledge—and each could be discussed more in depth in a chapter of its own—we will expand on only a few. The most important vehicles of this period to aviation in general, and to space travel in particular, were the X-1, X-2, X-3, and X-5, and they will be discussed in more depth.

X-1. In February 1945, the Army Air Force and NACA decided jointly to develop a research aircraft to fly faster than the speed of sound. A contract was let to the Bell Aircraft Company to build a research aircraft to explore the problems of high-speed flight. This aircraft, called the X-1 (fig. 80), made its first flight in January 1946.

The X-1 (six were actually built for the flight tests) was shaped like a bullet, had short, very thin, non-swept wings and was propelled by a rocket engine. Because its rocket engine consumed fuel at an extremely high rate, it could not take off from the ground like an ordinary airplane. It would have run out of fuel before it ever reached its operating altitude. The X-1 was carried to an altitude of 25,000 feet by a B-29 aircraft. The first flight tests were unpowered and designed to test its handling characteristics. The X-1 would glide to a landing on the dry lake beds at Edwards Air Force Base, California.*

Powered flights began on December 9, 1946, with the aircraft being flown a little faster on each flight. On October 14, 1947, with Air Force Captain Charles "Chuck" Yeager at the controls, the X-1 penetrated the "sound barrier", and man first flew faster than the speed of sound. The speed the X-1 reached on that historic day was 670 mph at 42,000 feet.

Flight tests continued with the X-1 and it was pushed to higher and higher speeds. It was discovered that once the aircraft passed the speed of sound, flight smoothed out and no further vibration problems existed. In June of 1954, Yeager pushed the X-1A to a speed of 2.42 times the speed of sound (1,650 mph). The X-1B was outfitted specifically to test the effects of frictional heating on an airplane at very high speeds. Testing with the X-1 aircraft continued until 1956.

X-2. This aircraft was designed to study heating in flight at three times the speed of sound. It was similar to the X-1 but had swept-back wings and a stainless steel airframe (fig. 81). Two of these aircraft were produced and both were destroyed in

*At the time of the first X-1 flights it was known as Murock Air Force Base. Its name was changed to Edwards Air Force Base in December 1949.

Figure 80. X-1

accidents during the test program. During its final flight on September 27, 1956, the aircraft reached its design goal of Mach 3, but disintegrated in flight killing the test pilot, Captain Milburn G. Apt. The speed record of 2,094 mph which was established on this last flight was not exceeded until 1961.

X-3. The *X-1* and *X-2* series of aircraft were rocket powered. The *X-3* (fig. 82) was designed to be the first jet-powered aircraft to fly at Mach 3. The *X-3* was built of titanium alloy to protect it from frictional heating. There were originally three prototypes ordered from Douglas Aircraft but only one was completed. The *X-3* flew for the first time on October 20, 1952, and made more than 20 experimental flights. However, because of the inadequate engine power, it never flew supersonically.

X-5. At the end of World War II, the plans for the German Messerschmitt P-1101 were captured by the United States. The Bell *X-5* was based on these designs and was the world's first aircraft with variable-angle wings (fig. 83).

The swept-back wings of a jet aircraft are very efficient at high speeds and, in fact, are almost a requirement for supersonic flight. However, the swept-back wings do not produce enough lift at low speeds to keep the aircraft flying. This means that the takeoff and landing speeds of the swept-wing jet are much higher than one with straight wings. One solution to this problem is to be able to change the wing of the aircraft from straight wings for takeoff and landing to swept-wings for high-speed flight. The *X-5* was built to test the problems of this theory and provide the answers necessary to build variable-wing aircraft.

Two models of the *X-5* were built and the first flight was on June 20, 1951. The first prototype crashed in 1953, killing the test pilot, Major Raymond P. Popson. The second aircraft flew for several years and provided the experience necessary to build the F-111 and F-14 variable-sweep wing aircraft.

GUIDED MISSILE RESEARCH

WW II research on missiles was continued after the war and led to concrete results in the 1950s. The Northrup SM62 *Snark* (see fig. 84) was a jet-propelled, tailless, pilotless airplane that flew 6,300 miles at Mach 0.94 under inertial and stellar guidance systems. It weighed only 50,000 pounds.

Figure 81. X-2

The GAM 63 *Rascal* was a small, rocket-propelled, supersonic-winged bomb developed in 1956. It was carried by B-47 squadrons in 1957 and was launched while the bomber was 100 miles away from target; once launched, the bomber crew guided it by teleradar. The change from aircraft to rockets was brought about by the development of smaller nuclear warheads, better rocket engines, and smaller inertial guidance systems, and they would take over some aircraft duties.

MEDICAL RESEARCH

It was not just in the area of aircraft design and structure that there were a lot of unanswered questions at the end of World War II. As the aircraft flew higher and faster, there was a growing concern about the pilot and how much the human body

Figure 82. X-3

Figure 83. X-5

Figure 84. Snark

could stand. The field of aviation medicine, and later aerospace medicine, grew right along with the other research areas in aviation. The United States Air Force did much of the pioneer work in aviation medicine, actually starting back in 1915.

As research in aviation medicine progressed, it became evident that man was not necessarily the limiting factor in supersonic and hypersonic flight, provided he could be protected from the environment. "G"-suits were developed to prevent the blood from pooling in the legs during high performance maneuvers. Partial, and finally, full pressure suits protected the pilot from the lack of atmospheric pressure at high altitudes. Ejection seats were developed to allow escape at high altitudes and high speeds.

Each step of the way that would eventually lead to space travel required new R & D in aerospace medicine. The developments were expensive and required long periods of research. They led directly to our astronaut training programs and the ability to *safely* place man into a hostile environment and return him *safely* to Earth.

CHAPTER 1-6

THE AEROSPACE AGE: 1958-PRESENT

The *Aerospace Age* has seen man move away from Earth on his first faltering steps into a new dimension. For the first ten years of this new age, man was cautious in his exploration. There were so many unknowns and so much to learn that care and restraint were needed. Each new step was built on what the prior step had taught us. We have now entered a new era in aerospace, a time when we have begun to use space rather than merely explore it. Communication, weather, and resource satellites are doing things for us that our fathers could only dream of.

Airline travel has become as routine today as automobile travel. We can be whisked across the continent in five hours or across the ocean faster than sound. The sleek jetliners are truly the magic carpets of the Twentieth Century.

The general learning objective for this chapter is for you to know significant developments and events in the Aerospace Age: 1958-present. To reach this objective, you must pattern your study of the material according to the *specific learning objectives* listed in Appendix I of this textbook.

PRELUDE TO SPACE

We have chosen to call the age in which we currently live the *Aerospace Age* because aerospace developments have more of an effect on us, and on all of the people in the world, than any other single aspect of our society. Others have called this age the *Computer Age, Electronic Age,* the *Age of Technology,* and other descriptive terms. These terms are all valid; we will not argue with them other than to say that to a great extent, computers, electronics, and technology are all products of aerospace developments.

Why do we choose to date the Aerospace Age from 1958 rather than 1957? There are two reasons. First, although Russia orbited the world's first artificial satellite in 1957, it was not until 1958 that the significance of that event was understood. As a result, in 1958, the National Aeronautics and Space Administration (NASA) was founded and the United States space effort got underway. Secondly, in October, 1958, the United States inaugurated jet

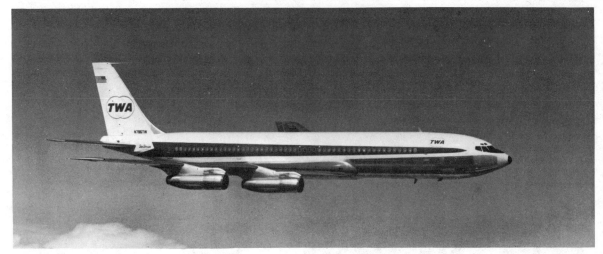

Figure 85. Boeing 707

passenger service within the United States and across the Atlantic in the Boeing 707. This aircraft ushered in a new age of commercial aircraft and revolutionized passenger travel by air (see fig. 85).

The exploration of space did not suddenly appear without warning. True, the launching of *Sputnik 1* (see fig. 86) surprised much of the world, but within both the United States and the Soviet Union there had been much preparation.

UNITED STATES EFFORTS

At the end of World War II, the team of German V-2 rocket experts (headed by Doctor Wernher von Braun) fled to the United States lines to avoid being captured by the Russians (see fig. 87). The United States also captured the V-2 assembly plant and 100 partially assembled V-2 rockets. The V-2s and the German scientists were sent to the U.S. where they would form the nucleus of United States rocket research during the late 1940s and early 1950s.

The United States Army established a team of scientists and engineers at the White Sands Proving Grounds, New Mexico, in 1946 for the purpose of conducting scientific research on the upper atmosphere. This team was headed by Doctor Wernher von Braun and used the captured V-2s to carry instruments into the upper atmosphere. This effort was a joint program involving the Army, Naval

Research Laboratory, Air Force, General Electric Company, and several universities and scientific institutions. Between 1946 and 1951 they fired 66 V-2s in this effort. Beginning in 1949, a second stage

Figure 86. Sputnik, suspended in Soviet museum

Figure 87. Wernher von Braun

contracted with the Martin Company to build an improved V-2 called the *Viking*. They also contracted with Johns Hopkins University to build a research rocket called the *Aerobee*. In 1951, both were launched successfully. The *Viking* reached an altitude of 136 miles and the *Aerobee* flew to 80 miles altitude.

The Army moved Doctor von Braun's team to their Redstone Arsenal in Huntsville, Alabama, in

rocket named the *WAC Corporal* was added to the V-2 (see fig. 88).

Beginning in the 1950s, the different branches of the service began going their separate ways in rocket research. The Naval Research Laboratory

Figure 88. WAC Corporal atop V-2 rocket

Figure 89. Redstone (right), and Pershing missiles

1950. The Army viewed rockets as an extension of their artillery, so they gave the Von Braun team the job of developing a liquid fuel, battlefield missile based on the V-2. The result was the *Redstone* missile (manufactured by the Chrysler Corporation) which was first flown in August of 1953. During the next five years, 37 *Redstones* (see fig. 89) were test fired. The *Redstone* had a 200-mile range and reached a speed of 3,800 mph.

In 1946, the Air Force began research on the first Intercontinental Ballistic Missile (ICBM). They awarded a contract to Convair Corporation to build a test vehicle, but in 1947, they had to cancel the contract because of a shortage of money. President Truman told the Air Force they could have the money to build either bombers or missiles, but not both. The Air Force decided the bombers had first priority. From 1947-1951 the Air Force had no ICBM program, but they did launch some *WAC Corporal's* from their new Long Range Proving Grounds at Cape Canaveral, Florida.

Two major occurrences changed the national priorities and made the money available for continued Air Force research. First, in 1949, the Soviet Union exploded her first atom bomb and we lost our nuclear monopoly. Second, the Korean War started in 1950. In 1951, the Air Force gave a new contract to Convair to build an ICBM. They called the missile the *Atlas* (see fig. 90).

By 1955, the Navy had perfected the *Viking* and the *Aerobee,* the Army had a successful *Redstone,* and the Air Force was beginning production of the *Atlas.* In August 1955, President Eisenhower announced that the United States would place several small satellites into orbit during the International Geophysical Year (IGY) which started on July 1, 1957. This project was called *Vanguard.*

There were two vehicles which seemed to be able to put a satellite into orbit. One was the Navy *Viking* (with an *Aerobee* second stage and a solid fuel third stage) and the other was the *Redstone* (with an upper stage). The Navy entry was selected in 1955 to launch the *Vanguard* satellite.

SOVIET UNION EFFORTS

The Soviet Army captured the German V-2

assembly plant and laboratories at Peenemunde at the end of the war. However, as we mentioned earlier, Von Braun and his team had escaped to the Allies. All the Russians captured were a handful of German engineers and hundreds of technicians. They also got a list of the manufacturers who supplied the parts for the V-2, and from these manufacturers, they got enough parts to build a few of the rockets.

The Russians also began upper atmospheric

Figure 90.

research in 1946-1947 using V-2s but, because they had so few, they had to begin building their own much sooner than the United States. In 1949, they developed an improved V-2 which they called the *T-1;* and in 1954, they started working on a large multistage rocket.

A few days after the United States announced its intention to launch satellites during the IGY, Russia announced that they would also launch satellites. Most people in the West did not believe this, thinking it was some more Russian propaganda.

In 1956, Premier Khrushchev warned in a speech that the Soviet Union had developed an ICBM and soon would have missiles with nuclear warheads. On August 26, 1957, the Russians successfully test launched their ICBM, and on October 4, 1957, they launched *Sputnik I* (see fig. 91), apparently using the same rocket. Then on November 3, the Russians launched *Sputnik II,* which carried the dog Laika.

Figure 91.

SPUTNIK I

OCT. 4 1957

AMERICAN REACTION

The reaction in the United States was immediate. Some people said we had been caught as flat-footed as at Pearl Harbor; the Senate immediately began an investigation and the White House announced that the Navy was preparing for the *Vanguard I* launch at Cape Canaveral. In reality, the Navy was preparing for a test launch of the *Viking/Aerobee* rocket and

was not ready to launch *Vanguard I.* On December 6th, when the Navy made its test launch, the *Vanguard's* first stage exploded, and the whole world saw on public television our "entry into the space age."

In November , 1957, the Secretary of Defense revised the Army's *Redstone* proposal and told Von Braun to get ready to launch as soon as possible. The Army had a *Redstone* with a solid fuel upper stage which they had been working on as a test rocket (renamed *Jupiter C*) to study some of the problems of reentry heating. They placed the

Figure 92. Explorer I mated to Jupiter C

satellite developed for *Vanguard* atop this *Jupiter C*, and only 84 days after they got the go ahead, they successfully launched *Explorer I* (see fig. 92). This was America's first satellite—the date was January 31, 1958.

THE SPACE AGE

The "space race" was on. The Soviet Union entered it with one big advantage—they had a rocket large enough and powerful enough to place very heavy objects into orbit. As an example, *Explorer I* weighed 31 pounds while *Sputnik II* (launched in May 1958) weighed 2,926 pounds. Eventually, however, this would prove their undoing because they were not forced to develop the miniature electronics and other lightweight materials which the United States was forced to produce. When we finally caught up with them in large rockets, we were far ahead in the amount of equipment we could take to the moon or into space with a single rocket.

One of the biggest reasons for the "space race" between the United States and the Soviet Union had nothing to do with national security or with who got to the moon first. It had to do with international prestige. During the late 1950s and early 1960s, there were many new nations emerging throughout the world. They were looking for someone to lead them, and that leadership went beyond who had the strongest army or the most atom bombs. The nation that could show the world they were first in science and technology would impress many of these small nations. The ability to put satellites into space was impressive, but the best way to demonstrate leadership was in the area of manned spaceflight. This is an area that even the most underdeveloped nation can relate to because spaceflight is an extension of flight through the air. As we mentioned at the beginning of this chapter, all mankind has a natural interest in flight.

NASA ESTABLISHED

As we mentioned earlier, the Soviet Union launched *Sputnik II* on November 3, 1957, with a dog aboard. This was a clear indication that Russia's goal was to place man in space. The launch of *Sputnik III,* six months later, demonstrated that they had a booster powerful enough to do it.

This knowledge prompted a reevaluation of our national priorities in the area of scientific research and started leaders in the United States looking for an agency to head up our space exploration program. Each of the military services had different ideas about what the priorities should be in space research. Their primary responsibility was the defense of the United States. The final decision was that our space exploration program should be headed by a civilian agency.

On July 29, 1958, President Eisenhower signed the National Aeronautics and Space Act into law, creating the National Aeronautics and Space Administration (NASA). NASA was now established as the agency to lead our civilian space program while the Department of Defense retained responsibility for space projects necessary for national security. The nucleus of NASA was the 8,000 employees of NACA who became employees of NASA on October 1, 1958.

MANNED SPACELIGHT: FIRST ERA

The United States, through NASA, proceeded to carry out systematic development of manned spaceflight. Five programs were developed and carried out successfully from 1961 through 1975. Russian spaceflight programs developed along the same lines as the American programs and occurred roughly during the same periods.

Phase I: Mercury/Vostok Flights. The Russians began the space race with the initial advantage of having large rockets—and they made the most of it. On April 12, 1961, *Vostok I*—with Major Yuri Gagarin on board—was successfully launched (see fig. 93). He was the first man to escape from Earth's atmosphere into space. Although he only stayed up for one orbit (108 minutes), he described sights no human eyes had seen before.

The United States had begun its *Mercury* program by this time. The *Mercury* was a one-man capsule launched by the *Redstone* and *Atlas*

APRIL 12, 1961
YURI ALEKSEYEVITCH GAGARIN
ORBITED EARTH

MAY 5, 1961
COMMANDER ALAN B. SHEPARD, JR.
CONTROLLED SUBORBITAL FLIGHT

Figure 93. (top) and 94.

rockets. The objective of the program was to put a man into Earth orbital spaceflight, observe his physical/mental reactions, and return him safely to Earth. NASA responded to *Vostok I* with Alan Shepard's flight in the *Freedom 7* (see fig. 94) on May 5, 1961, and a flight by Virgil "Gus" Grissom in *Liberty Bell* 7 on July 21, 1961. However, both of these missions were suborbital flights that reached a peak altitude of 115 miles and traveled only about 300 miles out into the Atlantic.

On February 20, 1962, John Glenn became the first American to go into orbit when he rode the *Friendship 7* capsule into space for three orbits (see fig. 95). The United States finally had sent a man into orbit, but this accomplishment was overshadowed by the *Vostok II* flight of 17 orbits which had been launched six months before *Friendship 7.*

In 1962, the United States and the Soviet Union each had two more orbital flights:

United States	Soviet Union
Aurora 7—Scott Carpenter—3 orbits	*Vostok 3*—Andrian Nikolayev—64 orbits
Sigma 7—Walter Schirra—6 orbits	*Vostok 4*—Pavel Popovich—48 orbits

At the end of 1962, the box score was United States—12 orbits and USSR—130 orbits.

The United States had only one manned space flight in 1963, but it lasted longer than all other United States flights combined. During May 15-16, 1963, Gordon Cooper flew *Faith 7* for 22 orbits.

The Soviet Union had two *Vostok* flights in 1963. *Vostok 5* flew for 81 orbits and on June 16, 1963, *Vostok 6* took the first woman, Valentina Tereshkova, on a 48-orbit space flight.

This flight completed the first phase of manned spaceflight for both the United States and the Soviet Union. The next Russian efforts would be the *Voskhod* series (three-man capsules), the first of

Figure 95. Mercury capsule

Figure 96.

which would be launched in October of 1964. The first manned launch in America's project *Gemini* would not take place until March of 1965.

Phase II: Gemini/Voskhod Flights. The Russians began their *Voskhod* series in 1964 while the Americans didn't get their first manned *Gemini* flight until 1965. The *Gemini* spacecraft were two-man vehicles and were launched by the *Titan II* rocket. The objective of the *Gemini* program was to develop techniques of joining (docking) spacecraft together in Earth orbit. This was called "rendezvous docking" and served to train space crews for the upcoming *Apollo* flights.

On March 18, 1965, Cosmonaut Leonov became the first person to "walk in space" when he spent 20 minutes outside his *Voskhod II* spacecraft. This was matched three months later by Astronaut Ed White who spent 21 minutes outside his *Gemini 4* spacecraft (see fig. 96).

For some reason, the Soviet Union had no more flights in the *Voskhod* series. It was over two years before they launched another manned capsule. Meanwhile, the United States launched eight more *Gemini* spacecraft and by the end of 1966 had established a sizeable lead over the Soviets. The United States total then stood at 656 orbits while the Soviets totaled only 163. Project *Gemini* provided the U.S. with the knowledge and technology necessary to proceed with project *Apollo* (the project dedicated to lunar exploration).

Phase III: Apollo/Soyuz Flights. Project *Gemini* concluded with the flight of *Gemini 12* on November 11, 1966, and it was nearly two years (October 11, 1968) before the first manned *Apollo* was launched. Part of this delay was due to a

Figure 97.

disastrous accident at Cape Kennedy on January 27, 1967. On that date the crew which had been selected for the first manned *Apollo* flight (Gus Grissom, Edward White II, and Roger Chaffee) were killed by a fire in their capsule during a training session.

The *Apollo* spacecraft were three-man craft, and their objective was to land and explore the moon. They were launched by the *Saturn* rocket series. Nineteen flights had been planned in the program, but only seventeen were completed.

Apollo 11 landed on the moon on July 20, 1969, and Astronaut Neil Armstrong became the first person to set foot on the surface of that heavenly body (see fig. 97). Astronaut "Buzz" Aldrin soon joined Armstrong and the entire world watched the end of the "space race" live on television sets.

There were five more successful lunar landings in project *Apollo,* the final one being the *Apollo 17* flight in December of 1972. Looking back, it now becomes apparent that if the Soviets ever planned to race the Americans to the moon, they gave up some time in 1965-1966 during the *Gemini* project.

The Russians began their *Soyuz* flights with a disaster. On the return leg of the *Soyuz I* flight (April 24, 1967), Vladimir Komarov was killed in a crash upon re-entry, becoming the first spaceflight fatality in history. The Russians did not resume their flights until October 26, 1968, when Beregovoi—at 47, the oldest man in space—maneuvered in *Soyuz 3* near the unmanned *Soyuz 2.*

Like the Americans in the *Apollo* program, *Soyuz* cosmonauts practiced docking techniques from 1968 to 1969. In 1970 they performed the longest-duration manned spaceflight up to that time—424 hours 59 minutes. But most of their *Soyuz 4* through *8* flights were in preparation for the next phase of the Russian spaceflight program—space laboratories.

Phase IV: Skylab/Salyut Laboratories. The basic objective of both Skylab and Salyut programs was the physiological study of long-term manned flight. The Russians launched their *Salyut I* "Space Station" April 19, 1971 (see fig. 98), and on April

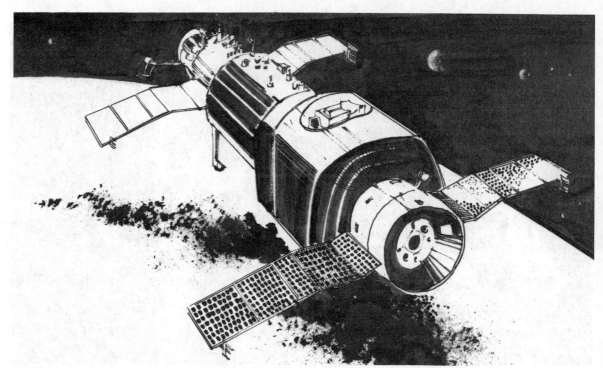

Figure 98.

22, 1971, *Soyuz 10* docked with the world's first space laboratory—although the crew of the *Soyuz* did not board the *Salyut.* In June of 1971, *Soyuz II* docked with *Salyut I* for 22 days. Unfortunately, the crew died as they returned to Earth when a faulty valve allowed air to escape from the cabin.

By the end of 1976, Russia had put up six *Salyut* space stations. These stations were experimental laboratories along the lines of the American *Skylab* and were the basis of Russia's long-term manned program. Despite setbacks in the program, they continued to pursue the *Salyut* project. By the time *Soyuz 23* failed to dock with *Salyut 5*—and had to make a quick trip home—there had been seven failures in 11 attempts to complete space station missions.

The United States as early as 1970 had made plans to establish a space laboratory program. This program was originally called the *Apollo Applications Program,* but was later renamed the *Skylab.* The intent of the program was to make some practical use of left over hardware from the Apollo moon landings. However, it gradually grew into a vital step in our mastery of the space environment.

On May 14, 1973, the *Skylab I* (see fig 99) unmanned orbital workshop was placed into orbit. There was a failure in the powered phase of the launch which ripped off one of the solar array wings from the workshop. Stop-gap measures were taken to control the solar radiation and prepare a repair kit for the astronauts who would go up and dock with *Skylab I.*

Unlike the Russians, the NASA only orbited one space station—the *Skylab Workshop.* There were four successful missions flown in the *Skylab* project with different Apollo command and service modules docking with the orbital workshop. Most of the objectives of the program were achieved and the crews established techniques and procedures necessary for the success of the planned *Space Shuttle* project.

Both *Skylab* and *Salyut* effectively demonstrated man's adaptability to extended working in manned space flight. *Skylab* was to have concluded the first

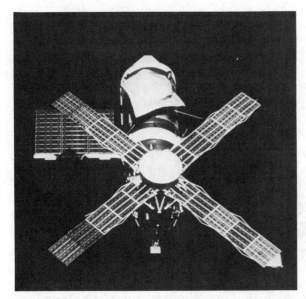

Figure 99.

era of manned spaceflight. However, there would be a long gap between the *Skylab* and the planned *Space Shuttle* program. For this and other reasons, an international venture would serve as the end to this era of manned spaceflight—the *Apollo-Soyuz Test Project*.

Phase V: Apollo/Soyuz Test Project. The plan for a joint U.S./Soviet spaceflight was included in an agreement on the peaceful exploration of outer space signed by President Nixon and Premier Kosygin on May 24, 1972—target date, July 15, 1975. The space flight was named the *Apollo/Soyuz Test Project* (APSTP). The flight would serve three purposes for America: Our scientists would have a chance to look at and learn something about the Russian's space program; it provided much-needed space activity during the long gap between *Skylab* completion and the *Space Shuttle* flights; and it allowed us to use left over *Apollo* spacecraft and hardware which would otherwise have been

Figure 100. Artist's rendering of Apollo-Soyuz docking

Figure 101.

wasted. The basic objective of the APSTP was the development of an international space rescue capability in the form of a common docking device and procedure. Formal approval for the plan came in 1972, and by early 1974 NASA reported the joint program had reached its half-way point.

On July 15, 1975 the *Apollo* and *Soyuz* spacecraft lifted off and headed toward the rendezvous point. The flight lasted nine days and included two dockings (see fig. 100). The two ships linked up by means of the Docking Module, and airlock with docking facilities at each end. July 17, the two ships docked and the objective of the mission had been accomplished—space rescue capability was now a fact. This flight marked the end of an era in U.S. spaceflight; it was the last *Apollo* flight and the final U.S. manned space activity until the *Space Shuttle* program began.

MANNED SPACEFLIGHT: SECOND ERA

The second era of manned spaceflight has produced an increase in manned spaceflight activity—by the Americans, Russians, and other nations. Long range plans of the United States and the USSR are geared towards space operations; most of their efforts in space up to 1983 were geared toward the solutions to a host of problems associated with space operations—from reuseable space vehicles to permanent space stations.

American Efforts. The United States' first project was the *Space Shuttle* component of the Space Transportation System (STS). The STS consists of the *Space Shuttle, Spacelab, space tugs,* and the *Tracking and Data Relay Satellite System* (TDRSS).

The *Space Shuttle* (see fig. 101) was designed to reduce cost and increase the effectiveness of using space for commercial, scientific, and defense needs. Because of its reuseability, it has the ability to inexpensively transport a variety of payloads to orbit and return them to be used again.

Preparation for building the Space Shuttle Orbiter began even before the Apollo missions were completed (early 1972), but years of study, preliminary designs, and proposal writing preceded these preparations. On September 17, 1976, the first Orbiter, the *Enterprise,* rolled out of the factory. The *Enterprise* was the first of five orbiters ordered for the program (*Columbia, Challenger, Discovery,* and *Atlantis* are the other four) and was used to demonstrate the approach and landing qualities of this design. The *Enterprise* was carried "piggy-back" on a Boeing 747 and then launched for approach and landing tests. On August 12, 1977, the *Enterprise* made its first free flight and landing.

On April 14, 1981, the *Orbiter Columbia* made the first successful orbital flight—the first spacecraft in the world to end an orbital mission by making a conventional airplane-like landing on Earth. It demonstrated its reuseability by making a second flight November 12, 1981, and three more flights in 1982 (March 22, June 27, and November 11). The November 11 flight, mission 5, carried two communication satellites—the SBS-3, Satellite Business System; and the ANIK C-3, Canada's Telsat. Mission 6 was the first flight of the Challenger. NASA has 15 more flights of the Shuttle Orbiters scheduled during 1983 and 1984.

Soviet Efforts. After the APSTP, the Russians continued their *Soyuz* flights and put up more *Salyuts.* Since 1975, they have put up so many spacecraft that we cannot discuss them all here. For example, in 1980 they carried out 89 space missions, mostly of a military nature (reconnaissance vehicles), and in 1981, 96 space missions were completed. In all, the *Soyuz* spacecraft have made 40 missions. The *Soyuz* has been replaced by the *Soyuz T* series—an uprated *Soyuz* design with more computational capability and outfitted to carry three cosmonauts. This is a tanker/transport design. The *Soyuz T-6* was the first mission to carry a French astronaut (July of 1982). (The Russians have begun a program to use foreign astronauts on their flights, both from the Western nations as well as the Eastern Bloc, such as Hungary and Romania.) The *Soyuz T-6* docked in May of 1982 with the new *Salyut 7* space station which was orbited in April of 1982.

While orbital assembly of a modular station is a near-term Soviet activity, a much larger, single station is their goal for the mid-80s. In order to get this single large station up to orbit, the Russians are developing a heavy booster more powerful than the Saturn 5. The booster will be launched in 1983 or 1984 and is keyed to the launch of the new heavy space station which will hold 12 cosmonauts.

To move personnel to and from this new large station, the Soviets are developing a new shuttle-type winged reuseable spacecraft which they launched for an orbital test in 1982. They have already built a new landing runway for the new "shuttle" at their Tyuratam launch site.

Fully operational space stations will probably mark the end of the second era of manned spaceflight; actual use of space, space colonies, and space travel will more than likely initiate the third era of manned spaceflight.

MINORITIES IN THE AERO-SPACE AGE

Since 1958, minority participation in aerospace activities has increased dramatically. This has occurred partly because of the international push for equality in employment by human rights advocates and, to a great extent, because of new laws passed by Congress which make it possible for groups previously excluded to enter into aerospace career fields.

COMPETITION

In May of 1963, Betty Miller made the reverse flight of Earhart's earlier attempt (California to Australia). This was a record solo flight for women and she was personally congratulated by President Kennedy. Jerrie Mock went around the world in her Cessna 180 in 29½ days in 1964 and was congratulated by President Johnson for this first by a woman.

Not to be forgotten during this era was the formidable Jacqueline Cochran. On June 6, 1960, she became the first woman to fly Mach 2, and, on June 15 of the same year, became the first woman to make an arrested landing and a takeoff on an aircraft carrier. By 1961 she had set eight major records in a Northrop T-38 and, on April 27 of the following year, she became the first woman to fly a jet across the Atlantic on a 5,120-mile flight from New Orleans to Hanover, Germany. During this flight she set 49 new intercity and straight line distance records. During 1963-64 she set five new speed records in her F-104G and established a new women's speed record of 1,429.2 mph on May 18, 1964. Jacqueline became a colonel in the USAF Reserve and finally retired in 1970. Her death August 9, 1980, closed out a career of more than 40 years in aviation.

AIRLINES

In 1961, Scandinavian Airlines hired its first woman pilot. Since that time, women have steadily increased their number in the airlines.

January 6, 1973, Emily Warner became the first U.S. female pilot, to fly for Frontier Airlines as a second officer aboard a Boeing 737. She later moved to the right seat of a twin Otter, and subsequently qualified for captain. She was also the first female airline pilot in the United States to earn four stripes. She then returned to the Boeing 737 as first officer. Also in 1973, Delta got its first woman flight crew member, Joy Walker—a flight engineer.

Daniel "Chappie" James

MILITARY

It wasn't until 1948 that the military services became integrated and until that time there was little chance for blacks or women to advance in rank. It has been even more recent that women have been trained as pilots in the military.

There have been several black general officers in the military but only one has reached the rank of a four star general in the Air Force. He was General Daniel "Chappie" James who had flown combat in both Korea and Vietnam. In 1975, he became Commander in Chief of the North American Air Defense Command. General James retired from the Air Force in 1978 and died only two months after his retirement.

Women also can now rise to general officer rank. The first USAF female general was Jeanne Holm. The second female general in the USAF, and the first to command an Air Force wing was Major General Norma E. Brown (1974). Since the military academies became integrated in 1976, more and more women have been admitted into these previously all-male institutions. The 1980 graduating class from the Air Force Academy contained 97 female officers.

SPACE

Space programs probably represent the area in which minority members have gained most publicity. Many women and blacks are actually involved in the space R&D and operating areas. Dr. George R. Carruthers, a black astrophysicist at the Naval Research Laboratories, developed the Far Ultraviolet Camera/Spectrograph for the Apollo 16 mission, thus contributing greatly to space knowledge and exploration.

The first black selected to be an astronaut aboard DoD's Manned Orbiting Laboratory Program was Major Robert H. Lawrence, Jr. Lawrence had a degree in nuclear chemistry and was a pilot-scientist. He was killed in an aircraft accident in 1967 before he had a chance to fly into space. Three blacks were named to the astronaut program in 1978. Major Guion S. Bluford, Jr., (now Lt. Colonel) was a 1964 graduate of Pennsylvania

Figure 102.

State University and earned a Ph.D. in aerospace engineering from the Air Force Institute of Technology. He was a Vietnam pilot with 144 missions. Bluford was named for the eighth Shuttle mission, which is to place a second series of radio relay satellites in Earth orbit. Qualifying for future space missions was Frederick D. Gregory, a USAF and NASA test pilot. Also named in 1978 was Ronald E. McNair, a Ph.D. physicist from M.I.T. who specializes in laser research; he is now mission qualified. Major Charles F. Bolden, Jr., was named in 1980 to the astronaut program and is pilot qualified for future shuttle flights.

The present team of female astronauts were selected in 1978. The team is composed of eight women. Included in this group are: Mary L. Cleave, Ph.D.; Bonnie J. Dunbar; Anna L. (Tingle) Fisher, M.D. (whose husband is also an astronaut); Shannon W. Lucid, Ph.D.; Sally K. Ride, Ph.D.; Margaret R. (Rhea) Seddon, M.D. (who is married to astronaut Robert L. Gibson); Kathryn D. Sullivan, Ph.D.; and Judith A. Resnik.

ADVANCEMENTS IN AERONAUTICS

The aeronautics research flights which were so important in the early 1950s continued into the late 1950s and early 1960s, but then they were reduced in number and in the variety of aircraft built. During the latter part of the 1960s, up to the present, the flight testing has been primarily of prototypes of various operational aircaft rather than of research aircraft.

AERONAUTICAL RESEARCH

There were two X-series aircraft that were flown during the 1950s and 1960s which should be mentioned—the *X-15* and the *XB-70*.

X-15. The *X-15* project was a joint Air Force, Navy, and NACA project aimed at building an airplane that could fly at a speed of 4,500 mph and reach an altitude of 250,000 feet. To accomplish this the aircraft would have to withstand a temperature of over 1200°F. On September 30, 1955, the *X-15* contract was awarded to North American Aviation. Three *X-15* aircraft were produced under this contract.

The *X-15* (see fig. 102) was 50 feet long, had a 22 foot wing-span, and weighed about 33,000 pounds, of which over 18,000 pounds was fuel. The *X-15* was rocket powered and was carried under the wing of a specially modified B-52. To protect it from the 1200° temperature, the *X-15* was constructed of a nickel-steel alloy called Inconel X.

The *X-15* was carried aloft by the B-52 four times before it was dropped for the first time. These captive flights were used to test all systems and check wind tunnel data. On June 8, 1959, the *X-15* was dropped for its first flight, which was a powerless glide back to Earth. The first powered flight took place in September 1959, and the aircraft reached a speed of almost 1,400 mph. The first eight flights of the *X-15* were piloted by a North American Aviation test pilot, Scott Crossfield. The first government flight was performed in March of 1960 by NASA test pilot Joe Walker.

Flight testing of the *X-15* continued through 1967, with the three *X-15*s performing over 200 total flights. Before flight testing ended, the *X-15* had exceeded both of its design goals. It had reached a speed of 4,534 mph (Mach 6.72), which is twice as fast as a rifle bullet, and it had reached an altitude of 314,750 feet, which is 59.6 miles straight up. The pilots on these record-setting flights were USAF Major Bob White for the speed record and NASA test pilot Joe Walker for the altitude record.

XB-70. In 1954, the United States Air Force requested bids on a contract to build a supersonic replacement for the *B-52*. This aircraft would have to fly three times the speed of sound and at an altitude of 70,000 feet. North American Aviation won the competition and received a contract to build three (later reduced to two) prototypes. The result was the *XB-70*—one of the largest, fastest, and most controversial aircraft ever built. The first *XB-70* had its initial flight in September of 1964, and the second one made its first flight in July 1965.

The *XB-70* had a delta wing with span of 105 feet, two vertical stabilizers, and a 185-foot long fuselage. Almost 80 feet of the slim fuselage stuck out in front of the wing. This required that a small balancing wing called a *canard* be fitted just behind the nose (see fig. 103). The nose of the *XB-70* drooped for better pilot visibility and this, together with the canard, gave it a cobra-like look.

There were several design features which were unique to the *XB-70*. The very thin delta wings were constructed of welded stainless steel honeycomb and were designed so that at supersonic speeds the wing rode on its own shock wave like a surfer on a surfboard. The fuel tanks were "blanketed" with nitrogen so the fuel could not ignite when the skin temperature rose due to frictional heating. The six turbojet engines were mounted side by side and buried within the fuselage/wing structure. Each engine produced about 30,000 pounds of thrust. The wing tips folded down in high speed flight to provide for better stability.

In 1964, Congress decided the Air Force did not need a supersonic bomber and cancelled the program. The two prototypes remained at Edwards Air Force Base, California, and were used by the Air Force and NASA for supersonic research. In October 1964, the *XB-70* reached its design speed (2,000 mph) and altitude (70,000 feet) requirements.

In June 1966, the second *XB-70* prototype was destroyed in a mid-air collision. Number one is now at the United States Air Force Museum at Wright Patterson Air Force Base, Ohio.

Aircraft research and design since the Wright *Flyer* has been one of continual change as aircraft designers determined which configuration produced the best performance characteristics—especially at high speeds. While performance had always been the major design factor in the past, today, other factors are also important. For the military, changing air tactics, advanced weapons systems, and new technology advantages in aerodynamics, structures, and propulsion have entered the design picture. Beginning in the mid-1970s, fuel efficiency and environmental considerations became driving

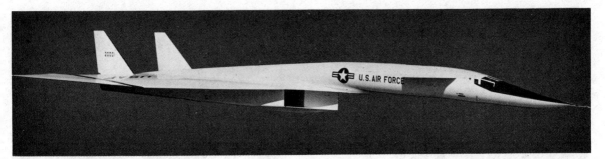

Figure 103. XB-70

forces in commercial aviation as well as in military aviation. Production and operating costs are very real factors in modern aircraft design and construction. By the end of the century, and well into the next, we may well see some departures from conventional aircraft designs. The developments in aeronautical research from the mid-1970s to the present are significant to civil and military aviation. We will briefly describe the major research projects from 1975 to 1982, beginning with one very important research project which has made many of the reseach projects possible.

Composites. Research direction in the past has always been limited by weight and structural stress limitations. Many designs that looked good on paper could not be tested because the aircraft would be too heavy and/or incapable of withstanding the inflight stresses. However, advances in construction materials in the 1970s have overcome some of these limitations. Super-strong, but lightweight, non-metallic, graphite epoxy "composite" materials have been developed that are stronger than many common metals used in aircraft construction. These "composites" are being tested in every major structural component of an aircraft—from wings and fuselage to helicopter rotor blades. Research tests have demonstrated their strength and thus have opened new doors either to go back to old designs which are more efficient or to advance to new, previously untestable designs.

Airfoil Designs. The new-directions research of the last ten years includes foreswept wings and oblique-wing aircraft.

Foreswept Wing. The foreswept wing (FSW) is also known as *forward swept, forward-swept,* *swept-forward,* or *fore-swept* wing. Sweeping wings forward goes back more than a hundred years to pre-Wright experiments of the 1870s. The concept was flight tested earlier in this century (about 40 years ago) and has theoretical advantages. Its use had been overshadowed by aftswept wings, since foreswept wings needed to be structurally stronger in high-speed flight. In the past, this meant making the wing heavier using conventional metal alloys. The FSW is now practical as the result of advances in composite material technology. This technology enables the wings to be made lighter, smaller, and less costly than equivalent performance planes with aftswept metal wings. The FSW design also reduces weight, cost, and drag. Test data show this technology provides an aircraft that can weigh less, fly longer ranges with given fuel loads, and turn very tight at supersonic speeds. One of the problems with FSW is "twisting"—the wing must bend without twisting, and this problem seems to have been solved.

The Defense Advanced Research Projects Agency (DARPA), the USAF, and NASA jointly investigated the FSW design and called on three companies for a demonstrator fighter design. Rockwell International's version was called the X-FSW *Sabrebrat;* General Dynamics' bid for the DARPA contract was a FSW version of its *F-16* fighter; and the Grumman Corporation's design was the *X-29A* (see fig. 104). All designs had wings sweeping forward instead of rearward, as conventional airplane wings do, and all used canard wings. On December 22, 1981, Grumman won the competition to build the first FSW aircraft. The *X-29A* will have a variable camber trailing edge that changes the wing

Figure 104. X-29A

shape to match flight conditions. Flight tests are scheduled for December of 1984.

Oblique-wing Aircraft. This type of aircraft is also known as "adaptive-wing," "skewed-wing," or "pivoting-wing" aircraft. The Oblique-wing Aircraft (OWA) changes form during flight for optimum lift under different circumstances and can be rotated to different positions for best aerodynamic characteristics. The ability to change the wing angle provides efficiency at both low and high speeds. For takeoff, landing, and low–speed cruise, the wing is perpendicular to the fuselage; at high speeds, the wing is pivoted to different oblique angles. In one projected Rockwell bomber design, the wing would actually be stowed for high supersonic flight and the aircraft's flat body would supply the needed lift.

NASA has flight-tested an oblique-wing aircraft, the *AD-1* "Scissors." The *AD-1* completed its 38-flight test program in 1982. It has been flown with the wing in the maximum 60-degree position. The wing rotates around its vertical axis, with one wing aftswept and the other foreswept. The *AD-1* was

designed to explore the feasibility of using an adaptive wing as a low-drag, supersonic airfoil for future transport airplanes. On such a transport, the wing would be pivoted 60 degrees at higher speeds to reduce air drag, thereby allowing higher speeds and a longer range for the same fuel expenditure.

Lighter-Than-Air Craft (LTA). You might have thought LTA airships were dead, but they have been revived. NASA is investigating the possibilities of applying modern technology to LTA ships. One application is a hybrid airship—combining helicopter and LTA components—which could lift cargoes weighing as much as 1,000 tons over short distances. NASA's limited LTA technology development program emphasizes research on the aerodynamic considerations of combining LTA hulls with large diameter helicopter-like rotors.

Solar Aircraft. Flight experiments have been conducted in powering an aircraft on the sun's rays alone. These experiments began as human-powered aircraft research (the *Gossamer Condor,* 1977, and the *Gossamer Albatross,* 1979) under the leadership of Paul MacCready. The *Gossamer Penguin* (1980) and the *Solar Challenger* (1981) have made successful, sustained flight powered only by the sun's rays.

The *Solar Challenger* weighs 194 pounds, is designed to fly at high altitudes, and is able to fly long distances through turbulent air conditions when necessary. Its maximum speed is 40 mph at a ceiling of 10,000 feet. It has a 47-foot wingspan and a glide ratio of 13.5:1 (which gives it characteristics of a sailplane—in case of a "short circuit"). The craft's weight was kept down by using new composite materials such as Kevlar and Dacron polyester fiber and graphite epoxy. Electricity for the *Solar Challenger* is generated from more than 16,000 solar cells (45 sq. ft. of cell surface) mounted on top of the wings and horizontal stabilizer. The craft needs about 1,350 watts of power (it produces up to 2,676 watts) to maintain sustained, level flight. Its France-to-England flight (in June of 1981) gave it the world's atmospheric record for solar-powered aircraft. On July 7, 1981, the *Solar Challenger* left Cormeilles-en-Vexin, France, and landed in Manston, England, five hours and twenty-two minutes later. It was a 180-mile trip at an average speed of 35 mph. The *Challenger* reached altitudes of 11,000 feet with its pilot Steven Ptacek.

MILITARY AVIATION

The development of military operational aircraft had started to lean toward the newer, faster, high-performance jets just before and after the Korean War. New military applications surfaced in both the Korean War and the Vietnam War which resulted in new categories of aircraft—such as the electronic warfare aircraft *EF-111A* (see fig. 105) and super-advanced aircraft in conventional categories—such as the *U-2/TR-1* and *SR-71* (see fig. 106) high altitude strategic reconnaisance aircraft, which fly above 70,000 and 80,000 feet respectively.

Faster and more maneuverable aircraft were built and sold to other nations even before they were entered into the American inventory. Some designs

Figure 105. EF-111A

Figure 106. SR-71

arrived at the prototype test-flight stage only to be blocked from production due to disapproval by political leaders. The *B-1* bomber was built and tested, but then production was shelved by Congress. Later, in October of 1982, President Reagan decided to go ahead with *B-1* production (see fig. 107) in the *B-1B* configuration.

CIVIL AVIATION

Commercial Aviation. In chapter 1-5, we mentioned the British Viscount turboprop. The first jet-powered American transport was also a turboprop-powered aircraft. This was the Lockheed *L-188 Electra* which entered service in October of 1958. Since that time, commercial aviation has gone on to develop and put into operation several categories of aircraft. Beginning with the long-haul jets such as the *Boeing 707, DC-8,* and *Convair 880,* the airlines moved on to short-haul jets; with an increasing passenger load by the mid-1960s, jumbo jets made their appearance. And when speed seemed to be the vital factor, the supersonic transports appeared. By 1978, European technology had come up to that

Figure 107. B-1

Figure 108. Boeing 707-120

of the United States; this prompted competition for the next category of aircraft—the family of the advanced-technology aircraft.

Long-haul Jets. In June 1952, the Boeing Company made a decision to go ahead and develop a commercial jet airliner using $16 million of their own money. At that time there was no indication that the airlines were even interested in a jet airliner as no one had approached Boeing with an order. The only commercial jets flying were the British *Comet 1s*, and they had only been in service for about a month.

This was a daring venture for an aviation industry to make and was totally different from the standard procedure of an airline placing a firm order before a manufacturer began production. However, Boeing had a lot of experience building large jet airplanes. They were producing both the B-47 and B-52 jet bombers and the government contracts for these airplanes had given Boeing the knowledge and technology to branch out into the commercial air-line field.

Construction of the prototype started in October of 1952, and the first flight took place on July 15, 1954. It was immediately evident that this was a remarkable airplane. First of all, it was huge compared with propeller driven airliners or even with the *Comet 1*. The first production model, the *707-120* (see fig. 108) had a wingspan of 130 feet, a length of 144 feet, and weighed 248,000 pounds fully loaded. It carried 179 passengers and had a cruising speed of 600 mph. By comparison, the *Comet 1* had a wingspan of 115 feet, was 93 feet long, weighed 105,000 pounds, and carried 36 passengers at 490 mph. The range of the *707* was over 4,000 miles compared to 1,750 miles for the *Comet 1*.

The *707* incorporated many revolutionary design features such as noise suppressors (to quiet the engine exhaust), thrust reversers, leading edge flaps, and an automatic landing system. The thrust reversers were to slow the aircraft down after landing and the leading edge flaps provided slower takeoff and landing speeds. The *707* also had an anti-skid braking system which allowed the aircraft to stop on slick runways without the wheels skidding.

Boeing immediately began an exhaustive testing program using the prototype and the first production models of the *707*. Some of these test flights were also used to demonstrate the capabilities of the 707 to the airlines and to the public. One of these demonstration flights was a speed dash across the United States from Seattle, Washington, to Baltimore, Maryland. The flight was completed in three hours and 48 minutes at an average speed of 612 mph. The run was only three minutes longer than the fastest military jet and was made in one-half the time of propeller driven airliners.

The first two airlines to order 707s were Pan American and American Airlines. On October 26, 1958, Pan American inaugurated transatlantic service with the 707, and on December 11, 1958, National Airlines flew the first domestic 707 flight. This flight was from New York to Miami in a 707 leased from Pan American. American Airlines began transcontinental 707 service on January 25, 1959. The 707 went on to become the standard long-range jet of the 1960s. More than 900 have been sold to 25 international and domestic airlines. More than 400 have been delivered to the Air Force as the military C-135.

Two other United States commercial long-haul jets appeared at about the same time—the *Douglas DC-8* and the *Convair 880*. The prototype *DC-8* flew in May of 1958 and the *Convair 880* in January of 1959. Here is a good example of the importance of timing in the very competitive commercial airline business. The *DC-8* was a successful airliner and several hundred were placed into service. The *Convair 880* and its larger version (the *990*), on the other hand, never quite made it, and only a few were ever manufactured. The airlines had already placed their orders for 707s and DC-8s; the *Convairs*, even though they were fine aircraft, came along about one year too late.

Short-haul Jets. So immediate was the success of the 707/DC-8 airliners that both Boeing and Douglas began working on smaller, short-haul jets. Actually the first short-haul jet was the French *Caravelle I* which first flew in 1955 and went into service with Air France in 1959. More than 200 *Caravelles* in four models were manufactured. They were a very successful aircraft with a jet engine attached to either side of the rear fuselage and carried between 65 and 90 passengers. United

Airlines was the only United States carrier to fly the *Caravelle I*.

In December 1960, Boeing announced they were going into production of a short/medium-haul trijet called the 727. The prototype flew in February of 1963, and in February of 1964, Eastern Airlines placed it into service. The 727 has been produced in five models and is the most successful jet ever built; over 1,700 have been sold. The other short-haul Boeing aircraft, the 737, is an 80-113 passenger, twin-jet airliner which went into service in 1968. More than 800 737's have been built. One thing that makes the Boeing jets so popular, in addition to their reliability, is that all models (707, 727, and 737) have the same fuselage and many of the components are interchangeable.

Douglas entered the short-haul market in 1962 with the announcement of their twin-jet DC-9. The DC-9 flew for the first time in February of 1965. The DC-9 resembles the *Caravelle* in the placement of the engines but is a larger aircraft carrying from 80-115 passengers. More than 1,000 of these very popular aircraft have been sold.

The final short-haul jet we will discuss is the *BAC-111*, built by the British Aircraft Corporation. This twin-jet aircraft went into production in 1961 and flew for the first time in 1965. Two hundred and twenty-seven *BAC-111s* have been built.

Jumbo Jets. By the mid-1960s jet airline travel had reached a peak and it looked like there was no end in sight. All aviation forecasts were that passenger (and cargo) traffic was going to continue to grow by eight-ten percent per year.

In April 1966, Pan American World Airways approached Boeing with an order for twenty-five giant jet airliners. With this firm order, Boeing announced they would begin production of the Boeing 747 (see fig. 109). This "jumbo jet" was huge even when compared to the 707. It had a wingspan 65 feet longer than the 707 and its fuselage was nearly 90 feet longer and almost twice the diameter. While the 707 weighed about 250,000 pounds, the 747 weighed nearly 800,000 pounds fully loaded.

The 747 made its first flight in February of 1969, and Pan American flew its first commercial flight from New York to London on January 22, 1970. The

Figure 109. Boeing-747

747 offered a new standard of luxury which included seating for 385 passengers and an upstairs cocktail lounge. There have been 540 747s built since 1969.

Both Lockheed and Douglas entered the "jumbo jet" field in 1966 with announcements of intent to build a medium-haul jumbo jet. Both manufacturers went into production in 1968; the Douglas DC-10 flew first in August of 1970 while the Lockheed L-1011 flew in November of 1970. American Airlines placed the first DC-10 into commercial service on August 5, 1971, and Eastern Airlines inaugurated L-1011 service on April 15, 1972.

In addition to following a very similar timetable, the two aircraft are very similar both in appearance and in performance. They are both trijets with one engine under each wing and the third on the tail. In the DC-10 the rear engine is mounted above the fuselage while in the L-1011 it is mounted inside the rear fuselage. They both carry about 350 passengers for distances up to 4,000 miles. Both aircraft have been very successful.

Advanced-technology Jets. Before 1978, the Americans had the technological edge over foreign aircraft manufacturers, with 85 percent of all world airliners of U.S. manufacture and design. But by 1978, the technology gap had narrowed to the point that U.S. aircraft makers began to feel a technological threat from abroad, especially from the A310 advanced-technology transport. This threat gave rise to the introduction of a new family of advanced-technology jetliners for the 1980s. The DC-9 Super 80, the Boeing 767, and the Boeing 757 are three aircraft which were developed to improve efficiency through the use of advanced technology.

The DC-9 Super 80 (see fig. 110) was the first of the new-generation jets which became operational in August of 1981. It looks like a DC-9 but has

Figure 110. DC-9 Super 80

Figure 111. Concorde

technological features which reduce noise levels, fuel use, and exhaust emissions. It also has a larger wing and is 43½ feet longer than the regular *DC-9.* Carrying 137 to 172 passengers, it has a range of 1,000-2,000 miles.

The Boeing *767* made its first flight September 26, 1981 and is the second member of the new-generation jets. First delivery was to United Airlines August 19, 1982, while Canada Air got its first *767* October 30, 1982. Seventeen airlines have placed orders for 173 of these medium-range, 211-passenger aircraft. The maximum takeoff weight of the initial transport was 300,000 pounds. A unique feature of the *767* is its two-man cockpit (normally airliners carry three cockpit crew members).

The companion to the *767* is the Boeing *757,* a standard-body jet carrying 185 passengers. Its first flight was February 19, 1982. Its first delivery was to Eastern Airlines in January of 1983. The *757* also has a two-crew member cockpit and a maximum takeoff weight of 220,000 pounds.

Supersonic Transports. In the early 1960s two

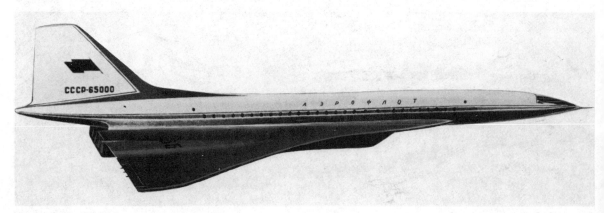

Figure 112. TU-144

European aviation manufacturers, the Bristol Aeroplane Company (which later became part of the British Aircraft Corporation) in England and Sud-Aviation (which later became Aerospatiale) in France, were both working on designs for a supersonic passenger airliner. They both came up with very similar designs for a delta-wing aircraft which could carry about 100 passengers and fly at about Mach 2.2 (1400 mph). They also both discovered that the development costs of such an aircraft would be so high that neither nation could afford to build it. In November of 1962, an international agreement was signed which would allow BAC and Sud-Aviation to jointly build the aircraft and the governments of Britain and France would share the development costs. Thus, the Concorde was born (see fig. 111).

At that time, unknown to anyone in the Western World, the Soviet Union was also working on a supersonic transport (SST) known as the TU-144. The TU-144 was very similar to the Concorde in size and shape but was designed to fly a little faster— Mach 2.35 (1500 mph) (see fig. 112).

The United States, not to be outdone, decided to enter the SST competition. However, the Concorde and the TU-144 already had a head start because the U.S. did not start its SST program until 1965. In May 1967, Boeing was selected over Lockheed in the competition to build the American SST. Boeing was awarded a contract to build two prototypes, with the federal government paying about 90% of the development costs. Boeing called their SST the Model 2707. It was evident that the 2707 could not beat either the British or the Russian SST into service so the U.S. decided to go bigger and better. The 2707 was designed to carry up to 350 passengers and fly at Mach 2.7 (1800 mph).

The TU-144 won the race into the air, flying for the first time in December 1968. The Concorde first flew in March of 1969. The 2707 never flew.

In March of 1971, by a very close vote of 51 to 46, the U.S. Senate cut off the government funds to continue the 2707 project. There were many anti-SST people in the United States, mostly environmentalists, and they made enough noise to make Congress hear their objections. Many of their arguments against the 2707 were completely false

but they prevailed. After an expenditure of over one billion dollars, the American SST was dead.

Because of a disastrous crash of a TU-144, the Concorde beat the Russian SST into commercial service. Both British Airways and Air France began Concorde service on January 1, 1976. On May 24, 1976, the Concorde began flying from London and Paris to Washington, D.C. The flight takes less than four hours.

GENERAL AVIATION

During this time period (1958-present), general aviation in the United States has grown into the largest segment of all aviation and continues to grow at a faster rate than military or commercial aviation. This is not generally true in other nations of the world (with the exception of Canada). There are three main reasons for this: (1) geography, (2) expense, and (3) freedom to fly.

The United States is a very large nation while European countries, on the other hand, are smaller than most of our states. To fly from Amsterdam to Rome would require crossing through four independent nations and asking permission of each to enter their airspace. This trip is shorter than the trip from San Francisco to San Diego in California. Because of the short distances and excellent ground transportation, there is no real reason to fly within any of the European countries.

The expense of owning and operating a general aviation aircraft is very high, and the U.S. is one of the few nations in the world with a standard of living that will permit the average person to own his own airplane. Most nations of the world do not have a developed aviation manufacturing industry, so if a citizen of one of these nations wants to own an airplane, he would have to import one from the U.S. Also, the cost of fuel in most foreign countries is almost twice as high as in the U.S.

And finally, many nations of the world are ruled by a government that does not want its citizens to have the right to fly whenever and wherever they want.

We mentioned in Chapter 1-5 that immediately following World War II, Beech, Cessna, and Piper began to build all metal, single-engine monoplanes.

Figure 113. Cessna 310

These aircraft evolved through the years to become more and more sophisticated. The pilots wanted them to fly higher, faster, and farther so many became turbocharged and were equipped with retractable landing gear. More instruments and electronic aids were added, all of which led to the general aviation aircraft of today.

In the 1950s, the manufacturers began adding twin-engine aircraft to their inventories. This was in answer to the need for business and executive types of aircraft. The first of these twin-engine aircraft was the Beechcraft *Twin Bonanza* in 1951. This was followed by the *Aero Commander* in 1952 and the Cessna *310* (see fig. 113) and Piper *Apache* in 1953. During the 1960s more and more innovations were added to these twins, and, by the end of that decade, most manufacturers had twin-engine aircraft as fancy as the commercial airliners.

It was also during the 1960s that the first turbojet business/executive aircraft were built. The first of these was the British *Hawker Siddley 125,* a twinjet which entered service in 1963. American business jets included the *Learjet* (1964), the North American *Sabreliner* (1966), and the Grumman *Gulfstream II* (1967). This meant that the corporate executive could not only travel in the same comfort as on the airlines, but he could also travel as fast. He could also land at many airports which were not served by the airlines.

Today, seventy-one percent of all general aviation flying is being done either directly or indirectly for some business purpose. Only 29 percent is done just for fun, or for personal transportation. We will discuss general aviation in considerably more detail in another Part of this text.

THE FUTURE??

There have been some remarkable accomplishments in the short time since the Wright brothers flew for the first time. As you have studied this unit on the *Heritage of Flight,* it should have become evident that the history of flight has always been filled with seemingly unsolvable problems. Each new accomplishment solved these problems but also created just as many new, seemingly unsolvable problems. Even today, we are still confronted with new problems like the energy crisis, noise pollution, and new and more terrible aerospace weapons. Are these problems unsolvable, or will new developments and accomplishments solve them just as they have all others? Only time will tell; but you can be sure that there will be even more amazing aerospace developments in the future.

This leaves us with but one final question to ask ourselves before we continue our study of this book—does mankind still have the inborn desire to fly free as the birds, or has the human spirit been dulled by the rapid advance of technology? The answer to this question lies partly in the continuation of individual and small-group flight activities which *use* technology to help satisfy the desire to fly. Within the past decade, several examples have taken place: the *Gossamer Condor, Double Eagle II,* a very special helicopter flight, and the advent of ultralight aircraft.

We mentioned at the very beginning of this book that, from the start of recorded history, mankind has been trying to fly using only muscle power. Hundreds of thousands have tried it and failed. At 7:30 a.m., August 23, 1977, a 77-pound aircraft called the *Gossamer Condor* (see fig. 114), powered only by the muscles of a young bicyclist named Bryan Allen, lifted off the Earth and performed a 7-minute and 22-second flight. The airplaine flew a figure eight pattern around two pylons set one mile apart and held an altitude of at least 10 feet during the entire flight.

At 7:50 p.m. (local time) on August 17, 1978, three American balloonist landed in a farmer's field in Evereux, France. This was the completion of a 3,233 mile flight which started in Presque Isle, Maine, 137 hours and 18 minutes earlier and was

Figure 114. Gossamer Condor

the first successful balloon crossing of the Atlantic Ocean. Interestingly, man's first balloon flight in history, in September of 1783, took place only 60 miles from where Ben Abruzzo, Maxie Anderson, and Larry Newman landed in the *Double Eagle II* (see fig. 115).

More recently, the first round-the-world flight by helicopter was made during the period 1-30 September, 1982. Ross Perot, Jr., and Jay Coburn took off from Dallas, Texas, in a Bell Longranger II helicopter, the "Spirit of Texas," and for the next 29 days flew 24,750 miles in their circumnavigation of the world. Their trip took them to 26 other countries and involved slightly more than 246 flying hours. The accomplishment of these young pilots is an example of how technology helps people pioneer in the realm of flight.

More and more "ultralight" aircraft are entering the airspace. The ultralight is a very lightweight airplane which technology has helped to develop. Some ultralights are constructed of exceptionally strong but relatively new materials. Pilots claim that the greatest appeal of this type airplane is that it gives the sensation of flying like a bird.

Yes, the desire to fly free as the birds is still with us. And, no, technology obviously has not dulled the human spirit.

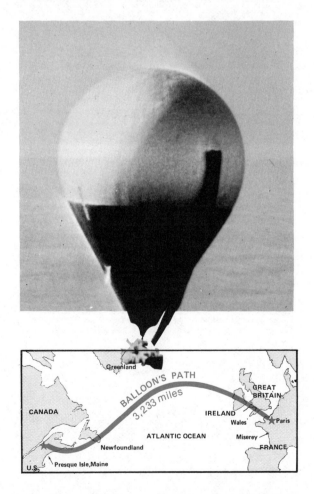

Figure 115. Flight of Double Eagle II

PART TWO

ROCKETRY AND SPACECRAFT

Rocketry is based on the propelling of a vehicle by a reactive force. It applies Newton's third law of motion—the action of the rocket's exhaust gases produce a reaction, forcing the rocket in the opposite direction. So a rocket engine, or motor, is a *reaction engine*. The jet engines which power most airliners are reaction engines, too. But there is a distinct difference: the jet engine generates its reactive force by burning a mixture of air with a fuel; the rocket engine does not use air. The rocket carries everything it needs to generate a reactive force; this allows the rocket to operate in the atmosphere and in space.

We owe the success of our space activities and the many benefits derived from them to research and development in rocketry. Rocketry is now, and will be for the forseeable future, the foundation of our space activities. Perhaps generations to come will develop new propulsion systems based on something other than rocketry. These propulsion systems of the future will most likely involve forces of the universe not as yet known or understood.

In this part we will survey rocketry from its beginnings and fundamentals to its future applications. The main learning objective for this Part is for you to Know the Fundamentals of Rocketry and Applications of Rocketry to Spacecraft. Upon completing your study of all six chapters in this Part, you should:

1. know the historical background, fundamental laws, and operating principles of rockets,
2. know the various types of chemical propulsion systems,
3. know the operational concepts of several advanced propulsion systems,
4. know how rockets are guided and controlled,
5. know the different types of orbits and trajectories,
6. know the various actual and proposed unmanned and manned spacecraft programs.

Chapter 2-1

ROCKET FUNDAMENTALS

There is an explanation for everything that a rocket does. The explanation is almost always based on laws of physics and the nature of the rocket's propellant, which usually is a combination of chemicals. But let us point out quickly that experimentation is required to find out whether a *new* rocket will or will not work. Even today, with all the knowledge and expertise which exists in the field of rocketry, experimentation occasionally shows that certain ideas are not practical.

In this chapter we will look back in time to the early developers and users of rocketry. We will review some of the physical laws that apply to rocketry. We will discuss selected chemicals and their combinations which may be used as propellants. Since each rocket is made up of systems, we will identify the systems and their components. And, we will look at the basics of rocket propellant efficiency.

The general learning objective for this chapter is for you to know the historical background, fundamental laws, and operating principles of rockets. To reach this objective, you must pattern your study according to the *specific learning objectives* listed in the Appendix of this textbook.

ROCKETRY'S BEGINNINGS

Rocketry is certainly not a new activity, nor was it born out of our efforts to explore space. As early as A.D. 1220, and perhaps even earlier, rockets were used by the Chinese. The Chinese were also the first to use rockets as weapons of war. In A.D. 1232 they used "fire arrows" (rockets) in a battle known as Kai-Feng-Fu.

Much later, in 1405, a German engineer by the name of Von Eichsteadt devised a rocket which was propelled by gunpowder and, in 1429, the French used rockets to defend Orleans against the British.

By 1630, rockets which exploded and sent small pieces of metal in all directions were developed for military use. During the Thirty Years' War (1618-1648), rockets weighing as much as 100 pounds were fired. Rockets also saw extensive use in the battle of Panipat in India where as many as 1,000 rockets were fired at one time. Rockets were used in 1807 at the battle of Copenhagen and, in 1812, the British formed a rocket brigade. This brigade saw action in the Napoleonic Wars at Leipzig in 1813 and at Waterloo in 1815.

Even during this early period of rocketry, research and experimentation constantly improved the quality and changed the nature of military rockets. Colonel William Congreve, a British artillery expert, developed a rocket with *fins* for more controlled flight or better stabilization. William Hale used *spin* stabilization for his rockets. Even with these improvements over the *stick* (skyrocket-type) stabilization, the rocket was seldom used for military purposes. Rockets of that time could not hit a specific target and therefore were not accurate enough for precision bombardment. However, the newly developed *rifling** for artillery pieces and shoulder weapons did provide the desired pinpoint accuracy. For this reason, the rocket was replaced as a significant military weapon. The rocket was, however, used to carry lifelines to ships wrecked along coastlines, and in World War I, rockets were used to carry signal flares to light up the battlefield at night and to carry messages. Some rockets were used for more typically military tasks against enemy airships and balloons. At least one World War I airplane was equipped with rockets. They were placed in holding tubes and the tubes were attached to the biplane's wing struts. The rockets were ignited electrically.

The turning point and the regeneration of interest in rocketry was brought about by the work of Dr. Robert H. Goddard in the United States and Dr. Hermann Oberth in Germany. Dr. Goddard, who is recognized as the "Father of Modern Rocketry," was the first scientist to use liquid propellants (liquid oxygen and gasoline) in a rocket. Dr. Oberth's work with liquid oxygen and alcohol propellants closely followed that of Dr. Goddard. These "firsts" in the use of the more powerful liquid propellants (as compared to solid propellants) took place in the 1920s.

While Dr. Goddard's work in liquid propellant rocketry was strictly a private venture, rocketry in Germany had the attention and support of the government. As war drew near for the United States, Dr. Goddard's work was directed toward developing quick-takeoff propulsion units for United States

*A system of spiral grooves in the bore of a gun which causes the projectile to rotate, or spin, about its longer axis. (This stabilizes the projectile's flight.)

Navy aircraft instead of rocket-powered launch vehicles for studies of the upper atmosphere and space. In Germany, however, rocketry went forward with the development of powerful engines for rockets. These rockets were ultimately known as the V-2 and more than a thousand fell on England as high explosive "bombs."

After World War II, both the United States and Russia acquired German personnel with rocketry expertise. These men formed the nucleus of the program that developed the powerful launch vehicles and space vehicles used today. Our modern rocketry, therefore, is the result of Dr. Goddard's and Dr. Oberth's pioneering work and the expertise of the men who developed the rocket as a weapon and eventually converted it to peaceful use.

SOME SEVENTEENTH-CENTURY LAWS

Rocket propulsion, flight, and control are achieved by obeying or applying certain physical laws discovered by Galileo (1564-1642) and Sir Isaac Newton (1642-1727).

GRAVITY

Gravitation is the term used to describe the force of attraction that exists between all matter within the universe. Why and exactly how this attraction force operates no one knows. But it is in effect at all times and a body of small mass (amount of something) attracts a body of large mass just as the large mass attracts the small mass. Said in another way, mutual gravitation exists between all bodies regardless of size.

When gravitation (or attraction force) involves Earth and a body or mass on or near the Earth, gravitation is referred to as *gravity.* We can theorize that when a pencil falls to the floor, the Earth attracts the pencil as the pencil attracts Earth. Theoretically, this is true. But, on the practical side, because the Earth has so much more mass than the pencil, we see the pencil falling toward Earth while Earth doesn't move at all.

According to legend, Galileo experimented with gravity by dropping a solid iron ball from the

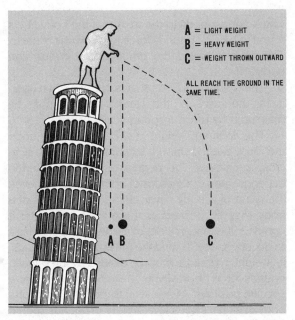

A = LIGHT WEIGHT
B = HEAVY WEIGHT
C = WEIGHT THROWN OUTWARD

ALL REACH THE GROUND IN THE SAME TIME.

A B   C

Figure 1. Galileo's experiments at the Tower of Pisa

Leaning Tower of Pisa. His experiments, as illustrated in figure 1, showed that objects of varying weights will strike the ground at the same time if they are released simultaneously and from the same height above the surface. This holds true even if one of the objects is propelled horizontally.

From his theoretical work, Sir Isaac Newton concluded that bodies in space (such as planets and their moons) are attracted toward each other in a special way. This attraction force is directly proportional to the product of the masses of the two bodies and inversely proportional to the square of the distance between them. In other words, the amount of mass involved determines how much gravitational attraction is possible; and the distance between the two bodies determines the effect of the gravitation—the greater the distance the less the effect.

Bodies like Earth and the moon are drawn toward each other by gravitation. The moon is kept from crashing into Earth by the moon's "forward" velocity (speed and direction), which creates the familiar centrifugal effect. Centrifugal effect, also identified by Newton, is the tendency of a rotating body to move away from its center of rotation. If it were not for gravity (and individual molecular attraction), the spinning Earth itself would come apart because of the centrifugal "force" created by its rotation. Virtually the same effect exists with the Earth-moon system. The moon "tries" to fly off into space, but the gravitational attraction keeps it from doing so.

You can see how this centrifugal effect/gravitation phenomenon works by tying a string to an object and swinging the object around and around. The object represents the moon; your hand represents Earth's center of gravity; and the string represents gravitational attraction. If you swing the object steadily and with sufficient velocity, it will "circle the Earth" and exert a constant pulling on the string. If you increase the swing (velocity) enough, the string (gravitation) will break and allow the object to fly off into "space." Slow the velocity and the object will fall. With this little experiment you have to consider the falling action to be toward the center of gravity (your hand).

Putting satellites into orbit around Earth or any other celestial body requires that certain velocities be reached, otherwise the satellite will "fall" and strike the body it is supposed to orbit. In other words, it is necessary to use rocketry and preplanned trajectories to balance the particular gravitational force with an orbital velocity that produces a counteracting centrifugal effect. We will discuss types of orbits in a later chapter, for now we should review Newton's laws and associate them with rocketry.

NEWTON'S LAWS

Reviewing Sir Isaac Newton's three laws of motion, the first states: A body in a state of rest and a body in motion tend to remain at rest or in uniform motion unless acted upon by some outside force. This really is an explanation of *inertia,* or the tendency of all things to remain in a fixed condition. The second law states: The rate of change in the *momentum* of a body is proportional to the force acting upon the body and is in the direction of the force. The third law states: To every action there is an equal and opposite reaction. As we stated in the introduction to this Part, this third law is the heart of rocketry because the action of the rocket engine produces the forward motion of the total rocket.

FORCE, VELOCITY, AND ACCELERATION

In order to understand these laws of motion and their relationship to rocket propulsion, one needs to grasp the proper meanings of the terms used by Newton to describe them. For example, Newton used the term "force" (F) to define the cause of motion. You experience the application of force by exerting your muscles to move yourself or some object.

Velocity (v) is the rate at which a body moves when a force is applied to it. It is expressed as a unit of distance per unit of time, such as feet per second, and it implies a specific direction.

The rate at which the velocity of a body increases is called *positive* acceleration. Acceleration (a) is expressed in unit of distance per unit of time, usually in feet per second per second. It occurs when a body is subjected to the application of a force over a continuing period of time. For example, the acceleration which results from the force of gravity upon a free-falling body is about 32.2 feet per second per second.

FORCE, WEIGHT, AND MASS

The relationship of force, weight, and mass is defined by Newton's law of universal gravitation. This law states, in effect, that any two bodies attract each other with a force directly proportional to their mass and inversely proportional to the distance between them. This relationship may be expressed by the equation $F = M_1M_2/r^2$, where F represents force in pounds, M_1 and M_2 are the masses of the two bodies in slugs,* and r is the distance between them.

The gravitational force of a symmetric sphere acts as though its entire mass was concentrated at its center. Since Earth approximates such a sphere, the distance between the Earth and a body upon or near its surface is equal approximately to the Earth's radius. The mass of the Earth, M_1, remains constant. From these values the force of the Earth's gravity,

which corresponds to the weight of the body M_2, is found to be 32.2 pounds-force for each unit of mass. This ratio is called the *gravitational conversion constant.*

The weight of a body, that is, the attraction upon it by the force of the Earth's gravity, may be measured by using a spring scale.

The apparent weight of a body depends upon the force exerted upon it by another larger body in close proximity. The degree of force so exerted depends upon the masses of both bodies. However, the mass of a body never changes. The mass of a body may be defined as the quantity of matter it contains. It is that property of matter which enables it to occupy space. To find the mass of a body in slugs, its weight in pounds must be divided by the value in pounds-force of gravity as these are observed at a specific position. At sea level to find the mass of a body in slugs, its sea level weight in pounds should be divided by sea level gravity effects in pounds-force. Therefore, a mass of one slug would weigh 32.174 pounds at sea level and at 45° latitude on the Earth's surface.

MOMENTUM

Momentum is defined as the product of mass and velocity. Newton found that the action of force on a body changes the body's momentum at a rate proportional to the force and the direction of the force. If the mass of a body remains constant, any change in momentum is reflected in a change of velocity. For example, if a worker drops a brick from the fifth floor of a building, the brick will be accelerated by the force of gravity at the rate of 32.2 feet per second per second. The mass of the brick does not change; its velocity and momentum change at a rate proportional to the force of Earth's gravity.

APPLICATION OF NEWTON'S LAWS TO ROCKETRY

We can relate Newton's three laws to rocketry as follows:

---

*A unit of mass. The mass of a body in slugs is equal to its weight divided by the acceleration of gravity (32.2 feet per second per second).

(1) The first law states simply that when launching a rocket vertically, the propulsion system must produce enough force (thrust) to overcome the inertia of the launch vehicle. Another way of expressing this is to say that the thrust (in pounds) must be greater than the weight of the rocket. As an example, the *Saturn V* rocket used to launch the *Apollo* spacecraft series weighed 6,000,000 pounds. In order for the *Saturn* to be launched vertically its engines had to produce more than 6,000,000 pounds of thrust. In fact, the engines of *Saturn V* produced 7,500,000 pounds of thrust.

(2) The second law is shown mathematically by the equation $F \propto ma$, where F represents force; m is mass; and a is acceleration. The symbol $\propto$ stands for "proportional to." What this formula says is that the amount of force required to accelerate a body depends on the mass of the body.

You have seen on television or at the movies how slowly the older, large rockets lift off their launch pads. At the moment of lift-off, the total mass (or weight) of the rocket is only slightly less than the force being produced by the engines. However, every second the rocket's mass is being decreased by burning and expelling the rocket's propellant as thrust. At the same time the amount of force being produced remains constant. Thus, the force becomes increasingly greater than the dwindling mass and this results in a rapid second-by-second acceleration until the propellant is used up.

(3) To relate Newton's third law of motion to a rocket, we must understand what is happening in a rocket engine. All chemical rockets develop thrust by burning fuel and expelling mass (exhaust particles) from their exhaust nozzles at a high velocity. The thrust (forward motion or push) produced is a reactive force acting in a direction opposite to the direction of the exhaust. Going back to Newton's second law ($F \propto ma$) we can see that there are two ways to increase the thrust (force)— either increase the mass of the exhaust or accelerate the exhaust particles to a higher velocity. When the rocket fuel burns in the combustion chamber, the gases produced are very hot and create a very high pressure inside the chamber. This high pressure forces the gases through the exhaust nozzle to the lower pressure outside the rocket. As these gases

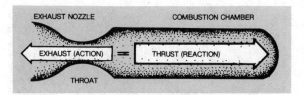

Figure 2. The basic rocket engine (or motor)

move out of the combustion chamber they pass through the throat (see fig. 2) which constricts (narrows) the exhaust and thereby increases its velocity. The "bell shaped" nozzle allows the escaping exhaust to expand which lowers its pressure. This accomplishes two important things—it keeps the pressure in the nozzle lower than inside the combustion chamber and, at the same time, permits only rearward motion of the exhaust gas, and thus develops forward thrust.

In figure 2 we can see what the aerospace engineer strives for in producing a powerful and efficient rocket engine—to create as high a pressure as possible in the combustion chamber and to design the throat and nozzle for maximum acceleration of exhaust particles.

ROCKET SYSTEMS

Modern rockets used for space applications or military purposes consist of four major systems. The systems are known as (1) the airframe, (2) the propulsion system, (3) the guidance system and (4) the control system. These systems exist to deliver whatever the rocket is carrying, which is called the *payload* (see fig. 3). Let's talk about these systems briefly.

THE AIRFRAME

The airframe system of a rocket, like that of an aircraft, serves to contain the other systems and to provide the streamlined shape. The airframe must be structurally strong and capable of withstanding heat, stress, and a great deal of vibration. At the same time, it must be as lightweight as possible. Every pound of weight saved in the airframe allows an additional pound of weight to be added to the payload.

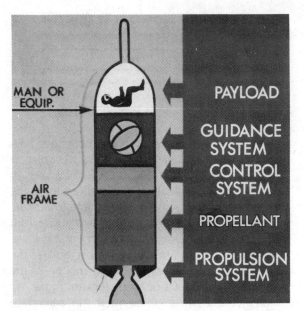

Figure 3. The payload and systems of a rocket

was the thrust structure which contained the vehicle's five F-1 engines. The thrust structure was a complex group of beams and bracing made mainly of aluminum alloy plus some steel. Surrounding the thrust structure was a *skin* assembly which provided additional strength and better aerodynamics — lessened the effect of drag caused by the rocket pushing its way through the air. Other aerodynamic features attached to the thrust structure included fairings and fins, as you can see in the illustration. The fairings were drag reducers, and the fins helped stabilize the rocket's flight while it was climbing rapidly through the atmosphere.

Fuel and oxidizer tanks made up the greater portion of the *Saturn's* first stage airframe (this is true with all liquid-propellant rockets). The walls of

The older Atlas rocket was a prime example of how engineers designed airframes that were both strong and lightweight. The skin of this rocket also served as the wall of the propellant tanks. This eliminated the need for separate internal tanks and provided a great saving in weight. The skin of the Atlas was thinner than a dime, and when it had no fuel aboard, it had to be pressurized to keep it from collapsing.

Precision is the watchword in making a rocket airframe. Techniques used to manufacture rocket airframe parts include machining, forging, casting, spinning, and extruding. To attain the needed precision, the knowledge of the scientist and the skill of the technician are required to insure the accuracy of each manufacturing technique.

To date, the most spectacular airframe ever constructed for a United States rocket was that of the massive *Saturn V* launch vehicle. In its *Apollo* lunar (moon) flight configuration, the *Saturn* stood 363 feet tall. Of course this included the *payload* of astronauts and the sub-vehicles that were delivered to the vicinity and surface of the moon.

The *Saturn's* first stage, as an example of its airframe, had a diameter of 33 feet and its length was 138 feet. Figure 4 shows the major components of the first stage's airframe. Beginning at the bottom

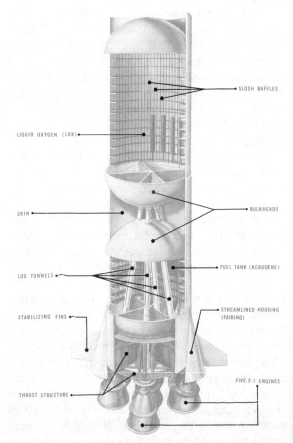

Figure 4. First stage of the Saturn V launch vehicle

these tanks formed a large part of the rocket's exterior surface or skin. Within each of the tanks were *slosh baffles* which added strength to the airframe while serving another purpose. The other purpose was to stabilize the propellants motion as the rocket vibrated and tilted in flight. The liquid oxygen (oxidizer) and kerosene (fuel) could, without such baffles, set up sloshing and swirling motions that could have made the rocket uncontrollable.

What is labeled *skin* in figure 4 was also known as the *intertank* structure. The *interstage* structure included that skin portion used to join the three rocket stages. Where the propellant tank walls exposed to the airstream were smooth, the metal "skirts" forming the intertank and interstage structures were corrugated. This corrugation was necessary to give greater strength to a relatively thin part of the structure.

Although the airframes of all liquid propellant rockets possess certain of the *Saturn V's* structural characteristics, there are differences. These differences depend on the size and purpose of the rocket. Again, in the design and construction of airframes for rockets, the primary objective is to build a structure that will withstand all anticipated stresses while using the least possible weight.

PROPULSION SYSTEMS

The rocket's propulsion system includes the propellant used, the containers for the propellant, all plumbing that may be required to get the propellant from the containers to the engine, and the rocket engine itself. In other words, everything directly associated with propelling the rocket is part of the propulsion system. From our previous discussion of the *Saturn V's* airframe, you can see that areas of the airframe may also serve as part of the propulsion system.

Propulsion systems used in rocketry may be generally classified as chemical systems, gas-heating systems, and electric systems. Those considered chemical systems usually involve the mixing and burning of a chemical fuel and a chemical oxidizer to produce the hot, expanding gases needed to provide thrust. The gas-heating system design would use an "external" heat source

to heat and cause the propellant to build the pressure necessary to provide thrust by exiting the exhaust nozzle at high velocity. Electric systems use magnetic fields and currents to propel matter in small amounts.

We will discuss certain aspects of propulsion systems more fully in later chapters within this Part of your text. For now, we will provide an overview of guidance and control systems.

GUIDANCE SYSTEMS

The "brain" of a large, sophisticated rocket is its guidance system. The guidance system is a self-contained electronic unit which employs a computer, an inertial platform, and may also have a star tracking unit for space navigation. The computer is programmed for the desired flight trajectory before launch. Of course, there is also a radio link between the rocket's mission controllers and its guidance system. This link allows changes to be made in instructions to the rocket's guidance system and it also functions, more or less, as a direct control in the event the on-board guidance system experiences a partial malfunction.

In comparison to the rest of the rocket, the guidance system is exceptionally small. The miniaturization of electronics is the explanation for its small size. The electrical power needed flows through miniaturized circuits and the "wire" connecting the various components is correspondingly lightweight.

Again using the *Saturn V* as an example, figure 5 gives an idea of how relatively small a guidance system is in comparison to the rest of the rocket. This photograph shows the entire instrument unit being fitted atop the 22 ft. diameter third stage. The actual inertial guidance system was only a part of the total instrument unit.

The rocket's motion is sensed by the system and fed into the system's computer. If the rocket is not flying according to the planned trajectory, impulses for correcting the trajectory are sent to the control system.

Coupled with an inertial guidance system may be an automatic celestial navigation unit, or "star tracker." However, a star tracker is justified only for

Figure 5. The Saturn V's instrument unit

space flight where it is exceptionally important to keep a spacecraft on the correct flight path. Although rocketry is involved in making course corrections for the flight of spacecraft, we are hesitant to associate the star tracker unit with the guidance systems for rockets. The spacecraft itself is really the *payload* of a rocket launch vehicle whose guidance system initially placed the spacecraft on the correct flight path. Even so, a star tracker unit can be linked to the primary guidance system of any rocket vehicle.

When we leave the larger, more sophisticated rockets and look at the smaller ones, we find there are several other types of guidance systems. These smaller rockets are within the area of military use; they are *missiles.* Of course, the largest of these missiles use the inertial guidance system, too. But these large missiles are capable of doing more than delivering a destructive device over intercontinental distances; they could be used (as some models have) as launch vehicles for spacecraft.

The smaller rocket missiles which have guidance systems usually are known as *short-range* missiles. Such missiles may be guided to their targets by the *command* of a human director. Other missiles' guidance systems may require that they

home in on the target which is radiating heat or light. And still other missiles are built to fly along a *beam* that is aimed at and kept on the target. These guidance systems, which are in addition to the inertial system, are the *command system,* the *homing system,* and the *beam-rider system.* We will look at these in more detail in the chapter on guidance systems.

CONTROL SYSTEMS

Again we must think of the guidance system of a rocket as being its "brain." It doesn't matter if this "brain" is within the rocket as a self-contained unit, such as the inertial system, or mainly outside the rocket, such as a command system. Whatever the rocket's guidance system decides should be done to keep on the correct flight path must be carried out by another system—the control system.

While in the atmosphere, control systems for rockets can work much like those of an airplane. Once the rocket climbs to where the air is very thin, other methods need to be considered. One way to change the rocket's flight path is to change the direction of the exhaust stream. Another way is to use small rockets along the side of the rocket near the nose and tail of the airframe to redirect the rocket. Variations or combinations of these systems control large and small rockets. (These same systems can also be used in the atmosphere.)

PAYLOADS

A rocket's airframe, propulsion system, guidance system, and control system all exist for one purpose: to deliver the payload. The payload is not one of the rocket's systems, but by its very nature it is the reason for the rocket's existence. The payload of the three *Saturn V* rocket stages was the *Apollo* spacecraft consisting of the command module, the service module and the lunar module. The rocket and payload arrangement on the return trip from the moon was the *service module* rocket and the *command module* payload. Of course, the ultimate payload was the astronauts and the materials and data returned from the moon.

Today the payloads of large United States rockets consist primarily of Earth satellites (including the Space Shuttle) and deep space vehicles. Most military rockets have payloads of explosives. These explosives include nuclear and thermonuclear "bombs." Of course, the payloads of the smallest military rockets are conventional-type explosives especially designed to destroy specific types of targets such as airplanes, tanks, and hardened defense or command posts.

Later on in this Part of your text we will talk about payloads again. At that time we will pay greater attention to details of certain payloads.

SPECIFIC IMPULSE AND DENSITY IMPULSE

Before going on to other chapters and expanding the subjects introduced in this chapter, we should define and give examples of specific impulse and density impulse. The word *impulse* means *thrust* and is the measure of how much thrust basically will be obtained from a propellant.

Specific impulse (I_{sp}) is the number of pounds of thrust delivered by consuming one pound of propellant (oxidizer/fuel mixture) in *one second*. If, for example, a pound of common black powder burns up in one second and produces 100 pounds of thrust, the specific impulse of this batch of powder is *100 seconds*. Packing one pound of this powder into a rocket "motor" and igniting it would give our rocket a 100 pound "kick" which would last for one second. Now, how high or far our rocket would travel would depend on several things. The total weight of the rocket and the design of the rocket motor would be major factors.

Let's suppose we do not want to burn all this powder at one time. We do not need 100 pounds of thrust to lift our rocket because the entire rocket weighs only two pounds, including the black powder propellant. What we want to do is spread the total thrust available over a longer period of time. For instance, we could use a long-tube design for the motor. This would allow only a small portion of the

powder's total surface to be exposed to the burning process. Let's say that this arrangement of the propellant extends the burning time to 10 seconds; in effect we have divided our 100 pounds of thrust by 10, which gives us 10 pounds of thrust per second until the propellant is burned up.

Taking this example to the extreme, if we could cause the same powder (propellant) to burn for 100 seconds, then we would have one pound of thrust per second. (However, our two-pound weight rocket would not move in the vertical direction.) When you see the symbol I_{sp} and a number following it, you should remember that the number represents the seconds during which *one pound* of thrust could be provided by burning one pound of propellant. For example, if a propellant has an I_{sp} of 500, it means that burning one pound of this propellant will produce one pound of thrust for 500 seconds or 500 pounds of thrust for one second.

Specific impulse is not the only measure considered when picking a propellant for a rocket. Density impulse is another measure of a propellant's thrust according to the *volume* involved. The propellants for the *Saturn V's* second stage are a good example. They were oxygen and hydrogen. This combination gives a specific impulse of 364 seconds. Yet, a pound of these propellants takes up a lot of space (volume) because of the relatively light weight of hydrogen, even in liquid form. The weight of the structure, or airframe, needed to contain this volume somewhat offsets the advantage of a high I_{sp}. The density impulse for oxygen/hydrogen is 90. Another propellant, composed of red fuming nitric acid (RFNA) as the oxidizer and aniline as the fuel, has a specific impulse of 200 and a density impulse of 310. So why wasn't the RFNA/aniline propellant used for the *Saturn V* second stage? Very simply, the people managing the program had to consider many factors other than specific and density impulse. These factors included cost, ease and safety of handling the propellant, and stability of the propellant. The decision reached, therefore, was a compromise after considering all factors and all possible combinations of oxidizers and fuels.

Chapter 2-2

CHEMICAL PROPULSION

With a few exceptions, propulsion systems for rockets and spacecraft today use chemical propellants. These propellants can be either solid, semi-solid, a gel, or liquid depending on whether or not they are pressurized. However, as we have indicated before, they are most often in solid or liquid form.

How rapidly a solid propellant will burn depends on how much of its surface is exposed to burning at any one moment. Of course, this depends on the design or molding of the solid propellant charge within its container. It is relatively easy to throttle or change the thrust of a liquid propellant rocket, but it is very difficult to control the thrust of a solid propellant type. Why and how these conditions exist will be examined in this chapter. We will also look at special factors and conditions influencing the use of liquid propellants, and we will cover some aspects of rocket engine (or motor) design and function.

The general learning objective for this chapter is for you to know the various types of chemical propulsion systems. To reach this objective, you must pattern your study of the material according to the *specific learning objectives* listed in the Appendix of this textbook.

OXIDATION AND COMBUSTION

Combustion is nothing more than very rapid oxidation. But, what is oxidation? Oxidation is the combination of oxygen with another substance. The time it takes for this combining process to take place determines whether the substance rusts or corrodes, burns as a fire, or explodes violently.

A chunk of rusting iron and the heat, pressure, and light of a functioning rocket engine are doing the same thing. It just takes one longer to become oxidized than it does the other. Another similarity between these two extremes of oxidation is that both require oxygen (oxidizer) and a substance to be oxidized. The substance to be oxidized is also known as the *reducer*. Thus, the iron in the example is the reducer and the oxygen in the air touching the iron is the oxidizer. For the rocket, one chemical compound is the reducer while the oxidizer is either another chemical compound or perhaps it is oxygen in pure form—liquid oxygen.

OXIDIZERS AND REDUCERS

Various oxidizer-reducer combinations can produce an endless variety of oxidation reactions. When it comes to rocketry, however, a few elements occurring in a wider variety of compounds (molecular bondings of two or more elements) dominate the field.

Oxidizers. The element oxygen exists in air as two molecules (O_2). To use it in its pure form as an oxidizer for rocket fuels (or reducers) it must be chilled until it becomes liquid. This means that the oxygen must reach and be kept at a temperature of -297° Fahrenheit. The reason why this temperature (or below) must be maintained is that the oxygen will boil (become gaseous) at any higher temperature. Temperatures in this range come within a classification known as *cryogenics.* Cryogenics is an area of science concerned with the production of low temperatures and the effect of such temperatures on matter. Thus, wherever you see *cryogenic* used with reference to an oxidizer, fuel, or propellant, you know that the substance is "super cold."

There are other oxidizers that do not have to be kept at as low a temperature as pure oxygen. These are chemical compounds which contain oxygen atoms as part of their molecular structure.

Reducers. Any list of fuels (or reducers) must begin with the elements hydrogen, carbon, and nitrogen. Certain compounds of hydrogen and carbon are called *hydrocarbons.* As you probably know, the fuels we use for heating and transportation are for the most part hydrocarbons and include coal and products obtained from crude oil. The first stage of the *Saturn V* rocket used the hydrocarbon kerosene as its fuel. The remaining stages all used hydrogen. Pure hydrogen (H_2) is an excellent rocket fuel but it is even more cryogenic than oxygen— hydrogen must be chilled to -423°F to liquefy it.

In the atmosphere, nitrogen (N_2) is inert, but it is highly reactive in other forms. It is very important to the manufacture of high explosives and other high-energy compounds and mixtures.

Propellant Combinations. Since it takes both an oxidizer and reducer to propel a rocket, it is correct to call either of them a propellant. However, the term propellant is most often used as a single reference to the oxidizer and reducer. For example, we could say "the rocket uses an oxygen-hydrogen propellant." We could also say that a rocket uses a thousand pounds of propellant. It is not necessary to say there are 500 pounds of oxidizer and 500 pounds of reducer. Nor is it necessary to say whether they are stored within the same container or in separate containers.

Speaking of propellant storage, other terms are used to describe the storage arrangement of a propellant's oxidizer and reducer. If the oxidizer is stored in one container and the fuel (reducer) in another, the term *bipropellant* is used. Bipropellants are not mixed until they reach the engine's combustion chamber. Back to the *Saturn V:* The first stage bipropellant was oxygen and kerosense, the second and third stage bipropellants were oxygen and hydrogen. For all three stages the propellants were pumped into the engines' combustion chambers where ignition and burning took place. We might add here that the majority of liquid propellant rockets use the bipropellant arrangement.

In some cases the liquid oxidizer and fuel can exist together in the same storage tank. Here the propellant also is pumped into the rocket engine's combustion chamber and ignited. However, the fact that separate storage tanks are not necessary qualifies the propellant to be called a *monopropellant.*

Chemically, even when oxidizer and reducer occur in a mixture, they are considered to be two separate ingredients, but there is such a thing as a *self-reacting compound.* In such a compound, one molecule contains atoms of both oxidizer and reducer and, upon ignition, reacts with itself, yielding energy as it breaks down or decomposes.

Let us return to fundamentals for a while.

NATURE AND EFFECTS OF OXIDATION

We have given rusting iron and a functioning rocket engine as extreme examples of slow and fast oxidation. To understand the process a little better, let us look at a third example, a charcoal fire. Its main reaction occurs between carbon in the fuel and oxygen in the air to form molecules of carbon dioxide (CO_2). In this process, a solid shrinks to ashes, but CO_2, in the form of an invisible gas, takes its place. Nothing is gained or lost in an oxidation. The total mass of all the ingredients involved in the reaction remains the same before, during, and after the oxidation process is completed. This classic principle, called *conservation of mass,* is an important one for chemical propulsion. A chemical reaction, then, is a process neither of creating nor destroying matter but of reshuffling and recombining it. As a *physical activity,* this process can be described as that of molecules clumping together to form larger molecules or splitting apart to form smaller molecules or atoms.

A *charcoal* fire in a backyard grill, however, is not started to produce carbon dioxide. It is the *heat* of this reaction that cooks the meat. The physical activity we mentioned is a vigorous one. *The heat of a chemical reaction is produced by atoms and molecules being stirred into rapid vibration or motion.* If the vibration becomes rapid enough the energy takes the form of visible light. Thus the charcoal fire has glowing coals and dancing flames.

In rusting iron, "heat" is produced. That is, molecules are stirred by the process into vibrating with slightly increased speed, but the reaction is so slight that no thermometer can record it. In a rocket, the reaction is swift and violent, producing thousands of degrees of temperature, brilliant light, loud noise (at lower altitudes where atmosphere is present), and, most important to all, *force*—that which moves mass. The energies produced differ, but they are all the results of one thing: the dance of the molecules—molecules vibrating, molecules swarming in helter-skelter flight, molecules rushing in headlong flight.

At this point, let us switch to a more descriptive word: *combustion* instead of oxidation. Actually they mean the same thing, with a meaning that can be stretched to include the rusting of iron. In normal usage, however, combustion means *rapid* oxidation. It produces visible light, and expansion of a liquid or solid into a gas. In short, it is fire.

There are many kinds of fire. Fires vary widely in speed of reaction, from slow broil to sudden explosion. They vary in means of ignition, and, above all, in the forms and proportions of their energy output. To demonstrate this fact, let us look at a couple of fast, energetic fires. A photo flashbulb's contents can be ignited by a tiny hot wire and yield high energy in the form of sudden, brilliant light. This reaction, however, produces very little force and does not burst the glass and plastic container. By contrast, a small quantity of TNT, a high explosive, would yield much greater force but not so bright a flash.

We might consider TNT's possibilities as a rocket propellant, if force was the only consideration. It carries its own oxidizer supply, being a self-reacting compound of carbon, hydrogen, oxygen, and nitrogen ($C_7H_5O_6N_3$). For all its violence, TNT is a sluggish reactor. The hot wire that can trigger a flashbulb would have no effect on it; neither would a match. It requires the shock of another explosion to detonate TNT. So far, so good; these qualities tend to make it safe and sure. Its main drawback is the suddenness of its explosion. Once it is properly triggered, it blows up all at once, with equal and shattering force in all directions. Unless weakened by adding other ingredients, it would blow up a rocket rather than propel it.

Let us now see how the energy of combustion can be harnessed for a kind of work different from cooking, photography, or demolition.

COMBUSTION FOR PROPULSION

The final objective in considering any combination of chemicals as a propellant is how much force can be obtained as the mixture oxidizes. But there are other considerations which are recognized as the qualities of a good propellant: (1) the propellant must contain oxidizer and fuel, (2) it must ignite correctly every time, (3) it must produce energy in the form of force, and (4) the force produced must be controllable. Let's consider these four qualities individually.

Need for Packaged Oxidizers. Aside from propulsion in space, where no free oxygen is available, there is another reason for putting oxidizer in a concentrated package. *An oxidizer-reducer* mixture will burn forcibly in a confined or semi-confined space in which an airbreathing fire would be smothered. Men knew this fact for centuries without knowing the reason why, and used it long before airbreathing engines were ever imagined. Old-fashioned gunpowder or "black powder" needs no air to burn its carbon and sulphur fuel ingredients because it has an oxidizer built into a third ingredient, potassium nitrate or saltpeter (KNO_3). The ability of this mixture to propel a rocket or hurl a cannon ball out of an iron tube was known and employed in warfare centuries before Lavoisier discovered oxygen and the principle of oxidation in the eighteenth century. To this day all chemical rocket propellants, all gun munitions, and all chemical explosives, contain an oxidizer, burn in confinement, and do their work by bursting out of confinement or rushing out of semi-confinement. "Rushing out of semi-confinement" describes rocket-propellant action. However, in a rocket propellant mixture the oxidizer outweighs the fuel something like 5:3. Because the package oxidizer is expensive and a rocket propellant needs so much of it, the air-breathing engine is much less expensive to operate than any type of rocket engine. Still, the air-breathing engine cannot operate within both the atmosphere and space, as does the rocket engine.

Ignition Characteristics. We have already noted that how fast a mixture burns is not necessarily related to how easily it starts. Well then, what properties of a propellant should be considered? Since the starting time of the rocket engine is important to controlling it, the propellant must start every time in the same way. Another factor that must be considered is a choice between a continuous or restartable propellant. Some propellants can be started but continue burning until all propellant is exhausted (burnout). Others can be repeatedly started and stopped. Safety is also a very important factor. This does not mean the propellant can stand up to any kind of rough or careless handling without igniting, but it does mean that its safety requirements should be known and feasible. Some propellants are ignitable the old fashioned way with a match flame or hot wire. Others require greater and more concentrated heat. Some require an explosive

shock. Some are hypergolic; that is, under normal temperatures, the oxidizer and reducer burst into flame the instant they meet. This sounds touchy, but the main safety requirement in this case is to keep the ingredients separated.

Energy for Force. Not light, not heat, but force is what we're looking for from a propellant's release of energy—the sheer momentum of moving molecules. What is desired is *mass flow* of combustion exhaust, but this mass can be no greater or less than the mass of ingredients before combustion. Although a designer might wish to lighten the propellant load aboard a vehicle, there must be a certain amount of propellant on board to produce the needed thrust. This load alone constitutes most of the initial weight of a launch vehicle. The only way to get more force per load is to increase the velocity of the mass flow; that is, to get more "speed" per molecule. Therefore, it is better not to increase mass flow by means of heavier molecules which are too sluggish. The ideal exhaust gas consists of plenty of lightweight molecules, which excel in energy and velocity.

Controllable Force. When a propellant burns, the speed of the combustion should not be excessive. Fast but not too fast is the rule of thumb. But how is this combustion process regulated? If a liquid propellant is used, the task of controlling the force is basically easy. All that is necessary is to govern the amount of propellant reaching the combustion chamber. This is similar to governing the amount of fuel/air mixture reaching the cylinders of an automobile engine through actions of the throttle and carburetor.

Controlling the force of a solid propellant is slightly more difficult. As we shall see later, there are ways of controlling the force desired from a solid propellant rocket. Basically, however, a solid propellant is selected (or developed) according to its ability to produce force without causing a massive, destructive explosion. In fact, solid propellants sometimes are called "low explosives." Modern solid propellants are considerably more energetic than the black powder type propellant used with very early rockets. Yet, they have the black powder's property of burning so that each particle ignites its neighbor particle and the burning continues as a swiftly spreading reaction. What are called high explosives, like TNT, are not suited as propellants because their contents "burn" all at once.

PRESSURE AND MASS FLOW

Adding pressure to a medium will increase its molecular activity and consequently temperature. Increase the temperature of a medium and its molecular activity and pressure will be increased—this is particularly true with a gaseous medium that is enclosed by a container. So this is the purpose of the rocket motor or engine: to provide a container in which the *temperature* (of the oxidizing propellant) increases the *pressure* of the gaseous portion of the medium.

If some means were not provided to relieve the constantly building pressure of a burning propellant, the container would burst. This is among the functions performed by the rocket motor's nozzle throat and nozzle—they provide an exit for the burned propellant mass, reduce the pressure within the combustion area, and direct the flow of the mass involved.

We can imagine what happens within the "business end" of a rocket on a molecular scale. Figure 6 shows what happens to a single molecule that has been energized by combustion and pressure. Loaded with this energy, the molecule zips about at location A. It beats madly at its prison walls, creating pressure. There is a way out of its prison, however, and the molecule will get there along with a crowd of its fellow highly active molecules. We see it again at location B and again at location C. Note that its path continues to be erratic but less and less so—more zig and less zag, one might say. Finally, it escapes.

This wandering molecule would seem to be going through a great deal of wasted motion and taking much too long to make its exit. Actually, it is making excellent progress. The whole journey is accomplished in a fraction of a second. More significantly, at each stage of the journey, it is *traveling faster than before in the right direction.* Furthermore, the greater the pressure in the chamber, the greater the velocity through the nozzle.

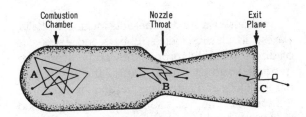

Figure 6. Concept of a molecule's path to exit a rocket engine

It is its speed out the nozzle that counts most. The net result, *acceleration,* is the essence of thrust. The mass of molecules is accelerating in respect to the motor, and the motor itself is moving. As long as combustion is going on inside it, and mass flow is passing out the nozzle, the motor adds velocity to velocity and accelerates.

Today, chemical systems are the most often used means of propulsion. When a lot of thrust is needed, rockets are usually propelled by a liquid fuel, such as kerosene, and liquid oxygen (oxidizer). The propellants are mixed as they enter the combustion chamber to be ignited. A spark or small flame is used to start the ignition process. From then on, continuing combustion ignites the fuel and oxidizer as they enter the combustion chamber. The drawback to liquid chemical systems is that they require expensive plumbing, turbines, pumps, and engines.

SOLID PROPELLANTS

The chemical system may have a solid rather than a liquid propellant. The fuel and oxidizer of a solid propellant are mixed together from the start. The skyrocket is a good example of a solid propellant; all it takes is ignition of the mixture. The combustion chamber and the propellant container are one and the same. This means that the solid propellant chemical system is simple, much less costly than the liquid type, and is very reliable. Today, solid propellants are used for our submarine launched ballistic missiles, the *Minuteman* intercontinental ballistic missiles, the first three stages of the MX missile, and as boosters for the Space Shuttle system.

Fuels used in solid propellants include asphalts, waxes, oils, plastics, metals, rubbers, and resins. The oxidizers for solid propellants come from two general sources: the organic, the source of nitrocellulose and nitroglycerine; and the inorganic, the source of chemcials such as sodium nitrate and potassium perchlorate.

Nitrocellulose and nitroglycerine are both used in the manufacture of colloidal* propellants. Each is said to be chemically balanced in that a single molecule contains both fuel and oxidizer and is thus capable of a complete reaction—oxidation.

Colloidal propellants may be either single-base or double-base. Single-base solid propellants will contain nitrocellulose only; a double-base propellant will contain both nitrocellulose and nitroglycerine. Because single-base propellants must be manufactured by the solvent process, the size of the charge that may be used is small. However, the size of the charge of the double-base propellant is limited only by the size of its manufacturing equipment.

Propellants using inorganic oxidants are mixed with substances readily oxidized, such as charcoal and asphalt.

Thixotropic propellants, usually referred to as semisolids or, more accurately, as gels, are colloidal suspensions that form a gelatin-type substance. Under pressure they become fluid. The gel bonds break down as the propellant is forced under pressure through pipes, and the propellant is converted to a fluid. When the pressure is removed, the fluid instantly returns to a gel. Gels, thereby, provide liquid propellants with the handling and storage characteristics of solid propellants.

CHEMICAL AND PHYSICAL PROPERTIES

A look at the contents of a typical double-based propellant tells much about the requirements of a modern solid propellant:

*A colloid is a substance made up of very small particles.

COMPONENT	PERCENTAGE OF TOTAL	FUNCTION
Nitrocellulose	51.38	Propellant
Nitroglycerine	43.38	Propellant
Diethyl phthalate	3.09	Plasticizer
Potassium nitrate	1.45	Flash depressor
Diphenylamine	0.07	Stabilizer
Nigrosine dye	0.10	Opacifier
Other	0.53	. . . .

Nitrocellulose and nitroglycerine are the active ingredients, and, as we said before, each contains oxidizer and reducer. The active ingredients comprise about 95 percent of the mixture; the other 5 percent is made up of additives which have specific functions in the mixture's burning process. The *plasticizer* helps give the mixture proper body and consistency—a thickener. The potassium nitrate *flash depressor* acts to cool the exhaust gases and reduce the wear and tear on the nozzle. The *stabilizer* function reduces the tendency of the propellant to absorb moisture during storage. The *opacifier* keeps the heat of the burning propellant mostly confined to the exposed edges. Without this opacifier radiant heat would bring the deeper layers of propellant to combustion temperature and the mixture would explode.

Other solid propellant combinations may not contain these particular additives in these proportions, but they must have the properties which these additives supply.

More typical of today's solid propellants are composites in which the fuel and oxidizer are two different compounds. Usually the oxidizer is crystalline in form (like salt or sugar) and is imbedded in the fuel base. Specific impulses of a double-based and several composite propellants are as follows:

FUEL	OXIDIZER	SPECIFIC IMPULSE
Asphalt	Potassium perchlorate	200
Nitrocellulose and Nitroglycerine	(same as fuel)	240

Polyurethane	Ammonium perchlorate	245
Boron	Ammonium perchlorate	270
Metallic hydride	Fluoride	300

In a solid rocket motor, the propellant substance is molded into its motor and casing as a single solid mass, called a grain. The shape and consistency of the grain determines its burning properties.

The polyurethane fuel base of the most common solid fuel mixture is a type of synthetic rubber. It maintains about the same consistency as that of tire rubber. Various other rocket propellants have similar plastic consistencies. It is very important that this consistency be even and free from internal bubbles or surface cracks. Exposure of more burning surface than intended could result in the danger of uncontrolled burning or explosion. The casing into which the grain is molded must be tough and heat resistant. A lining material is used as an insulator, and the case itself is made of various materials such as special steels, titanium, and fiberglass.

GRAIN DESIGN AND THRUST CONTROL

Once a solid propellant is ignited it is going to burn. It can't be turned off and then restarted as is done with liquid propellant systems. Some burning solid propellants can be stopped by dousing them with water, but others cannot be stopped. So, how does one control the burning rate of a solid propellant? How can the amount of thrust produced be controlled? The primary way of doing this is to *mold* the propellant into a shape that will provide the desired burning rate.

The flame—front (where actual oxidation is taking place) of a solid propellant always eats its way into the mass in a direction that is at a right angle perpendicular to the surface. The flame eats its way into a mass at a fixed rate depending on the contents of the propellant. For example, a typical double-based propellant's burning rate is about 0.40 inch per second; a dense polyurethane composite burns at about 0.22 inch per second. Since these rates do not change the only way to control the amount of

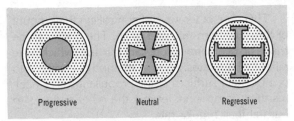

Figure 7. Grain designs for solid propellants

Progressive   Neutral   Regressive

force (or thrust) generated is to control the surface area exposed to the burning process.

The grain of a common skyrocket more than likely is a solidly packed propellant, with a space for ignition between the *charge* (or grain) and the nozzle. Once ignited this grain can burn only straight forward and the flame front is limited to the surface diameter. Thus, the burn rate (whatever it is), does not change until *burnout.* Since the burn rate doesn't change and the flame-front area doesn't change, the amount of thrust produced is constant. When this type situation exists the grain design is *neutral.*

What if a hole is bored the length of the grain, or charge, along its "longitudinal" axis? There will be a virtually instantaneous spread of the flame-front along the entire surface of the hole. This, of course, provides a larger surface area of flame and greater force. As the grain continues to burn more and more surface area is exposed so more and more thrust is produced. This is called a *progressive* burn rate.

Suppose a considerable amount of thrust is needed but the designers want the thrust to be neutral? The design shown in figure 7 might be used. Ignition produces a large amount of thrust very quickly but the design keeps the surface area constant—remember, the flame eats its way into the mass perpendicular to the surface.

The third design in figure 7 is one for a *regressive* rate. With this design the most thrust is produced shortly after ignition and diminishes thereafter. A similar approach is used for the Space Shuttle's solid rocket boosters. The most thrust is produced upon ignition and during the first 55 seconds of the two-minute burn. The grain of these boosters is shaped so that it then reduces thrust by approximately one-third until burnout.

There are other ways of controlling the amount of thrust or burn rate of a grain. The grain can be made up of different propellant mixtures which have different burn rates. Another method of control is to paint certain surfaces of the propellant with a heat-resistant compound, leaving the other surfaces to burn at their regular rate.

Control of a solid rocket motor's thrust depends primarily on the design and composition of the grain, as we indicated earlier. It is also *possible* to stop thrust in a solid propellant by injecting a high-pressure inert (or neutral) gas into the chamber. A grain stopped in this manner could be restarted. However, such arrangements have not proved worth the effort. So, once the grain is ignited it continues to burn and produce the amount of thrust for which it was designed. Control of the direction of thrust is another matter.

Thrust directional control for the solid propellant rocket *can* be obtained from the same type devices used with liquid propellant rockets.

IGNITERS

Solid propellants are ignited by a composition that both heats the grain to ignition temperature and increases the pressure in the combustion chamber until propellant reaction is assured. A few of the older solid propellant mixtures could be ignited by the heat of a short *resistance* (hot) electrical wire. Today this type ignition device is found in model rocket-launching devices, but the "real rockets" use devices like the *squib*. The squib consists of an enclosure filled with a combustible powder, which is ignited electrically. The flame of the burning squib in turn ignites the grain.

Two igniter compositions frequently used are common gunpowder and a metal-oxidizer mixture such as magnesium and potassium perchlorate. Each of these has advantages over the other. Each also has certain disadvantages. Gunpowder is inexpensive but it tends to absorb moisture, which can affect its performance adversely. Metal-oxidizer igniters are generally more efficient and their ignition delays are shorter. However, they are more hazardous to handle than black powder igniters. If magnesium is used in igniter composition, surface oxidation is likely to occur. Once oxidized, the igniter doesn't work very well.

A critical part of an igniter is the case which contains the composition. Manufacturers of igniters have a variety of material to choose from, ranging from paper to metal. Container strength must be sufficient for demands made upon it. For example, rapid ignition requires the container to be strong enough to remain intact until all the composition has ignited. However, the container must be designed so that no pieces of it are large enough to block the exhaust nozzle. Such blocking could cause extremely high pressures and damage the engine. The location of the igniter depends upon the design of the grain.

LIQUID PROPELLANTS

You will remember that there are two general classifications of liquid propellants—bipropellant and monopropellant. When the oxidizers and fuels are separated, we refer to the two as a *bipropellant.* And any rocket that uses a bipropellant has a liquid bipropellant propulsion system. However, it is not necessary for all liquid propellants to have their oxidizers and fuels kept separate. When we find a liquid propellant that contains its oxidizer and fuel in one solution, it is called a *monopropellant.*

Bipropellants have an advantage over mono-propellants in that they are more stable and capable of better performance. Bipropellants are of two types: The non-hypergolic (non-self-igniting) and the hypergolic (self-igniting). Each of the two types of bipropellants has advantages and disadvantages. Malfunctioning of equipment and accidents involving a system using either type of bipropellant can be disastrous.

An ignition delay, even a brief one, results in a sufficient accumulation of non-hypergolic fuel and oxidizer in the combustion chamber to cause a damaging explosion. The components of a hypergolic propellant catch fire when brought into contact one with the other.

The design of a liquid-monopropellant system is much simpler than that of a bipropellant system (see fig. 8). A monopropellant system requires only

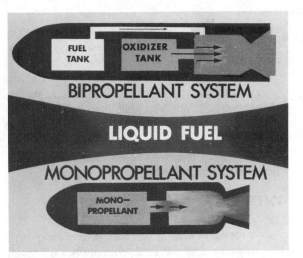

Figure 8. Comparison of bipropellant and monopropellant propulsion systems

half the storage, pumping, and controlling equipment required by a bipropellant system. It doesn't require metering to keep the fuel and oxidizer in correct proportion.

The drawback of a monopropellant is its sensitivity to temperature and shock. This senstitivty results in instability and restricts its handling. Generally, monopropellants also require more heat for ignition and react more slowly than bipropellants. These characteristics mean that monopropellants require larger combustion chambers.

Just as there are two general types of bipropellants, there are two general types of monopropellants: Those that obtain energy by combustion and those that obtain energy by *dissociation reaction* (decomposition).* The dissociation reaction is initiated by a catalyst.**

To ignite a liquid propellant it is only necessary to raise the temperature of a small part of the mixture to its ignition point. The flame then spreads throughout the total mixture. Mixtures that contain liquid oxygen have a high reaction rate, so these mixtures are easy to ignite. An ordinary spark plug, for example, can be used to ignite a flow of oxygen and alcohol.

*Dissociation is the process by which a chemical combination breaks up into its elements.
**Catalyst is a substance which produces and may accelerate a chemical reaction without undergoing significant change itself during the process.

One method of igniting a liquid-propellant mixture is to inject a limited amount of hypergolic fuel into the combustion chamber along with the oxidizer just before the main fuel flow starts. Another method uses a pyrotechnic fired electrically from an external circuit. If repeated ignitions are required during flight, a small precombustion chamber makes the ignition of a small amount of the propellant possible by means of a spark plug. The flow into the main chamber is delayed until the propellant in the precombustion chamber is ignited. The flame from the precombustion chamber is then used to ignite the mixture in the main chamber.

THE LIQUID - PROPELLANT ENGINE

The essential units of a liquid-propellant system include propellant tanks, a combustion chamber, and a means of forcing propellants from the tanks through control valves to the combustion chamber. The simplest liquid-propellant engine system transfers oxidizer and fuel from tanks to the combustion chamber by pressurizing the tanks with an inert gas such as nitrogen. More complex systems employ turbopumps to transfer propellants to the combustion chamber (see fig. 9).

The nature of the propellant determines to a great degree the structural design of the engine or propulsion system. Quite often the use which will be made of the liquid propellant engine determines both the nature of the engine's design and the type of its liquid propellant. There are many kinds of liquid fuels and a number of liquid oxidizers that are available for use in liquid propellants. It is possible for a single oxidizer to react with many different fuels. Also, a single fuel can react with a number of different oxidizers; for example, kerosene—a fuel—reacts with *liquid oxygen, hydrogen peroxide, or nitric acid.* For this reason, many combinations of fuels and oxidizers are possible. The basis for choosing a certain fuel-oxidizer combination might include economy, safety, ease of handling, and purpose, but the fundamental factor underlying the choice of a propellant combination is generally the performance of such a combination.

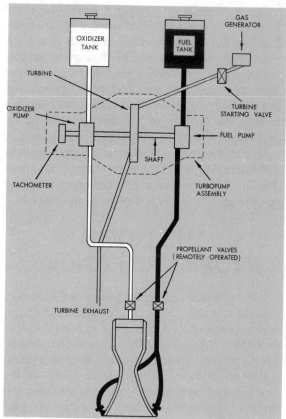

Figure 9. Major components of a liquid bipropellant propulsion system

COMBUSTION CHAMBERS

The combustion chamber is the "heart" of the liquid-propellant engine. Within this chamber several phases of the combustion process take place. These phases include (1) atomizing, (2) mixing, (3) pre-heating to ignition temperature, and (4) reaction of the propellant.

Combustion chambers may be uncooled or cooled. Combustion temperatures of propellants used in uncooled combustion chambers frequently are under 1,000°C. When it is desired to construct uncooled combustion chambers that will withstand relatively high temperatures over a comparatively long period of time, they are given an inside coating of a ceramic or carbon. There are several methods of cooling combustion chambers, but the most

commonly used method is by *regenerative cooling.* In this method, fuel or oxidizer is circulated within small passageways between the inner and outer walls of the combustion chamber, throat and nozzle. As the propellant flows through the passageways, it absorbs heat, thereby cooling the combustion chamber. The absorbed heat also adds energy to the fuel or oxidizer before it enters the injector and increases the velocity of injection into the combustion chamber.

VALVES

A propellant system's tanks and plumbing must be constructed of materials that are not adversely affected by the nature of the fuel and oxidizer the system uses. The nature of the fluids a system uses also determines the kinds of materials used to make valves. The scope of both the operating temperatures and operating conditions to which they are subject makes it necessary to use high-precision techniques in valve manufacturing.

Valves used in propellant systems range in type and size according to the use required of them. Comparatively large valves, for example, are used to control the high flow of fuel and oxidizer. A coupled valve, consisting of two propellant valves opened by a single piston, operates through a crosshead, causing fuel and oxidizer to enter the combustion chamber at the same time.

INJECTORS

The function of the injector of a liquid-propellant rocket engine is similar to that of the carburetor used with some automobile engines. Just as a carburetor atomizes (reduces small particles) and mixes fuel and air, preparing the mixture for combustion, the injector atomizes and mixes fuel and oxidizer.

The type of injector used depends upon the type of propellant. Lightness, simplicity, and low cost are factors that need to be considered by manufacturers of rocket engine injectors. However, just as is the case with valves and other rocket engine components, precision and exactness of construction of the injector are very important.

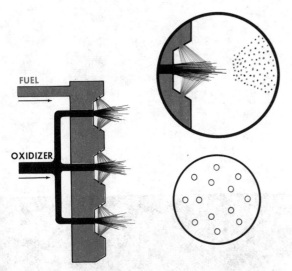

FUEL

OXIDIZER

Figure 10. Operating principle of the impinging-jet type injector

Two types of injectors are in common use. The difference between them is the difference between the methods each uses to mix fuel and oxidizer. In the *swirl jet* type, each propellant is introduced into the chamber in an inverted-cone-shaped spray, finely atomized and sufficiently diffused for adequate mixing with the adjacent spray. In the *impinging jet* type (see fig. 10) the fuel and oxidizer enter the combustion chamber direct, but through openings arranged in such a way that the streams of fuel and oxidizer strike each other (impinge on one another). Their collision causes the required atomization and mixing.

Improved injection systems have contributed to the development of throttleability (variable control) in liquid propellant engines. One such system mixes, in a specially designed manifold, gas under high pressure with liquid fuel before it is injected into the combustion chamber. Depending on the ratio of gas to liquid fuel, the engine may be throttled from a low to full thrust and may be stopped and started in flight.

HYBRID PROPELLANTS

Hybrid propulsion systems use both liquid propellants and solid propellants in combination within the same engine. Usually, solid material is used as the fuel, and a liquid is used as the oxidizer. However, there are systems which use liquid fuels and solid oxidizers. When solid fuel is used, it is packed into the rocket engine as an inert material, without its oxidizer. The liquid oxidizer is stored in a separate tank. To create combustion and generate thrust, the oxidizer is fed into the solid-fuel combustion chamber at a desired rate. In one such system, the solid fuel and the oxidizer do not come into actual contact. Instead, the heat of ignition vaporizes the oxidizer and the fuel. These gases, approaching each other from opposite directions, unite and burn just above the face of the fuel grain. The thrust produced by the hybrid rocket can thereby be increased or decreased simply by increasing or decreasing the flow of oxidizer over the fuel charge. Thrust is stopped when the flow of oxidizer is closed off.

The hybrid propulsion system combines in a single rocket engine many of the advantages of both liquid-propellant rockets and solid-propellant rockets. It has the flexibility, controllability, and high performance of liquid rockets, plus the simplicity, reliability, and relative economy of solid-propellant rockets. Flexibility probably gives the hybrid rocket its biggest operational advantage. It can be throttled, like a liquid rocket, from zero to full thrust; and it can be stopped and started in flight.

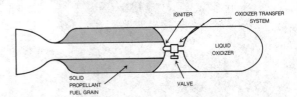

IGNITER · OXIDIZER TRANSFER SYSTEM · LIQUID OXIDIZER · SOLID PROPELLANT FUEL GRAIN · VALVE

Figure 11. Diagram of a hybrid propulsion system

Figure 11 is a very simple diagram of how the parts of a hybrid propulsion system might be arranged. In the system illustrated the "valve" controls how much oxidizer is allowed to come in contact with the fuel. This amount, or rate of oxidizer to fuel, determines how much thrust the system produces. In this particular design the grain has been molded for a *progressive* burn rate. To maintain a steady thrust could require less and less oxidizer as the process continues.

2-24

Chapter 2-3

ADVANCED PROPULSION SYSTEMS

In the second chapter of this Part, we talked about some of the propulsion systems in current use. Our main interest then was chemical propellants and whether they were in solid or liquid form. In this chapter we will discuss some ideas about the construction of larger-than-Saturn rockets to lift tremendously heavy payloads into orbit—still using chemical propulsion systems.

Chemical systems so far are the best for getting payloads away from Earth's surface. The chemical system is now the *only* propulsion system that produces enough thrust for this type of work. Out in space, and far from the major gravitational influence of a celestial body, less powerful propulsion systems become much more efficient.

As we think about the term *advanced propulsion systems*, we normally are speaking of something new—something quite revolutionary. Of course, a new means of developing thrust would be advanced. But how about putting together a *combination* of propulsion systems within one vehicle and calling the combination an advanced propulsion system? We believe this would be a valid application of the term. We also believe that the building of a launch vehicle even larger than the *Saturn,* using the same type of chemical propellants, would be an advanced propulsion system.

Therefore, we will consider the *different* and the *bigger* as *advanced.*

The general learning objective for this chapter is for you to know the operational concepts of several advanced propulsion systems. To reach this objective, you must pattern your study of the material according to the *specific learning objectives* listed in the Appendix of this textbook.

HEAVY-LIFT LAUNCH VEHICLES

In our introduction to this chapter we said that the combination of propulsion systems should qualify a vehicle as using an advanced propulsion system. By our own definition, therefore, the Space Shuttle vehicle is really an advanced propulsion system. After all, the combination of solid propellants, liquid propellants and an aerodynamic vehicle had not been tried until the Shuttle.

The Space Shuttle system is the present-day result of studies done a number of years ago. Similarly, studies are going on today in preparation for the propulsion systems of tomorrow. Today's planners see a requirement for getting very heavy payloads into orbit if there is to be true space utilization. These payloads will consist of construction materials, supplies and even sub-assemblies for various types of "stations" in space. The vehicles no doubt will be automated (no crew aboard) and will deliver their payloads to orbits where "space workers" will take over and use the payloads.

Planners see the future need of an uprated (more advanced) Space Shuttle for delivering to space the people who work there. Of course, the uprated Shuttle system would be reusable and it would be capable of higher orbits and a greater payload (of spaceworkers) than the present Space Shuttle system.

UNMANNED HLLVs

If funds are available, almost anything imaginable can be accomplished. Perhaps the people of Earth will someday realize a need to build heavy lift launch vehicles from a totally new design. Perhaps this totally new HLLV will use a new engine design, and perhaps it will use propellants other than oxygen, hydrogen, and kerosene.

On the more practical side, we can see that any future HLLVs will use existing hardware along with conventional propellants. What will make such a system "new" and "advanced" will simply be the arrangement of the parts. Suppose, for example, that we took seven of the *Saturn V*-type first stages and fastened them together as one giant launch vehicle. Simultaneous (at the same time) ignition of all these 35 F-1 engines could produce as much as 52.5 million pounds of thrust. This, we do believe, would qualify such an arrangement as an HLLV.

An entirely different design (or arrangement) may be used. Figure 12 shows an HLLV that is really a large cluster of smaller propulsion units. This idea also uses present-day propellants, and its stubby look actually detracts from our concept of the streamlined look that a rocket should have. On the other hand, we should remember that a rocket or propulsion system's appearance need not indicate anything in particular about its overall performance. Recall that the only reason for streamlining any type of vehicle is to reduce atmospheric drag. With the HLLV shown in figure 12 the configuration is a compromise. Its "nose" could be made longer and

Figure 12. Idea for heavy-lift launch vehicle design

therefore less blunt. Making the nose longer would be better aerodynamically but in turn it would increase the dead (useless) weight of the total vehicle and result in less payload. Too, by the time an HLLV reaches a very high velocity it will be beyond the Earth's atmosphere so atmospheric drag will not be a significant factor at that time.

Will special HLLVs be built? Probably. But we believe that the really large ones are many years away from lift-off. The current trend of cost reductions wherever possible and the emphasis on conservation no doubt will bring about something like the designs shown in figures 13 and 14. Recall that the Space Shuttle payload is something like 65,000 pounds. Of course, the manned reusable payload delivery vehicle (Orbiter) of the Shuttle system can be used over and over again. But let's suppose that we want to use off-the-shelf Shuttle components to power an expendable (non-reusable) payload delivery vehicle. This is what we have in figure 13. The design uses slightly modified liquid propellant tanks (called external tanks when on the Shuttle), and it uses the Shuttle system's solid rocket boosters. Notice that the Shuttle Orbiter's engine cluster (with modifications) is attached to the

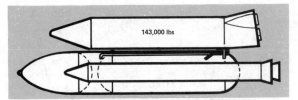

Figure 13. HLLV design based on Space Shuttle

payload container. This approach, therefore, allows 143,000 pounds of payload to be placed in low Earth orbit.

You might think that this type modification is still a waste of resources because we said that the payload delivery vehicle was expendable. It would be expendable in the sense that it would not be used again to deliver to orbit a payload from Earth's surface. On the other hand, it still would be quite useful as a space tug (shifting payloads to different places in space) or as a structural element for something like a space station. The solid rocket boosters of this design also would be parachuted back to Earth for subsequent flights. Thus, the liquid propellant tank would be the only truly expendable component of this system. Actually, it is possible that the liquid propellant tank could be modified to be reusable.

Still using components of the Space Shuttle system, a true heavy lift launch vehicle could be "put together." This is the idea shown in figure 14. Here four solid rocket boosters have been attached to a Shuttle external tank. A four-engine thrust element is connected to the rocket end of the tank while the 264,000 pound payload with aerodynamic cone is attached to the other end. Again, the solid rocket boosters return to Earth for subsequent reuse. It is possible that the liquid propellant rocket portion and the payload container will be used in space as elements of some other purposeful structure.

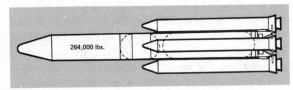

Figure 14. HLLV design that would use Space Shuttle propulsion units

MANNED HLLVs

It is a very good possibility that future HLLVs will be used to take relatively large numbers of space workers into orbit and possibly on to permanent space stations. A payload is a payload, so any HLLV could deliver a human cargo. On the other hand, a different approach probably will be used. By this we mean that the vehicle used more than likely will be "Super Shuttle." It will be a combination rocket and turbine engine craft. Such a vehicle would be capable of flying much like a large jet transport within the atmosphere. It would be completely controllable throughout all modes of flight, including conventional takeoffs and landings.

To give an idea of how such a system could be constructed, we refer you to figure 15. This is an early idea submitted as a Space Shuttle design, but we can imagine something similar being a winged, manned HLLV of the future. The vehicle shown would have used a modified *Saturn V* first stage — same propellants and same engines. From this point on, however, things would have been considerably different. The craft's wings apparently would have a more conventional appearance — approaching that of a delta wing fighter but much larger. It would have had ten large turbofan engines to provide thrust for conventional flight in the atmosphere. The extensive elevon system and rudder would have provided positive and complete aerodynamic control. The landing gear was to have been similar to a conventional jetliner. All together, the features of this particular design would have allowed its pilots to make a leisurely return flight to the designated landing area. (Remember that current Space Shuttle flights are unpowered or deadstick landings.)

We do not want you to think that future manned HLLVs will look exactly like the vehicle shown in figure 15 because there are many ways of doing the job. For example, the cost of delivering the payload with a certain vehicle design will usually determine whether or not that particular design is used.

From the perspective of today, it seems that future heavy-lift launch vehicles will use already-developed engines and existing propellants. When it is not necessary to move a payload from Earth's

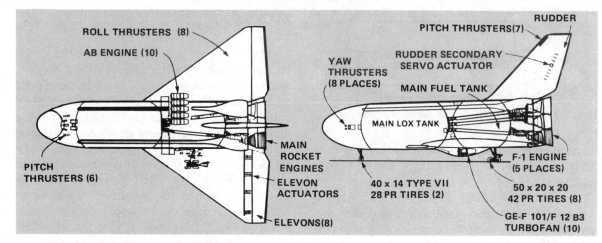

Figure 15. Idea for a manned HLLV

surface into space, propulsion systems with much less total thrust but longer duration thrust are very efficient. Such "advanced" propulsion systems will be discussed in the remainder of this chapter.

THRUST IN SPACE

Generally speaking, very little thrust applied to a vehicle in space can have a great effect on the vehicle's ultimate flight path. Of course, this small amount of thrust has to be with the purpose of a long-term change. A slight nudge to one side of even a very large interplanetary spacecraft will cause little movement off the line of flight. Yet, this slight movement will mean a great change in the arrival point at the craft's destination. The farther the distance the greater this change will be.

Why is it that objects in spaceflight can be moved about so easily? First of all, we should remember that Newton expressed the reason when he said that any amount of force will produce a change in proportion to the force. On Earth this small force may not be shown in movement of the "acted upon" object because of the influence of gravity or friction, or both gravity and friction. In spaceflight the effect of gravity is lessened by distance from Earth or the counteracting centrifugal effect (in orbit) to such an extent that it can just about be ignored. So, when a force is applied to the

side or rear of the spacecraft its flight path will change.

Notice that we have been applying this imagined force to the sides or the rear of the "spacecraft." It takes much less force to effect an immediately noticeable change in direction or speed at these points than on the nose of the vehicle. Again, why? The answer is that the vehicle's mass is exerting a tremendous amount of inertial force toward its direction of travel. A small force directed against this large force will have an effect of some type. To slow a spacecraft noticeably, however, requires application of a very large force against the direction of travel. This type of force is applied when it is desired to slow a spacecraft's velocity so that it will go into orbit around a planet. The *Apollo* spacecraft's main engines had to be turned on full blast to slow it enough to stay in orbit around the moon. When our astronauts in the Space Shuttle want to come out of orbit, they have to fire the craft's engines *toward* the direction of orbit.

We can see, therefore, that even in space there are times when a large amount of thrust is needed. With present-day technology the only way to deliver a large amount of thrust is to use the conventional chemical propulsion system. You have realized by now that the "lifespan" of chemical propellants is short, so the use of a chemical propellant system on a deep spaceflight would have to be planned very carefully. This is to say that a manned flight for an orbit of Mars, for example, would have to use powerful chemical propellant rockets to slow the craft to orbital velocity. Low thrust rockets simply would not do the job.

Continuing with the manned-flight-to-Mars example, low thrust rockets would be effective for course changes and vehicle attitude changes because little thrust is required. Just short bursts will do. Apply the same low thrust, continue it over a period of time, and the spacecraft's velocity will be increased. The amount of the increase will be proportional to the length of time the thrust is applied. Going back to Newton's third law, if this thrust in space is kept up long enough, the forward velocity of the spacecraft should eventually be equal to the exhaust velocity of the propellant mass. This may be a little difficult for you to imagine, but theoretically, this is what happens under the proper conditions.

Propulsion systems which actually produce little thrust are, therefore, useful for increasing the velocity of a spacecraft. Of course, we should always remember that low thrust rockets (thrusters or reaction control engines) are essential to flight attitude and course changes. They are also quite necessary to the proper orientation of satellites to insure that the areas the satellites are monitoring or broadcasting to are always the right ones.

So, how to develop a propulsion system that produces thrust over a long period of time is the problem. At this time there are two ways of doing this, either by using *electric propulsion* or *nuclear propulsion.*

ELECTRIC PROPULSION

The electric system uses the electrical power generated by an on-board source to establish magnetic fields and apply electric currents to matter so that the matter exits the engine at high velocity.

The primary drawback to electric propulsion is that comparatively little thrust is produced; on the other hand, the velocity of the propellant is very high and over a long period of application the vehicle being propelled by an electric system would achieve very high velocity. In other words, the electric rocket (suitable to in-space propulsion only) would get a

slow start but would eventually achieve a higher velocity for the vehicle than a rocket with a chemical propulsion system.

It should be obvious that any type of propulsion which uses electricity must have a source of electricity. Let's discuss these possible sources before examining the types of thrusters being used today or planned for the future.

SOURCES OF ELECTRICITY

Depending on the space vehicle, batteries may be found as the backup or intermediate source of power. Silver-zinc batteries were used during the Apollo flights for short-duration power needs.

Nickel-cadmium and silver-zinc batteries have powered many satellites over the years. But the drawback to any battery is its relatively short life span. This may change dramatically in the future, because research continues toward improving the durability and reliability of storage batteries.

The battery for an automobile or airplane is recharged by a mechanical alternator or generator but batteries for spacecraft operations are generally recharged by an array of solar cells (which change the sun's energy into electricity). For example, when a space vehicle (satellite) is in Earth's shadow its sensing instruments are powered by the battery. Upon coming out of Earth's shadow, the craft's solar cells again generate sufficient electricity to operate the instruments and to recharge the battery.

Solar cells (or photovoltaic cells) are the most popular method of generating electricity for spacecraft. At the distance of Earth's orbit from the sun, the sun radiates the equivalent of 130 watts of electrical energy per square foot on any surface that is perpendicular to the sun's rays.

Although solar cells have been improved significantly in their power output, each cell is relatively small. In addition, the individual solar cell is not 100% efficient, so it is necessary to connect hundreds or thousands of them together in order to generate a significant amount of electricity. Such an arrangement of solar cells is called an *array* or a *paddle.* In addition to arrays or paddles, solar cells can be mounted directly on a spacecraft's body surface.

To reach their highest efficiency level, the solar cells must be perpendicular to the sun. Even a slightly oblique angle can result in a great deal of power loss. Therefore, spacecraft body-mounted solar panels, because they face the sun at various angles or not at all, are less efficient than an array which can be oriented toward the sun. Sun-oriented arrays, however, also have their disadvantages, mainly in that they add to the mechanical complexity and power requirements of the vehicle. Another problem is that portions of the vehicle and its solar array may throw shadows on other portions, including the sensors and antennas. For these reasons, the less efficient but more reliable body-mounted solar cell panels are often used.

One drawback to the use of solar energy is that solar energy decreases as distance from the sun increases. At the range of Mars, solar energy is about half that at Earth, and out near Saturn about a hundredth. For space travel this side of Mars, however, solar energy has shown itself to be highly useful.

Another device which, like the storage battery, provides electricity from chemical reaction is the fuel cell. Fuel cells, unlike batteries, use chemical fuels and oxidizers which are stored outside the cell.

In a fuel cell, two porous nickel electrodes are immersed in a solution of sodium or potassium hydroxide (see fig. 16). Pressurized hydrogen and oxygen are fed to these electrodes and diffused through them. Chemical reactions between the hydrogen and the solution and the oxygen and the solution take place on the electrodes. Positive ions migrate through the solution, and negative electrons flow through the external circuit to provide power.

From a weight standpoint, fuel cells are best suited for uses requiring up to 10 kilowatts of power for operating periods between a few days and several months. Another advantage of the hydrogen-oxygen fuel cell is that the chemical reaction product is water, useful on manned missions. (Note: the Apollo space program used the fuel cell as a primary source of in-space electrical power and drinking water.)

Nuclear energy is a fourth means of generating electricity. Basically there are two ways of using

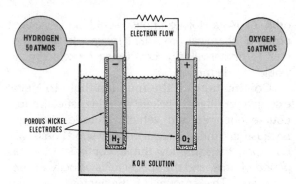

Figure 16. Principle of fuel cell operation

nuclear energy to generate electricity: the radioisotop method and the nuclear fission method. A radioisotope thermoelectric generator depends on the *decay* of certain radioactive metals. As these metals decay—turn into new isotopes—energy is given off as heat. The resulting heat is changed to usable power by thermoelectric or thermodynamic means. The radioisotope method of creating usable heat is slow and creates less heat than do other applications of nuclear power. This means that the radioisotope method generates relatively small amounts of electricity and must be used where low power will suffice. On the other hand, the radioisotope method can last for years; this feature makes the method particularly applicable as a power source of probes going to the outer planets.

Nuclear fission is the splitting of atoms as in the process which takes place in an atomic bomb. Nuclear fission can be slowed, however, to the point where the fission process is extended over a long period of time and the tremendous heat resulting from the process can be used to produce large amounts of electricity. It is the nuclear fission method which powers ships and electric generating plants on Earth. The drawback of this nuclear process is the heavy shielding required to protect against harmful radiation. The weight of this shielding poses a problem for fission reactors on space vehicles launched from Earth; for one thing, the thrust required to counteract the extra weight is very costly.

Whatever the drawbacks in the use of nuclear power sources, they are still the greatest hope for space power and propulsion in the future.

Remember, the nuclear unit does not have to rely on an outside source—such as the sun—and it can operate for years. It can be throttled up or down and the heat it produces can be used in many ways. One of these ways is as a source of electricity for electric propulsion systems.

ELECTRIC PROPULSION UNITS

Chemical propulsion units produce large amounts of thrust over short periods of time. Electric propulsion techniques produce very little total thrust but the amount of thrust which an electric unit develops is extended over a very long time. This long duration, low thrust situation, if you recall, works well for long voyages in space because constant thrust means constant acceleration.

No propulsion system, electric or otherwise, can work without a propellant mass—although in some instances of electric propulsion, the notion of mass is one that is stretched very thin. Nevertheless, the concept of a working fluid, a substance that is heated or otherwise energized and propelled at high velocity through an exhaust nozzle, is basic to all kinds of electric propulsion. Therefore, the specific impulse, the "yardstick" more commonly thought of as a measure of chemical energy, is applicable here, too.

Just as with chemical propellants, the specific impulse of a working fluid is proportional to the ratio of combustion chamber temperature (T_c) to the average molecular weight of the combustion products (m). This ratio is stated as T_c/m. Subject to these conditions, a pound of working fluid will yield so many pounds of force in one second. Stating the same quantity another way, a pound of working fluid will sustain one pound of force for so many seconds. In space, as we have noted, *sustained* thrust is even more desirable than *intense* thrust. Therefore, we are now more interested in specific impulse as an index of propellant economy or "mileage" than we are in the same value as an index of boosting power. Where specific impulses of chemical propellants may never exceed 600 seconds—a theoretical limit—electric engines are expected to yield specific impulses of 2,000 to 30,000 seconds, or more.

Before describing the different approaches to electric propulsion, let us point out certain basic features they all have in common. Instead of heating propellant in huge volume—a great roaring fire—an electric engine energizes a very small amount of propellant. This *working fluid* is fed into the engine slowly in a thin stream. Thus, a relatively small tankful of working fluid might be enough for months of operation.

TYPES OF ELECTRIC ENGINES

A number of different types of rocket engines labeled as "electric" are under development. Some have already found limited practical application with low-level power sources; others might be called more "futuristic." The future development of all engines in this class depends on improvement in electric power sources.

Perhaps the simplest concept to understand is electric heating of hydrogen, examples of which are the *resistojet* and the *arc jet*. As in chemical propulsion, the energy behind the rush of particles through the exhaust nozzle is in the form of heat. Other forms of electric propulsion not only employ heat but also use electrical energy itself as a means of moving particles.

Resistojets. This is the name given miniature thrusters designed to deliver precisely controlled thrust for spacecraft attitude control and station keeping. In a resistojet engine, heat is generated by passing an electric current through a special wire or tube, which presents high resistance to the current's passage. This resistance develops heat. A stream of hydrogen or ammonia is passed over the heating element and energized to high velocity as it travels out an exhaust nozzle similar to that of a conventional chemical rocket (see fig. 17).

Resistojets may be about six inches long and two inches in diameter and weigh about a half a pound. This size unit provides about 10 millipounds (1/1000 of a pound) of thrust at specific impulses of 300-575 seconds, depending on the propellant used.

Resistance heating is the principle on which electrical heating appliances like toasters, coffee percolators, and irons operate. The practical resistojets currently in use or under development use low-level power sources. As with all electric

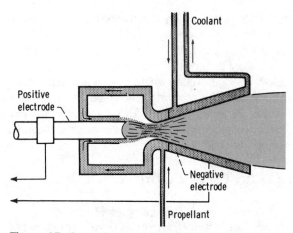

Figure 17. Operating principles of the resistojet

rockets described here, future development will depend on development of nuclear-reactor power sources. In this respect, however, the arc jet is more promising because it can deliver higher temperatures.

Arc Jet. The arc jet differs from the resistojet in that instead of a resisting wire or tube, there is simply a gap between electrodes. Electricity jumping this gap or "arcing" creates very high temperatures. Hydrogen passing through this arc is heated to thousands of degrees and expanded through a nozzle. Theoretically, extremely high exhaust velocities and high thrust as well as long endurance, with specific impulses up to 2,000 seconds, far excelling any known chemical or nuclear-fission system, are possible. With both the arc jet and the resistojet, the operating time is limited more by the fuel supply than by the duration of the power source. Nevertheless, these devices get the most mileage out of a supply of liquid hydrogen. Present power sources are not sufficient to realize the arc jet's possibilities to any practical degree. Teamed with a nuclear reactor, the arc jet might some day compete with more direct means of nuclear propulsion.

Ion or Electrostatic Engines. Ion engines are in use as auxiliary propulsion sources for north-south satellite station keeping and attitude control. The practical models, however, are of very low thrust and are limited to the kind of chores they are now performing on spacecraft and to the slow, prolonged acceleration in deep space that may be desired in some instances. Because their rate of fuel consumption is low, they can sustain thrust over

long periods. Among other desirable features of ion "rockets" are their lightness of weight and the ease with which they can be stopped and restarted.

The ion rocket is the first example cited here of propulsion by some means other than gaseous heating. It produces thrust by *electrostatic* acceleration of charged atomic and subatomic particles (see fig. 18).

When subjected to heat, the fuel for an ion engine is vaporized and ionized; that is, the heat causes the atomized fuel's atoms to give up an electron. The atoms are then positively charged ions. These ions pass through an electric grid, which accelerates their movement toward the exit nozzle to tremendous speeds. The stripped-off electrons follow another path and are fed back into the exhaust stream to produce an electrically-neutral exhaust. (Otherwise, the engine and the whole vehicle with it would build up a dangerous electrical charge.)

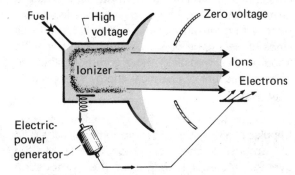

Figure 18. Operating principles of an ion engine

Plasma or Electromagnetic Engines. A *plasma* is not made up of molecules but of ions, free electrons, neutrons, and other subatomic particles. Some of these particles are positively charged, some neutral, and some negative so that the general mixture is electrically neutral. A plasma engine first employs electric power to heat a gas and break it down into a plasma. Then it subjects the plasma to electromagnetic fields of force, which accelerate the plasma to super velocities (see fig. 19). Specific impulse is directly proportional to exhaust velocity. It is the extremely high exhaust velocity of electric

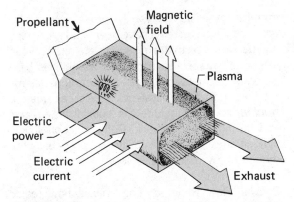

Figure 19. Operating principles of a plasma engine

Labels on figure:
Propellant
Magnetic field
Plasma
Electric power
Electric current
Exhaust

engines of the ion and plasma types that give them such high specific impulses.

Pulsed plasma thrusters, in the thrust level range of a few tens of micropounds, have a number of significant advantages in long life missions requiring precise maneuvers. This is particularly true where a large number of accurately controlled thrust pulses are needed such as on a spin-stabilized spacecraft. This plasma thruster has no valves, requires little power, and needs no warm-up time of function. The initial application of the plasma thruster was on a NASA Synchronous Meterological Satellite (SMS), for station keeping and for pointing control (proper aiming of antennas).

A later application of the plasma jet was launched in 1981. The still-functioning pulsed-plasma thrusters on the satellite NOVA-1 are used to control the satellite against drag and solar pressure (force of the sun's radiations). Another function of the two thrusters is to trim (adjust) the satellite's orbital period (time of one complete orbit).

We should see more and more applications of electric propulsion in the future. Scientists are working to improve the efficiency of this type propulsion, along with their own understanding of it.

NUCLEAR PROPULSION

The primary and now practical technique of using nuclear power for propulsion is to heat a working fluid. This method results in tremendous amounts of heat from the standard fission process.

Nuclear propulsion has been developed. It works and it could be used now but there are drawbacks to its use. We will discuss these drawbacks in this section. In addition we will look at other possibilities for nuclear propulsion.

NERVA

The acronym NERVA represents *Nuclear Energy for Rocket Vehicle Application*. It is first of all a *program* which was started in 1961 to develop a nuclear propulsion unit. The engine (or system) which resulted from this program is called NERVA. In the NERVA rocket, the reactor applied direct heating to hydrogen for rocket propulsion. Such a system is sometimes called a *gaseous heating* or *nuclear thermal* system. The NERVA could develop 75,000 pounds of thrust with a specific impulse of 825 seconds—double that achieved so far with chemical propulsion, but not as high as that of electric propulsion. In this instance, however, the objective is to combine both high thrust and high specific impulse to achieve a super rocket. This rocket would be capable of carrying heavy payloads deep into space, achieving high acceleration rapidly, and possibly of relaunching from another planet. It would achieve all of these with a bonus of good propellant economy. By propellant, of course, we mean the liquid hydrogen supply, which would still remain the critical factor. It would have to be conserved for use in high-thrust situations, but it would still have a great advantage over chemical propellants in this respect. The NERVA engine's capability for easy stopping, restarting, and thrust regulation plus high specific impulse give it the means of using a propellant supply with utmost efficiency.

Weight is a problem with all nuclear rocket propulsion systems. Another drawback to the NERVA concept is radioactivity. The hydrogen working fluid, as it passes through or around the reactor and is heated, is also irradiated—loaded with radioactive particles coming from the reactor's fissioning atoms. If a NERVA engine (see fig. 20) were to be used as a first-stage launcher, the hydrogen exhaust would spew a dangerous amount of radioactivity over the launching area. Thus, it

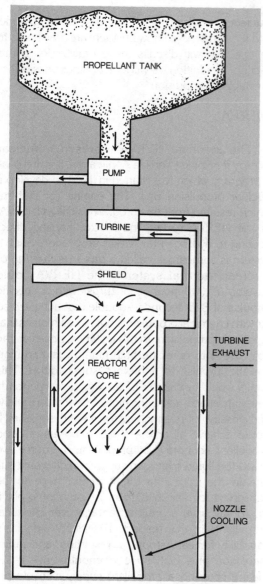

Figure 20. Schematic drawing of the NERVA engine

Text labels in figure: PROPELLANT TANK, PUMP, TURBINE, SHIELD, REACTOR CORE, TURBINE EXHAUST, NOZZLE COOLING

impulse of the NERVA-type system to around 1,000 seconds. Two concepts have been studied in which the fuel would be in the gaseous state and for which the potential specific impulse is as high as 5,000 seconds. (Actually, hydrogen and uranium plasmas are involved.) These systems, labeled as *gas core nuclear rockets,* include the coaxial flow reactor and the light bulb reactor. Both concepts involve difficult questions of feasibility and probably would require many years to develop.

Coaxial Flow Reactor. The coaxial flow reactor would consist of a large, nearly spherical cavity surrounded by a moderator-reflector system to control and confine the radiation and the high temperatures at work. Vaporized uranium would be centered in the cavity, held there by the action of the hydrogen propellant flowing through the porous walls of the cavity. Heat generated in the fissioning uranium plasma would be transferred to the hydrogen by thermal radiation. Some of the uranium would be exhausted with the hydrogen.

Nuclear Light Bulb. The light bulb reactor would consist of several cylindrical cavities, each containing a transparent wall of fused silica (glassy mineral) used to separate the gaseous uranium from the hydrogen propellant. (In contrast to the coaxial concept, no uranium would be carried away with the hydrogen stream.) Thermal radiation would pass through the transparent wall in order to heat the hydrogen to desired temperatures. This construction—the transparent wall surrounding the hot reactor core—is similar to a light bulb's construction and gives the engine its name (see fig. 21). While the silica wall transmits heat to the hydrogen working fluid flowing around it, it also blocks radiation. Thus NLB, as it is sometimes called, would be safe for first-stage use in launches from Earth.

An NLB-powered vehicle is seen as a totally recoverable, winged combination airplane and spaceship, with a single-stage power plant to carry it through all phases of aerodynamic and spaceflight. It would takeoff and land horizontally from an airport without radiation hazard. The NLB engines would have the thrust, the duration, and the ease of

could be used only as an upper-stage rocket at a safe altitude. Its initial use could be for boosting a heavy vehicle (possibly a manned vehicle) out of orbit into an interplanetary flight.

GAS CORE NUCLEAR ENGINES

Structural limitations associated with solid nuclear fuel elements presently restrict the specific

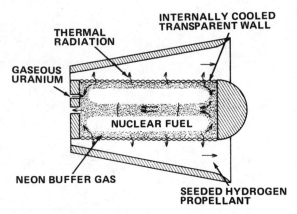

THERMAL RADIATION

INTERNALLY COOLED TRANSPARENT WALL

GASEOUS URANIUM

NUCLEAR FUEL

NEON BUFFER GAS

SEEDED HYDROGEN PROPELLANT

Figure 21. Concept of the "nuclear light bulb" gas-core engine

stopping and restarting needed for launch, prolonged or deep space flight, and aerodynamic reentry and landing.

FUSION AND PHOTON "ENGINES"

A fusion engine is a concept which goes far beyond NERVA or NLB in that it proposes use of a reactor for controlled thermonuclear energy. This is the energy of the so-called H-bomb, many times as powerful as the fission reaction employed in present-day nuclear reactors or the NERVA concept. It is based on the fusing of nuclei of the hydrogen-isotope atoms called deuterium and tritium (rather than the splitting of heavy atoms of uranium or plutonium). Perhaps the immense heat needed to begin such a reaction could be somehow generated, and the reaction then controlled and contained by means of an electromagnetic field. Through introducing or cutting off a coolant/working fluid in the exhaust flow, specific impulse could be controlled for either extremely high thrust levels or extremely high specific impulses—up to a million seconds or more.

Another decidedly "could be" propulsion system is the *photon* system. This is, so far, a very into-the-future thing. The idea is to convert matter into radiation or light energy. Photons are the elements of light and their velocity is that of the speed of light. If a means is found to effectively change matter into radiant energy, then the photon system will be developed. Although the thrust value would be low, the speed of a spacecraft propelled in this manner would eventually be quite fast.

If this dream of a photon engine ever comes true we will have an engine that can take us to other solar systems. After all, the highest velocity of a vehicle thus propelled would be very close to that of light, since photons would be its propellant.

Yet another system is a passive one; it really doesn't fit under any of the systems we have discussed but the idea does involve photons. It is called the *solar sail* and would rely on the pressure of the radiant energy coming from the sun for propulsion. The scheme involves a massive reflective area which would look something like the sail of a boat. Photons and other forms of radiant energy coming from the sun would strike the sail with enough force to push the sail and its attached spacecraft outward from the sun. However, the solar sail idea has drawbacks. The force of the sun's radiation diminishes drastically the farther away from the sun one gets. Also, a spacecraft using the solar sail would have to have another type of propulsion system in reserve if its occupants wanted to travel toward the sun.

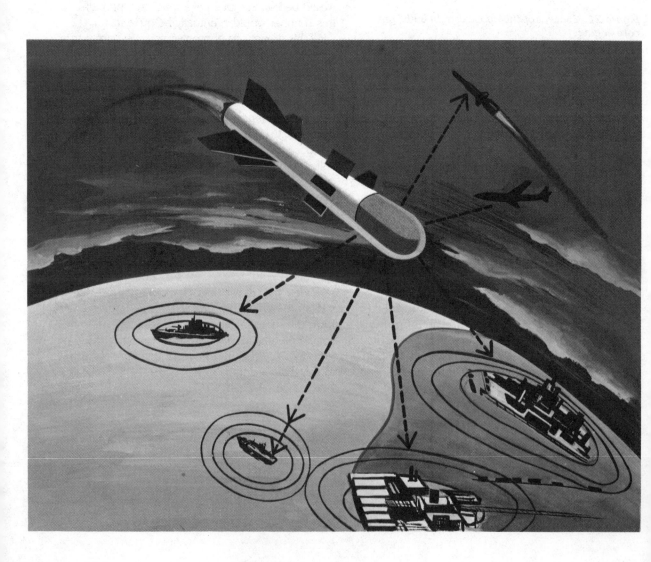

Chapter 2-4

GUIDANCE AND CONTROL

The first chapter of this Part provided a brief overview of a rocket's systems, including its guidance and control systems. In this chapter we will take a closer look at guidance and control. The mission of an aerospace vehicle, whatever that mission may be, depends heavily on its guidance and control system(s). The system(s) must function perfectly to insure the successful completion of the mission.

Coverage of guidance and control in this chapter will begin with *homing* guidance. From this point we will progress to *command* and *inertial* guidance. Then, we will reexamine control systems.

The general learning objective for this chapter is for you to know how rockets are guided and controlled. To reach this objective, you must pattern your study of the material according to the *specific learning objectives* listed in the Appendix of this textbook.

HOMING GUIDANCE

Homing guidance systems are used on short-range missiles. The homing-type must have something coming from the target which the guidance system can detect.

The infrared sensors on "heat seeking" missiles pick up infrared radiation which is given off by any object that generates heat. Sensors on the missile detect the direction from which the infrared radiation is coming. Other parts of the on-board guidance system compare this information with the missile's current heading. If the two directions are in line, no command is sent to the on-board control circuit for course change. However, this is rarely the case because most homing guidance systems are directed toward moving targets.

If you pay close attention to newscasts and special subject shows on television, you may get to see a demonstration flight of a heat-seeking missile intercepting an unpiloted target airplane (or another missile). The path of the missile will not be straight and in fact may be "weaving" as its control system carries out the orders of its guidance system. The source of infrared on modern jet aircraft is the tail pipe. If the missile is fired from directly behind the target airplane, then so much the better for the missile's guidance system. Its infrared sensor has a more positive lock on.

Where the early infrared, or heat-seeking, missiles required rather positive sources of infrared radiation, the modern ones do not. Today, the sensing portion of the missile is cooled to make it highly sensitive to very weak radiation. This enables the missile to pick-out or distinguish a target much more accurately.

What if the sensor picks up two sources of infrared, such as two aircraft in close proximity? More than likely it will track the strongest source. On the other hand, it could become confused and miss the target altogether. If the target airplane has the means to do so it will eject a high-intensity thermal device which will detract the incoming missile. Too, if the target aircraft's pilot knows that a "heat seeker" is in pursuit, a rapid climb or change of direction toward the sun could cause the missile to fix on the sun as the pilot takes another direction rather quickly. A very quick reaction by the pilot could also cause the heat seeker to miss—assuming that the pilot knows the missile is on its way and the evasive action is taken at the right time. The "right time" is very important because the missile probably is fitted with a proximity device which causes it to explode when near the target.

A homing system actually can be devised and set to home in on almost anything. It could home in on radio signals emitted by a ship or ground radio station. It could be set up to home on sound waves or light waves reflected from the target. The choice of homing guidance systems is very wide.

We shall assume that the infrared heat seeker which we have been talking about is of the *passive type*. This simply means that the homing system does nothing but detect whatever the target is emitting, if it is emitting what the system was developed to detect.

Some homing systems may use their own source of illuminating or "painting" the target. That is, the missile with this type of system sends an electromagnetic signal ahead of itself. A portion of this signal is reflected from the target back toward the missile. The missile's sensors pick up this signal and cause the control system to steer toward the target's surface which is reflecting the signal. Any type of homing guidance system which has the capability of generating and receiving a signal in this manner is known as an *active* type.

Nature's example of an active homing guidance is found in the common bat. The bat, as you may

know already, "broadcasts" high frequency sound waves. Its very sensitive ears (sensors) pick up the sound waves bounced back from a possible target—for example, an insect—and the bat heads toward the target. But the bat's active homing guidance system far surpasses that of any man-made system. This is because the bat can refine its signals to determine whether or not the target is suitable for further pursuit.

A third type of homing guidance system is *semiactive*. The signal bounced off the target is sent from some place other than the missile. A radar beam, for example, could be directed to the target and the missile's sensors could detect the "blip" thus formed and home in on it.

Whatever the homing guidance system used, it is also known as a *terminal guidance* system. Terminal guidance means that the missile is in controlled flight up to the point of impact with the target.

COMMAND GUIDANCE

The missile or rocket which does not have the capability of sensing and directing itself is subject to flight instructions from some outside source. Its control system must receive direct *commands* to alter the course being flown. These commands can be transmitted by radio or by a wire trailing from the missile.

If the command type missile has a rather long distance to travel to the target, a radar command system may be used. Antiaircraft surface-to-air (SAM) missiles are directed by radar. The system could use three separate radar units: one to detect the target at long range, another to track the target as it comes into range of the missile, and a third to monitor the missile's progress after launch. With the target-tracking and missile-tracking radars feeding information into the third primary component, a computer, command signals are sent to the missile to insure that its flight path intercepts the target's flight path.

Figure 22 shows the basic arrangement of a command guidance system for a surface-to-air missile, or "SAM." Here we have shown only two of

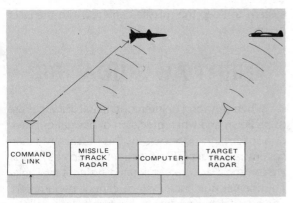

Figure 22. Basics of a command guidance system for a surface-to-air missile

possibly three radar units and this probably would be the arrangement on a mobile, battlefield anti-aircraft missile launcher. In this illustration, one of the radar units picks up the image of the target. Information on the target's direction of flight and its altitude is fed into the command system's computer. This information enables the missile aiming process to begin immediately. That is, the launching unit can be pointed toward the target's flight path and begin to move with the target as it approaches. We can think of this aiming process being very similar to a hunter tracking or following a duck in flight—with a shotgun.

Since the range of the missile is known, launching is delayed until the target is within effective range. Almost from the moment the missile is launched it is tracked by the unit's missile track radar. This radar feeds the computer data on the missile's trajectory. Thus the computer knows where the target is at that moment and it can predict where the target will be at some future time. Knowing where the target will be at X minutes or seconds from now, the command unit is fed course change information which is radioed to the missile's onboard control system. The missile's flight path is adjusted to place it at the point where the target is expected to be at a future time. If the target changes course in the meantime, new course changes are sent to the missile. When everything works as planned, the missile and target arrive at the same place at the same time and the missile's warhead explodes to destroy the target.

There are several ways of interrupting or confusing this type command system. The most modern is called electronic countermeasures (ECM). The target airplane (or missile) may carry very sophisticated systems for generating false signals,or there may be a special ECM aircraft within a group of aircraft which has the job of generating such signals. The basic idea here is to confuse the "other side's" target tracking equipment. In effect this is like throwing something into the eyes of an opponent. The right electronic signals directed toward the target tracking device could make it think it is seeing hundreds of targets, so it would not know which of the hundreds to single out. This may be called "jamming" an enemy's radar.

One of the most effective methods that a *piloted* target has for avoiding destruction by a command type SAM is to *dodge* it. This is precisely what many U.S. pilots did during the Vietnam conflict. The Russian supplied SAMs were large vehicles capable of striking very high flying targets. However, the distance between the launch sites below and the size of the missile allowed pilots to see some of what they called "telephone poles" coming at them from far below. At the right moment a very sudden change in direction would cause the missile to miss. In effect the target airplane did not arrive at the point where the command system had "told" the missile the airplane would be.

It's possible that the command guidance system is employed for only part of a missile's flight. Antiship missiles, for example, may be launched from aircraft and guided by radar toward the target. Upon nearing the target, the missile's own radar guidance system is activated. From that point to impact, the missile's guidance system concentrates on the target ship and provides instructions to the missile's control system which adjusts the flight path to insure a direct hit.

The *wire command* guidance system is used for close-range targets. Especially designed to give combat troops a fighting chance against tanks, there are several types of wire-command antitank missiles. These missiles contain spooled wire which trails from the missile as flight toward the target continues. The "missileer" observes the missile's flight toward the target. Any corrections are sent electrically over the wire to keep the missile on course. These commands, according to the missile design, may cause movement of aerodynamic fins or the firing of small pyrotechnic jets to change the missile's course.

Wire-command missiles are very popular with the armed services of various countries. Efforts continue toward improving this type of guidance system and it is evident that these efforts are concentrated on making the wire command as automatic and foolproof as possible.

A television camera mounted in the nose of air-to-surface missiles has for many years been part of a type of command guidance system. After all, if the target can be seen through the missile's "eyes," the operator can guide the missile straight into the target.

Television-type command guidance is also used for what are called "glide weapons." The glide weapon is an unpowered missile launched from an airplane. The operator sees the target through the weapon's television camera and transmits commands to the weapon's control system as it glides to the point of impact.

We will end our discussion of *Command Guidance* with the beam-rider command system. It is possible to have a missile whose sensory equipment detects and causes the missile to be steered according to the centerline of a radiation beam. The beam, of course, would be directed toward the target, and if kept on the target would cause the missile to fly true. The problem with the beam-rider approach is getting the missile locked on the beam quickly after launch. Otherwise, control is not possible.

Modern beam-riders use the now familiar laser technology. Laser generating units have been miniaturized and are highly portable and easily employed in field combat situations. The laser beam is directed at the target. The operator fires the missile. The missile's sustainer motor ignites several yards beyond the container-launcher tube. By this time its laser sensor has picked up the beam. The sensor detects the missile's position with regard to the laser beam's centerline and feeds this information to the onboard computer. The computer then "instructs" the missile's control

system to keep the missile centered with the laser beam.

INERTIAL GUIDANCE

When very long or intercontinental distances are to be flown and when precision of navigation, such as a space flight, is necessary, the inertial navigation system is a must. This is because inertial systems are the most accurate guidance systems available. The inertial guidance system cannot be jammed. The only defense against an intercontinental ballistic missile is to intercept and destroy the missile sometime before it reaches its target. You probably are familiar with news coverage of efforts to devise systems for defense against intercontinental ballistic missiles and cruise missiles. Such efforts concentrate on destruction. This is the only approach for a defense. The inertial system carries its own electric power source for those components which need electricity— such as the computer. The inertial guidance system does not have to have further communication to find its destination, or target, once it has been programmed. The system's primary advantage when used on a missile directed at an enemy target is that it cannot be interfered with by the enemy. This is not true for other types of guidance systems.

The first application of inertial guidance occurred in World War II. The German V-2 rocket bomb used a primitive system based on the missile's velocity. This system was preprogrammed to shut down the rocket's engine when the velocity required for the proper *ballistic* (unguided) trajectory had been attained. Essentially, this same approach is used today for intercontinental ballistic missiles. The guidance system is now much more complex or sophisticated, but it does *not* guide the warhead all the way to the target. Part of the flight of a large missile is still ballistic.

Truly reliable, highly accurate inertial guidance systems were not developed until the 1950's. Prior to this time they were not really needed. However, the moment rocketry developed the capability of sending a payload across continental distances, the inertial system was needed. Dr. Charles S. Draper's work at the Massachusetts Institute of Technology is

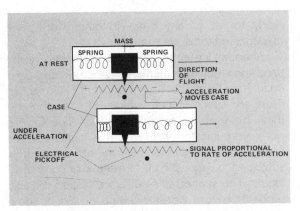

Figure 23. Schematic drawing of a single-degree-of-freedom accelerometer

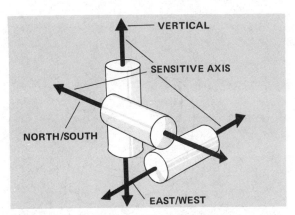

Figure 24. Arrangement of accelerometers to sense movement in all directions

credited with developing the world's first inertial guidance system capable of the accuracy required of an ICBM.

What an inertial system does, or must be capable of doing, is to measure (1) changes in direction and distance, (2) the velocity or *rate* at which change in position is taking place, and (3) acceleration—the rate at which the velocity is changing. To do all of this measuring, accelerometers, gyroscopes, a stabilized platform and a computer are needed.

Let's first talk about accelerometers. Figure 23 shows a *single-degree-of-freedom* accelerometer. The drawing may be simple but it does show the operating principle. The *mass* is fixed so that it can move in a linear (along a line) direction only. Its case is, in effect, attached to the total vehicle, so when the vehicle accelerates (+ or -) the case moves with it. The springs return the mass to its neutral position as acceleration ceases.

There has to be a means of measuring how much the mass is displaced, or moved. Our illustration shows that this is accomplished by "electrical pick-off." The amount of displacement is expressed by an increase or decrease in electrical current. This displacement information is fed to the system's computer where it is compared to the flight program. If the acceleration's time of onset, amount, and duration are correct, the control system will not have to be involved. If the acceleration is in error, however, control inputs will be made to correct the error.

A vehicle in flight moves or can move in three dimensions; therefore, it can accelerate in any or all directions. Figure 24 shows how accelerometers must be aligned to measure such movements. One accelerometer is aligned for north/south acceleration, another for east/west and a third for the vertical. The "north" and "east" accelerometers, therefore, provide information on movement of the vehicle anywhere on the horizontal plane. The unit's computer uses this information to establish the vehicle's position and to keep the position information updated. Information about a missile's vertical acceleration is essential to the guidance unit's knowing whether or not the arc of the trajectory is correct. As we have said, part of the ballistic missile's flight is unguided. So if the true ballistic portion of the flight is to be accurate, the guided portion must be perfect.

Accelerometers cannot do their jobs unless they are properly oriented and kept that way. This is the job of the inertial platform, or stabilized platform as it may be called. Here gyroscopes, with their "rigidity in space" characteristic, are positioned on the platform to detect movement of the platform itself. As shown in figure 25, the entire platform must be suspended by gimbals—as if it were a three-axis gyroscope—to let its parent vehicle move in any direction without the platform moving.

Electric motors not shown in our illustration are also part of the system and their purpose is to rotate the gimbal rings (labeled A and B in fig. 25). Suppose the missile (or airplane) vehicle were to

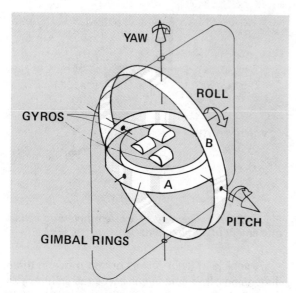

Figure 25. Arrangement of gyros on an inertial platform

pitch (pivot) upward. The appropriate gyro located on the platform would sense such movement and immediately activate the motor for gimbal A. The motor would turn gimbal A just enough to compensate for the pitching movement. Our explanation has taken a long time, but you should remember that all these sensings and corrective movements of the inertial units' components are taking place *instantly* and *constantly* as its vehicle follows the planned flight path.

An inertial guidance system must be set for the course over which it will guide its vehicle. This amounts to telling the unit where it is and where it should go. It also includes the initial or starting velocity. An aircraft's starting velocity is zero, but for a missile launched from an aircraft the situation is different; the velocity of the launching aircraft must be "programmed in."

The inertial system must know in what direction its accelerometers are pointed, so the platform has to be leveled and aligned before its vehicle is launched. Making such inputs to the system is called initialization. This process takes *time.* It might take 10 to 30 minutes for an aircraft, but an extra-long-range missile might require hours for warmup and initialization. Intercontinental missiles, which are kept ready for firing, have their guidance systems

ready to go at any time—in other words, the guidance systems are running.

Although it may be difficult for you to believe, the precision required of inertial guidance systems used on intercontinental ballistic missiles (ICBMs) exceed those for space launch vehicles. If you stop and think, however, the reason is obvious. The ICBM is not communicated with after it is launched. The space launch vehicle, on the other hand, is subjected to various kinds of external or *command* inputs. The spacecraft's guidance system will also probably have a celestial navigation aid of some type. The *star tracker* is one such aid. The star tracker uses a set of optical lenses and photodetectors to acquire and maintain a fix on two (or more) "stars." Since no two celestial bodies radiate or reflect light in exactly the same way, the *star tracker*, using photodetection can determine when it has acquired the celestial bodies for which it was programmed. Once this is done, the guidance system can determine the vehicle's position from the angles formed between the vehicle and the celestial bodies. This position can be relayed to the appropriate control center on Earth. All the while, tracking of the vehicle is going on at the control center. Personnel responsible for guidance can therefore command the spacecraft's control system to change or correct the trajectory.

CONTROL SYSTEMS

Any control system must get its instructions on what to do from a guidance system. The guidance system can vary from a human being to a self-contained electromechanical unit.

We might compare the control system of a rocket to a pilot's muscles and an airplane's control surfaces. Electrical impulses from the guidance system open and close switches which start or stop what are called servomotors. These servomotors may in turn operate the valves or pistons in a hydraulic system, or they may directly operate a control surface.

The small, short-range rocket missile can be controlled by aerodynamic control surfaces because its flight is within the atmosphere. The movement of control surfaces on the rocket's

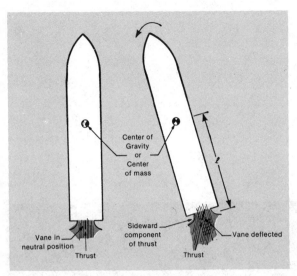

Figure 26. Action of an exhaust vane

stabilizing fins causes aerodynamic action/reaction. The rocket is thus moved about its center of gravity, changing the direction of thrust produced by its motor.

If less aerodynamic drag is desired, designers may use smaller or no stabilizing fins. The rocket's thrust can be changed by other means. A movable surface (or surfaces) can be placed within the rocket motor's exhaust. Of course, such *vanes* have to be made of special heat-resistant materials, but movement of them *deflects* the exhaust. In other words, deflection of the thrust produced changes its direction. This causes the rocket to rotate around its center of gravity or center of mass (in space). Once the new direction is established, the vane is moved back to the neutral position and total thrust is concentrated on motion in the new direction. Figure

26 shows the basics of how the exhaust vane system works.

Other methods of deflecting the rocket's exhaust stream include a collar-like device which surrounds the stream. This is called a jetavator and tilting the jetavator forces the exhaust stream in a different direction.

Controlling thrust direction on the large liquid propellant rockets is basically simple. The entire rocket engine is moved. This means that the engine has to be gimballed—movable in any direction. You can imagine how complicated and strong the actual mechanism (hydraulics, etc.) must be to move the operating engines of large rockets.

It is not necessary to change the direction of the exhaust stream itself to change a rocket's flight path. A force applied at some other point along the length of the rocket—its longitudinal axis—will also cause the rocket to change direction by pivoting about its center of gravity. Thus, small rockets, or *thrusters*, can be positioned near the rocket's nose or tail to apply a force against the airframe. In addition to being called thrusters, such small directional control rockets may be referred to as *reaction control engines*. In practice, reaction control devices are most effective within the space environment while the main engine is not operating. This is because the thrust produced by such "rockets" is indeed small. They can be used to change the vehicles attitude while the main engine is shut down. Upon reigniting the main engine, the new direction is taken up.

Flight beyond the atmosphere requires reaction-type control. Flight within the atmosphere also requires reaction control if the vehicle does not have wings. The Minuteman missile is one example of a vehicle which must use reaction control to keep it on course.

2-44

Chapter 2-5

ORBITS AND TRAJECTORIES

I n this chapter we will look more closely at what happens, and why, when rocketry is used to send payloads to other parts of this planet, the upper atmosphere, or to destinations in space. *Velocity* is one major factor in this process; another major factor is the *direction* of the trajectory. These two factors, you should remember, must always work *with* the forces of nature which are present at all times. The people responsible for predetermining the trajectory of a vehicle to deliver a payload must make certain that all factors have been planned for before launch.

The general learning objective for this chapter is for you to know the different types of orbits and trajectories. To reach this objective, you must pattern your study of the material according to the *specific learning objectives* listed in the Appendix of this textbook.

ORBIT AND TRAJECTORY DEFINED

The word *orbit* means "a path described by one body in its revolution about another body." All matter within the universe is in motion. This motion begins somewhere "down" in what we might call the submicroscopic universe. Certainly it includes the orbiting of electrons about the nuclei of atoms, but the beginning may be even "lower." It may be many times subatomic. On a much larger scale, orbits exist throughout all known space.

In effect, an orbit is a balancing of forces. Where space is concerned, it is a compromise between gravitational attraction and the inertia of a movement, which may be called centrifugal force or more correctly centrifugal effect. The path described by an orbiting body may also be called a trajectory because any trajectory is "the path of a body through space." (In general application of the term trajectory, space includes the atmosphere.) Thus, we will see orbit and trajectory combined as *orbital trajectory.* A trajectory that does not result in an orbit (closed trajectory) must have a beginning and an ending. This is generally known as a ballistic trajectory, particularly if the flight of the object begins and ends on Earth.

BASIC ORBITAL TRAJECTORIES

Our first question about orbits should be, "Why does one body orbit another?" We answered this question when we said that an orbit effects a balance between gravitational and inertial forces. But we believe that a further explanation with examples will provide a more complete answer.

Newton's law of universal gravitation states that the attraction between any two bodies is directly proportional to their masses and inversely proportional to the square of the distance between them. Another way of saying the same thing is that the farther away two objects are from each other the less effect their mutual gravitation will have. Applying this to Earth, we find that the force of gravity on the planet itself is less on a mountain top than it is at sea level. Granted, there is very little difference, but the difference exists.

If an object is taken to an altitude of 100 miles, or 1,000 miles, above the Earth and dropped, it would fall to Earth. At 1,000 miles the attraction would be even less than at 100 miles; therefore, the object would accelerate (or gain speed) more slowly. Nevertheless, it would still fall to Earth. The only way to keep the object from falling to Earth is to produce a force which is equal and opposite to the gravity and which balances the gravitational attraction. This is exactly what is done in keeping a satellite in orbit and the equal and opposite force is the inertial force or centrifugal effect. Inertia and centrifugal effect are both related to Newton's first and second laws of motion. The relationship between gravity and inertia in keeping a satellite in orbit can be visualized in figure 27 as follows:

Suppose you could build a tower on the Earth which was 100 miles high and you climbed this tower equipped with a supply of baseballs. If you dropped a baseball from the top of the tower, gravity would cause it to fall to the Earth. If you threw a baseball from the tower—Newton's first law says that the ball would travel in a straight line (a-b), and at a constant velocity unless acted on by some outside force. The outside force here is gravity, so the ball would start off traveling in a straight line but gravity would pull it into a curved path and it would strike the Earth at point c. Throwing the ball harder gives it more inertia and changes the curved path; therefore, the ball would strike the Earth farther from the tower (points d and e) but the results would be the same—eventually it would strike the Earth. If it

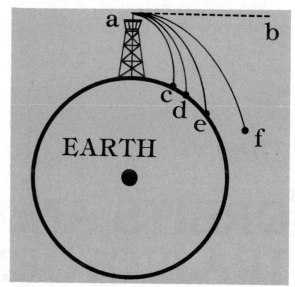

Figure 27. An orbit is achieved when inertial and gravitational forces are in balance

were possible to throw a ball from the tower at about 18,000 mph, it would have sufficient inertia to follow path f, and gravity would pull it toward Earth's surface at about the same rate as Earth's surface curves. The result is that the ball remains at a fairly constant distance (altitude) from the surface even though it is constantly "falling" toward it. But this balance of forces continues only as long as the velocity is maintained. Slow the ball by some means and gravity will get the upper hand and pull the ball to the surface. Add velocity to the ball and *something* else will happen. We say something because there could be several trajectories that the ball would follow according to how much *force* was applied and the direction in which the force was applied. Enough force in the right direction would accelerate the ball on a trajectory that might force it out of even the solar system. Less force in a different direction might place it in a trajectory that would eventually bring it crashing into Earth again.

You can imagine the possibilities of an object's trajectory or flight path when you consider all the variables with regard to velocity, direction, and existing gravitational attraction (throughout the universe). These are the possibilities which specialists must consider when launching spacecraft and/or satellites. Orbits within cislunar space (the space between the Earth and the moon) are relatively standard—the procedures and computations for most any type trajectory and resulting orbit or encounter probably have been done before. To program a trajectory that results in a spacecraft orbiting one of the moons of Jupiter, however, requires many computations to determine the amounts and directions of thrust required.

Concerning thrust, we should talk about velocity requirements for achieving selected trajectories and orbits. First, let's define some of the terms which will be used in discussions which follow.

Circular orbit. An orbit which maintains a virtually constant altitude above Earth's surface.

Elliptical orbit. An elliptical orbit is any *closed* orbit which is not circular. All elliptical orbits around Earth have an apogee and a perigee.

Apogee. That point in the orbital trajectory or flight path where the orbiting body is most distant from the body being orbited.

Perigee. The opposite of apogee—that point where the orbiting body is closest to the body being orbited. (NOTE: Apogee and perigee are used only to describe orbits around Earth.)

Apoapsis. Same meaning as apogee but applies to *other planets.*

Periapsis. Same meaning as perigee but applies to *other planets.*

Aphelion. Same meaning as apogee and apoapsis but applies to the sun only.

Perihelion. Same meaning as perigee and periapsis but applies to the sun only.

Parabolic and Hyperbolic Trajectories. Refers to open-ended or Earth escape trajectories.

VELOCITY REQUIREMENTS

Velocity requirement means the velocity required in order to travel a certain path. Here on Earth, the idea of such a velocity requirement may seem odd. On the highway, your destination may be 100 to 1,000 miles away, but you can take as much or as little time as you wish without fear of falling short of or overshooting your target. An airplane

must achieve a certain "velocity" in order to keep flying. But, within broad limits, it can also vary its airspeed without changing course. In space, on the other hand, *how fast* you go determines *where* you go. To reach the moon in the shortest possible time demands the complicated art of figuring the best trajectory to hit a moving target, then applying exactly the right amount of thrust needed to propel the spacecraft along the chosen trajectory. To circle the globe in one hour instead of the present minimum of 90 minutes seems to be impossible. Any increase in velocity is translated into a higher orbit instead of a "faster" orbit. For example, let's suppose that we have a 90-minute circular orbit established. If we try to increase the vehicle's "speed" at any point in this orbit, it is kicked out of the circular path and goes into an elliptical path. Though the vehicle will travel faster than before at perigee it will be considerably slower at apogee. The total time for a complete circuit of Earth in this new orbit will be longer than 90 minutes.

BURNOUT VELOCITY

At the moment a rocket engine ceases to produce thrust it is at "burnout." The velocity that is required to place a spacecraft on its intended trajectory must be attained at burnout. If something goes wrong and the proper velocity has not been reached by the time burnout occurs (either propellant is exhausted or automatic cutoff is activated to cause burnout), the payload is not going to reach its intended destination—orbit, moon, planet, etc. Today, this type failure is not likely to occur unless there is a major breakdown in the system because rocketry systems have been perfected to the point where there is a great deal of control over what happens. But whether or not direct control exists, the required velocity must be present upon reaching a certain point and/or time.

Of course it is possible to start, stop, and change the thrust of some rocket engines. This gives a great deal of ability to adjust the flight of a satellite or spacecraft. Suppose, however, that we had several one-shot, solid propellant rockets and we wanted to use them to launch different types of space missions. Let us "suppose" some more and consider each rocket capable of reaching a different velocity at burnout. The following velocities would be required to:

a. place a satellite in a circular orbit at 100 nautical miles (NM) altitude— 17,454 miles per hour (mph).

b. place a satellite in orbit with 1,000 NM apogee and 100 NM perigee— 18,409 mph.

c. place a satellite in orbit with 10,000 NM apogee and 100 NM perigee— 21,954 mph.

d. place a satellite in orbit with 100,000 NM apogee and 100 NM perigee— 24,273 mph.

The above examples could be carried further, but suppose we wanted to send a payload somewhere other than into orbit about Earth. What would then be the velocity requirement? Of course, it would depend on the ultimate destination of the payload but the minimum velocity to the moon is 24,409 mph—with burnout at 100 NM altitude. Such velocity requirements continue to increase until a velocity more than 36,000 mph is required to leave the solar system. Now, 36,000 mph is a respectable velocity but it could take a velocity of almost twice this much to send a payload crashing into the sun. Surprised? Most people are because we tend to forget that Earth's orbital velocity about the sun is more than 66,000 miles per hour. Before we ever launch any rocket, therefore, we must remember that its initial velocity is the same as that of Earth. And to get a payload to the sun really means that this "Earth velocity" must be counteracted so that the sun's gravitation field will pull the payload into the sun.

All the velocity requirements stated above are for a given set of conditions. No allowances were made for several variables. One variable is the velocity that can be added according to the direction of launch; another is the location of the launch site. If a launch vehicle is fired toward the east it will have the velocity of the Earth's rotation added to whatever velocity it obtains from the vehicle's propulsion system. At Earth's equator this velocity is roughly 1,000 miles per hour; a launch north or south of the equator would reduce this added velocity. How much reduction there would be depends on the distance from the equator of the launch site. The azimuth or

angle in relation to true east would also affect how much "natural velocity" would be added.

Suppose the mission of a payload required that it be launched toward the west. Everything that we said about a to-the-east launch is reversed. Finally, what about a true north or true south launch direction? The specialists responsible for calculating the desired trajectory would still have to consider Earth's rotational velocity because it would be more of a deflecting force instead of a plus or minus velocity change force.

TOTAL VELOCITY REQUIREMENTS

In planning a space mission, it is necessary to calculate *total* velocity requirements. This total figure represents the adding together of all the velocity requirements for all stages of the mission. It does *not* represent the velocity at which the vehicle travels at any one moment in its journey but it would be in excess of that velocity. All the velocities in such a sum would not be in the same direction. Nevertheless, the sum is essential in computing the needed propellant for the mission.

Placing a payload into a low orbit about Earth might be a "one-shot" deal. That is, the total required velocity would be realized at burnout and the payload would be injected into the proper orbit. This could very well be the case for certain types of *elliptical* orbits. On the other hand, a trajectory for a very long spaceflight or the need to change the shape of an object's orbit, will require a change in velocity—in other words, the application of thrust.

Perhaps we can better demonstrate the concept of the need to know total velocity requirements by examining a flight to the moon and return: Injection into a trajectory that will take the spacecraft to the moon could require a burnout velocity of 36,000 feet per second (or 24,545 mph, with variables considered). To land the vehicle on the moon would require 8,700 feet per second (5,932 mph) of retrothrust (opposite-direction thrust). Another 8,700 fps would be required for liftoff and insertion into a return-to-Earth trajectory. In this example, we will go along with the technique of using Earth's atmosphere to slow a returning spacecraft to softlanding velocity, so no velocity requirements exist for the return trip. Earth's gravitational force has provided most of the velocity requirements. Thus, we have a total velocity requirement of 53,400 fps (36,409 mph). If the flight plan did call for a slowing of the spacecraft prior to entering Earth's atmosphere this velocity requirement would have to be included. So would any velocity requirements for changing or correcting the vehicle's course on the way to or from the moon.

So what does a total velocity requirement mean to flight planners? In effect it tells them how much thrust is going to be needed for the trip. This thrust and the vehicle/payload masses determine what kinds and sizes of engines will be needed and how much propellant will have to be used. The amount of propellant will probably be slightly more than is calculated as the bare minimum.

BALLISTIC TRAJECTORIES

The term *ballistic* pertains to the science of ballistics. Trying not to complicate your mental picture too much, ballistic is the study of the arc of a non-orbiting body. Ballistic flight is primarily concerned with propelling an object from one place on Earth's surface to another place, or target, on Earth's surface. The moment a bullet leaves the barrel of a rifle the bullet is in ballistic flight. It is no longer powered so it is under the influence of natural forces only—gravity, primarily. The same ballistic-type flight occurs with rocket propelled missiles used to hit a distant target. If there is no way of changing the payload's flight path after main rocket burnout, the remainder of the flight is ballistic. On the other hand, if the missile is guided all the way to impact with the target, we can't consider any of its trajectory as being ballistic. This is because any ballistic influences will be counteracted by the guidance and control systems.

All ballistic trajectories behave as if they were going into an elliptical orbit around Earth's center of gravity. What keeps them from doing this is the presence of Earth's surface. We can see this tendency to orbit the center of gravity if we examine the trajectory of a large ballistic missile.

Any missile that has a range of several hundred miles or more, rises above the Earth's atmosphere in its trajectory, and is designed to reach its target in the shortest time possible is a long-range ballistic missile. It must obey certain laws in its flight. Such a missile cannot be under continuous propulsion and guidance during the entire course of its flight. Its launch and trajectory, during the time the propulsion system is functioning, will be guided. The guidance system is somewhat like an individual keeping the sights of a rifle on target while a control system is performing the same function for the rifle barrel.

Burnout of the propellant system will occur well below the top of the missile's trajectory. The rest of the payload's flight will be like that of a bullet or an orbiting space vehicle—unpowered and determined primarily by the force of gravity.

It will describe a high, arching trajectory toward its target, possibly reaching a peak of several hundred miles above the surface of the Earth. The path of the reentry portion of the flight will be affected by atmosphere.

The launch velocity of a ballistic missile is less than that required for an orbit, although in the case of a missile with a 10,000 nautical mile range, it is only a little less. The missile is also launched into a higher flight path angle than the more horizontal angle that is usual for orbital launches. Lacking the velocity to clear the Earth, it will fall back to Earth along a path determined by gravity. If it could continue falling—that is, follow an imaginary path within the sphere of Earth—it would fall faster and faster to a "perigee" point, describe an imaginary ellipse around the center of the Earth, and be carried by its own momentum right up through the Earth back to the point where it started. This trajectory is of course impossible, but the fact remains that the actual flight of the missile does describe the exterior portion of such an imaginary orbit around the center of the Earth (see fig. 28). Therefore, the missile's ground track—that is, the route of its trajectory projected downward and plotted on the surface of the Earth—would be a part of a great circle, somewhat modified by the effect of Earth rotation. The missile could not follow a trajectory due east or due west along some parallel of latitude other than

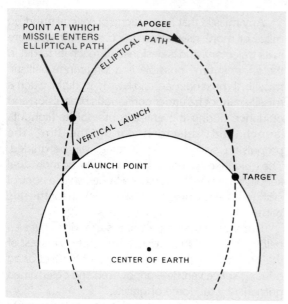

Figure 28. A ballistic missile's imaginary orbit about Earth's center

the equator (which is a great circle). Nor could it follow an eccentric or irregular path designed to fool an enemy defense system.

These facts tell us two things about ballistic missiles. One is that propulsion and guidance are available to place a missile into a trajectory toward any target on Earth with great accuracy. The second is that, since the route the ballistic missile must fly is predictable, defense measures can be taken against it.

SOUNDING ROCKET FLIGHTS

If the trajectory of a rocket does not send its payload into orbit, or to some destination well beyond Earth, or to another point on Earth's surface, where does the rocket send its payload? The only direction we have left is straight up. Essentially, this is the trajectory of a sounding rocket—straight up.

Now, why would anyone want to use the term sounding rocket anyway? *Sounding* is an old term associated with measuring or sampling the depths of a body of water. Somehow, and at some time, this

same term was applied to sampling Earth's "ocean of air." Thus, a rocket sent into or even beyond the atmosphere on a one-way trip to gather information is now identified as a sounding rocket.

Instruments carried aboard a sounding rocket are designed to observe and measure various natural phenomena at different altitudes above the surface and transmit these findings to ground stations. After reaching its maximum altitude, the rocket simply falls back to Earth and is destroyed by either reentry and/or impact forces. Now, we can't say that the total sounding rocket is destroyed in this manner every time. It is possible that at least part of the payload section could be designed to survive the force of reentry.

Launch velocity requirements for sounding rockets are of interest, for these are requirements to reach a certain distance from Earth's surface *without* going into orbit. For example, if the altitude chosen for the rocket's "apogee" is high enough the thrust/burnout velocity is more than adequate to go into orbit. To reach a 1,000 nautical mile altitude (100 NM altitude burnout) requires a velocity of 11,114 mph. We know that this isn't enough velocity to achieve orbit (17,454 mph). But suppose a mission to sample the magnetosphere at 10,000 nautical miles altitude had to be flown. What burnout velocity would be required in this case? The answer is 31,000 feet per second or 21,136 miles per hour—much more than enough to achieve orbit.

Why does this very high altitude sounding rocket not go into orbit? The reason is that a sounding rocket is launched at a very high angle and does not have the horizontal velocity needed to put it in orbit. Like any other sounding vehicle, it eventually reaches a point where gravity overcomes its upward momentum, and it will return to Earth. Its trajectory is not necessarily straight up and down but is rather like a high, narrow arch, with a return path that would not carry it beyond the Earth. If the complete path of the sounding rocket trajectory were plotted it, too, would describe an extremely narrow ellipse within the Earth around the center of Earth's mass.

It is also interesting to note that it does not require ten times as much velocity to reach 10,000 miles as it does to reach 1,000 miles but less than twice. Gravity's effect weakens with distance from its center.

Some economic factors can also be noted. Since the sounding rocket velocity for 1,000 miles is suborbital, it is the cheapest way of reaching such an altitude. Using a sounding rocket to reach a height of 10,000 miles, however, is questionable; and, for reaching still higher altitudes, it is definitely more economical to put the vehicle into orbit.

TYPES OF ORBITS

As far as satellites of Earth are concerned there are two basic orbital flight paths involved: the elliptical and the circular. If you will think about our previous introductory discussions on trajectories and orbital velocities, you will realize that an elliptical orbit can be achieved with one "shot," if the angle used (to the vertical) is correct. Get away from the one-shot-type approach to orbital insertion and thrust will again be needed. Let's find out why this is true.

The lowest Earth orbit that we have talked about is an approximate circular one at 100 nautical miles altitude, for which an injection velocity (the velocity that will place it in orbit) of 17,454 mph is required. Therefore, let us use this orbit as a starting point for learning more about Earth orbits. In this one instance, the injection velocity, the apogee velocity, and the circular orbit velocity are all the same. At this altitude, the pull of gravity is only slightly less than it is at the surface of the Earth. The velocity represents the speed at which the vehicle must "outrace the horizon" as it "falls" around the curving Earth, always maintaining the same altitude above it. It is important to note that the injection into orbit must be "horizontal" (tangent to the orbit). Any effort to extend range by giving the vehicle an upward trajectory without added thrust would only rob it of some of its vital forward velocity and bring it to Earth before one orbit was completed.

For any higher orbit, we have this basic paradox: higher and higher velocities are required to reach successively higher altitudes, but lower and lower velocities are required to stay in orbit at successively higher altitudes. This phenomenon is due to the weakening of Earth's gravitational effect with distance.

Let us describe what happens when a vehicle is boosted off the Earth to achieve an apogee of 1,000 nautical miles. A boost velocity of about 18,400 mph is needed to hurl the vehicle to that height. After burnout, the vehicle coasts outward along an *elliptical* path, moving slower and slower as gravitational pull gradually overcomes the force of the launch. At its planned 1,000 NM apogee it will have a speed somewhat less than 15,000 mph and will begin to lose altitude. Sliding down the far side of the ellipse, it will move faster and faster as it approaches closer and closer to Earth. It will then whip around perigee at top speed. Perigee in this case will be the original point of injection, altitude 100 NM, and top speed will be the original injection velocity. The vehicle will then begin another climb toward its 1,000 NM apogee. Discounting the slow effect of faint atmospheric resistance at perigee, it will keep on swinging around this ellipse indefinitely without need for burning an ounce of propellant.

Let us continue to assume that injection and perigee are at 100 NM. More and more launch power, then, will shoot the vehicle out to more and more distant apogees. The orbits would describe successively longer ellipses. How is it possible to achieve a circular orbit at a desired altitude?

CIRCULAR ORBITS AND TRANSFERS

To change what is certain to be an elliptical orbit into a circular orbit when the satellite reaches after-launch apogee requires the addition of thrust. Of course this thrust must be applied toward a specific direction. That is, when the vehicle reaches apogee, its engine is restarted to give it some additional velocity to thrust it outward and circularize the orbit. Circular velocity minus apogee velocity gives the amount of "kick" needed to circularize an orbit at a given altitude.

To show how to figure the total velocity required to attain a circular orbit, let's work a problem using simple arithmetic. The velocity required to boost a vehicle to an apogee of 300 NM is 17,659 mph. To this number add the difference between apogee velocity and circular velocity at 300 NM (273 mph).

The sum, 17,932 mph, is the *total velocity requirement*—that required for launching a vehicle into a 300 NM circular orbit, in two steps—but the vehicle never travels that fast. The total velocity requirement is merely an engineer's figure useful in determining how much energy is needed to perform a given task with a given payload weight. Now, before someone claims that we have made a very bad error in expressing velocity in miles per hour, let us explain: spaceflight velocity is usually not given in miles per hour but in feet per second (fps). However, we wanted you to visualize the fantastic velocities required in space flight according to miles per hour, an expression of measure with which everyone is familiar. If you need or want to find out what fps is in mph, divide the fps by 88 and multiply the answer times 60 (88 fps equals one mile per minute or 60 miles per hour).

We want you to understand that the velocities we have given are "ballpark" figures. In actual flight situations, much more precision is necessary. The amount and the point at which thrust is applied to an orbiting vehicle are critical. For example, if thrust applied at apogee is a little less than that required for circularizing the orbit, the result will be a wider ellipse with the same apogee and a higher perigee. If it is a little more, the vehicle will be boosted to a higher apogee.

Achieving a circular orbit at any height above that of launch burnout (original perigee) is done in two steps—launching into an elliptical trajectory and applying another spurt of rocket energy at the desired altitude to circularize the orbit. It might also be done in three steps. The vehicle could be launched into a lower orbit, called a parking orbit, then boosted to a higher apogee, then circularized at that apogee. Moving a vehicle from one orbit to another is called a transfer. Such maneuvers accomplished within the same orbital plane are called *coplanar (same plane) transfers*. All the movements are on the same plane, like the sheet of paper on which you see them in figure 29. (If viewed from the side, the plane would appear as a line.)

The Hohmann Transfer. Back in 1925, when space travel was only a theoretical dream, the city engineer of Essen, Germany, published a scientific paper on

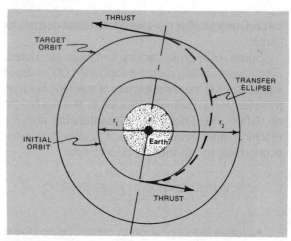

Figure 29. The Hohmann transfer (coplanar)

the most economical way to boost a satellite into a chosen circular orbit. The method proposed by Walter Hohmann is quite similar to the one described above. It has been called the "minimum energy transfer." The Hohmann transfer, or slight variations of it, is a practical method of space maneuver to this day. In a Hohmann transfer, the vehicle is first placed in a low elliptical, parking orbit. When the vehicle swings around to perigee, sufficient thrust is applied to push the vehicle to apogee at the desired altitude. When the vehicle reaches the high point of this transfer ellipse, thrust is applied again, and the vehicle moves out on a circle tangent to the transfer ellipse.

All this talk of ellipses, circles, and tangents should remind us again of the fact that all space travel is in curves. Moving in a straight line in space would require constant application of deflected thrust, a tremendous and wasteful expenditure of propellant. The curves chosen by Hohmann are those that actually permit thrust to be applied in a straight line. A vehicle with a rigid engine or nozzle, incapable of changing direction of thrust, would be able to accomplish a Hohmann transfer by thrusting straight ahead at the proper transfer points. Momentarily the vehicle would move out on a straight line tangent to its former course, but almost immediately the particular new balance achieved between the forward momentum and the pull of gravity would set the vehicle on a new curved trajectory.

Other Coplanar Transfers. Before we leave the subject of coplanar transfers, we might mention other ways of accomplishing transfers and maneuvers within a given plane of orbit. One is the fast transfer applied in modern satellite maneuvering (see fig. 30). Instead of choosing a transfer ellipse tangent to both the lower and higher orbits, a trajectory is chosen that intersects or crosses the two orbits. In a direct ascent, more launch velocity would be built up than needed to reach a given apogee. At the desired altitude the kick would thus be applied lower than apogee, with deflected thrust to aim it into the desired circle. Because all the energy would not be working in a straight line, extra energy would be needed to make the desired turn. The maneuver boosts the vehicle into higher orbit faster than a Hohmann transfer. Actually, most fast transfers are only slightly different from Hohmann transfers. The turn is not very sharp at either transfer point.

There is also a method of reaching a higher orbital altitude by using one of the low-thrust electric engines described earlier. As long as a vehicle has enough velocity to stay in orbit, a low-thrust engine can be used to move it higher. The engine does not work in spurts but is capable of prolonged low thrust. As long as the electric rocket keeps thrusting, the vehicle's course keeps changing toward higher and higher altitudes. In brief, it spirals out to the desired altitude in an ever-widening orbit.

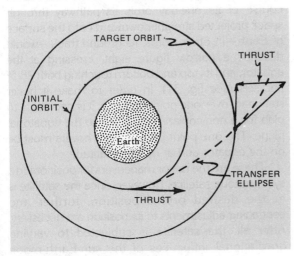

Figure 30. The fast transfer

Mention should also be made of moving down from a higher to a lower orbit. To do this, negative, or retrothrust must be applied to kill off some of the velocity that keeps the vehicle in the higher orbit. The vehicle is then drawn by gravity into an orbital path that matches its new velocity. As it moves lower, however, it moves faster. This is another interesting paradox: putting on the brakes in order to go faster. Actually it is a practical maneuver. Suppose that two vehicles are attempting to meet (rendezvous) in the same orbit, and one is a thousand miles ahead of the other. The chase vehicle can never hope to catch up with the target vehicle while both are in the same orbit. Therefore, the chase vehicle applies retrothrust to get drawn into a downward transfer ellipse. This allows it not only to follow a short-cut route but also to be moved by gravitational pull faster along that shorter, lower route to a point where the two orbits are again tangent. At this point the two vehicles will come within maneuvering range of a rendezvous. The pre-computed route selection as well as the guidance and control mechanisms used to accomplish the rendezvous itself must be extremely precise.

Non-Coplanar Transfers. Up to this point we have thought of satellites being in the same plane. In actual satellite flight this isn't true. We have Earth satellites at many different altitudes and at various angles to the equator. Some have circular orbits but others are in elliptical orbits with apogees and perigees of varying distances.

We must remember that the plane of any orbit around Earth must pass through the center of Earth. If a satellite is launched due east from Cape Canaveral in Florida (the launch site of many space vehicles), which has a latitude of 28.5° North, it is impossible for it to keep traveling due east around the world at the same latitude. Its orbital path will bring it south across the equator to reach a latitude of 28.5° South before it swings north again. The orbital plane of such a launch is said to have an angle of inclination (slant) of 28.5° with respect to the plane of the equator. Aiming the satellite at launch in any direction other than due east will produce a steeper angle of inclination, causing the satellite to overfly latitudes higher than 28.5° on either side of the equator. A northward or southward injection will put the satellite in a polar orbit.

Obviously, no launch from Cape Canaveral could put a vehicle directly into an orbit around the equator, or at any angle of inclination less than the latitude of Cape Canaveral itself. To put a vehicle into equatorial orbit requires a non-coplanar transfer. The vehicle would first be launched at its minimum angle of inclination of 28.5⁰. Then, on either its first or a later revolution at one of two points where it crosses the equator, thrust would be applied at the proper angle to put the vehicle into an orbit coplanar with the equator. Think of this transfer maneuver as kicking the vehicle sideways instead of upward, as in the coplanar transfer. Similarly any angle of inclination can be achieved by means of non-coplanar transfer, but not necessarily in one such transfer. If the angle of change is too extreme, the vehicle may have to orbit Earth two or more times, changing its angle of inclination by a certain amount at each intersection of planes, before the desired inclination is achieved. If both a change of inclination and a change of orbital altitude are desired, the non-coplanar and altitude transfers can be achieved in one orbit by calculating the thrust angles three-dimensionally.

SPECIAL ORBITS

This is *our* term for those orbits in which a satellite must be placed to accomplish a special mission. These orbits almost always are circular. This is especially true for those satellites which provide services in the forms of communications, environmental monitoring, and navigation.

Geosynchronous Orbit. There are certain tasks which satellites can do best if they are in an orbit that will keep them stationed above one point or area on Earth's surface. These are called geosynchronous satellites or geostationary satellites. The two terms mean the same thing for a satellite in an equatorial orbit at a distance where the satellite's period of revolution is the same as Earth's period of rotation—24 hours. Three geosynchronous satellites, spaced 120 degrees of longitude apart, can give 24-hour round-the-world service over most of the

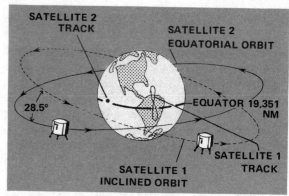

Figure 31. Examples of geosynchronous orbits

surface of the globe. Now that you have studied something about orbits and transfers, you may be able to guess how such satellites are put into position.

Again, for a satellite to be "synchronous" with the Earth—that is, keep time with the rotation of the Earth so perfectly that it always remains directly above a certain point and never drifts east or west of it—it must have a *circular* orbit at one altitude. That altitude is 19,351 nautical miles (or 22,300 statute miles), which gives it a period of 24 hours. If such a satellite is launched from Cape Canaveral without a non-coplanar transfer, it will have an inclination of 28.5⁰ and will not appear perfectly stationary over the Earth. It can be timed to reach the right orbit at the desired point, but its inclination will take it above and below the plane of the equator by 28.5⁰ in the course of its one-day orbit. Its pathway through space projected straight downward onto the surface of Earth—in other words, its ground track—would describe a narrow figure eight, crossing at the equator, and its top and bottom touching both 28.5⁰ parallels (see fig. 31). In order to make it hover stationary over one point on Earth, it is necessary to plan for a non-coplanar transfer into the equatorial plane. The one point over which it hovers must be on the equator and at no other latitude.

These are the major maneuvers for positioning a synchronous satellite. However, once the satellite is in the desired orbital position, further and continuing adjustments to its position are necessary. After all, the satellite is subjected to varying gravitational influences of the sun-Earth-moon system. In addition, the pressure of the sun's

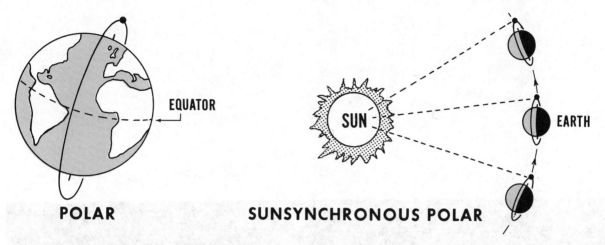

POLAR

SUNSYNCHRONOUS POLAR

Figure 32. Polar and sunsynchronous orbits

radiation disturbs the satellite's position. All of which means that "station keeping" maneuvers have to be made periodically. Such maneuvers are effected by the satellite's small reaction control devices, or thrusters.

Polar Orbit. As the name implies, a polar orbit (see fig. 32) involves a path that crosses or nearly crosses the North and South Poles during each orbit. This type orbit offers the satellite's cameras—if it is carrying cameras—a chance to photograph all of Earth's surface. The reason this is true is that Earth is turning on its axis as the satellite sweeps over the poles and each orbit of the satellite puts it west of its previous sweep. (Earth is rotating toward the east.)

Sunsynchronous Orbit. This is another form of polar orbit that keeps a satellite exposed to constant sunlight. This may be difficult for you to visualize, but Earth is not a perfect sphere. It bulges slightly at the equator and is flattened slightly at the poles. The resulting not-perfect sphere contributes to the fact that Earth's gravitational force is not constant at all points of a satellite's orbit. A satellite placed in the proper polar orbit (direction and altitude) will remain exposed to constant sunlight as Earth revolves around the sun. (See the sunsynchronous orbit in figure 32).

The sunsynchronous orbit is appropriate for those satellites that need constant sunlight to generate power for on-board operations. This orbit could also be used for those satellites which monitor the sun's activities, and the sunsynchronous orbit may be one of those chosen for in-space electric power generation.

Chapter 2-6

CIVILIAN SPACECRAFT

Launching and retrieving information gathered by spacecraft are very costly operations. Added to these costs are those of designing and building the launch vehicles and their payloads. Guidance systems and other systems needed to perform electronic functions are, pound for pound, the most expensive of the total vehicle/payload program. But these expenses are justified many times over when we think of the value provided by the payloads the launch vehicles send into space. This value is in the knowledge and services which can be gained or rendered only by spacecraft.

The general learning objective for this chapter is for you to know the various actual and proposed unmanned and manned spacecraft programs. To reach this objective, you must pattern your study of the material according to the *specific learning objectives* listed in the Appendix of this textbook.

SPACECRAFT: SOME DEFINITIONS

When we specify *civilian spacecraft,* we are, perhaps, stretching the definition somewhat. In this chapter, any spacecraft which does not have a military function, such as communications, will be considered to be in the civilian category. On the other hand, there are few private corporations in the world that could afford the expense of developing, launching, and operating a complete system. Therefore, governments must use some of their total resources to develop such systems to the point where their services can be *sold* to nongovernmental civilian users. This is precisely what has happened in several fields. Private corporations *pay* to have their operational and experimental packages or spacecraft launched by a governmental agency. In the United States this governmental agency is the National Aeronautics and Space Administration or NASA. It also launches payloads for governments of other nations. What we are saying then, is that our term civilian spacecraft might be more accurately expressed as *government spacecraft with civilian missions.*

Generally speaking, spacecraft (any type vehicle which travels in space) are either scientific types or application types. By scientific we mean that the spacecraft gathers information which may or may not have immediate use, or application. The application type performs some type service of immediate and/or continuing use—such as communications. Now, let's confuse this "neat category" somewhat: A satellite, or spacecraft, could be an application type which also gathers strictly scientific information. On the other hand, a scientific satellite might provide information for which a user would have immediate application. Still another possibility exists, that of civilian users obtaining data from military satellites, and vice versa. The point is that we should think of spacecraft as *useful vehicles* before assigning them to a category because such assignments tend to limit our conception of a spacecraft's capabilities.

Finally, our use of the term *satellite* refers to those spacecraft which orbit Earth. *Probe* is the general term we will use for those spacecraft which either fly by, orbit, or land on a celestial body *other* than Earth.

UNMANNED SATELLITES AND PROBES

Thousands of unmanned satellites and planetary probes now occupy various orbits or sit silently on distant celestial bodies. There are so many old satellites that concern has been expressed for the survival of new satellites being placed into certain orbits. It is feared that collisions could occur between the new craft and those now considered "space junk."

Many of the older satellites and probes have continued to function well beyond their intended lifetimes. Some of these craft have had to be silenced because no funds were available to continue processing the data they returned.

This area of unmanned satellites and planetary probes has grown so rapidly over the years that it is now difficult to describe. What we will do in this section is first review some of the purposes and accomplishments of the earlier vehicles. Then we will discuss a very few of the newer and the yet-to-be flown craft.

APPLICATIONS SATELLITES

"Applications" is the term we have chosen for all those satellites which provide services that can be or are used immediately by our society and the societies of other nations. But what types of services

are important to society and can be provided by satellites? We can group them into the areas of communications, natural resources, navigation, environmental services, and search and rescue services.

Before true applications satellites could become a reality, a lot of testing had to be done. Some of the tests were directed specifically toward improving sensing and communications systems to be used on later satellites. A special testing program was begun in 1966 with the first of a series of Applications Technology Satellites (ATS). The ATS-1 was placed in geosynchronous orbit and conducted communications and meteorological tests. Subsequent flights in the series helped make possible the abilities of today's "applications satellites."

Communications Satellites. The beginning of what is now a most complex communications satellite system occurred in 1958 when taped messages were broadcast from orbit. The "Score" satellite operated for only 13 days, but its messages excited the people of our nation.

Echo 1, a very large reflective balloon, was placed in orbit during 1960. This was what is called a *passive* communications satellite because its function was nothing more than that of a reflector of radio and TV signals. And, since the satellite was in low Earth orbit, it could only be used for a short time as it flew over broadcasting and receiving stations.

The *Courier 1B* was also orbited in 1960. This early communications satellite was the first of the *repeater* types. It received signals from ground stations, amplified the signals, and rebroadcast them to receiving stations on Earth.

In 1965, the *Early Bird* was launched. This satellite was placed in geosynchronous orbit where it functioned as a commercial communications satellite.

Amateur radio enthusiasts were rewarded in 1970 when the first of the *Oscar* series was orbited. The Oscar satellites are reserved for amateur radio communications and new ones are orbited periodically as the older ones become inoperative. Until a satellite retrieval and repair system is functioning, this problem of satellites "going dead" or malfunctioning will continue. Recall that all satellites must have consumables in the form of propellants for station keeping and electrical power sources. When a satellite uses up its consumables, the owners must go through the costly process of replacing instead of repairing it.

Today the communications satellite business is large and it is growing. National and international corporations are financing the construction, launch and operation of several types of "comsats," as they are called. It is impossible for us to describe all the comsats now functioning but we can introduce a few:

Intelsats. This is a series of satellites owned by the International Satellite Corporation. There are 12 of the Intelsat V model. Each craft can relay the output of two television channels and 12,000 simultaneous telephone conversations.

SBS series. A partnership of IBM Corporation, Comsat General Corporation, and Aetna Life and Casualty owns this system. The Satellite Business System (SBS) series consists of three spacecraft in geosynchronous orbit. Communications through the system are at user or subscriber cost and pertain to business matters only.

RCA Satcom series. The RCA Satcoms form part of a distribution system for video programing to cable TV systems.

TDRSS. This is a new system which can serve both government and private commercial users (see fig. 33). Its long name is Tracking and Data Relay Satellite System. A private corporation owns and operates the system and leases tracking and data relay services to the National Aeronautics and Space Administration.

If you recall from Part One of this volume, the TDRS system was introduced as an element of the Space Transportation System. It is used by NASA to relay data and communications to and from the Shuttle Orbiter during each flight. This new system eliminates the need for some of the Earth stations required for earlier flights.

Again, the number of communications satellite systems and individual spacecraft is growing year-by-year. Technological advances cause improvements in each model of a series—providing higher and higher capacities for transmitting video, data, and voice communications. Growth in satellite

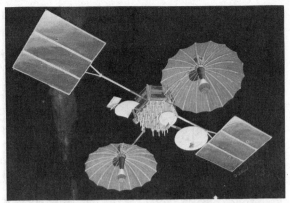

Figure 33. The Tracking and Data Relay Satellite
(Courtesy of TRW Inc.)

communications, according to one source, is expected to become a 10-billion-dollar industry by 1990.

Natural Resources Satellites. Our total planet is a natural resource. The processes of locating, removing, and disposing of materials taken from this resource must be understood and controlled for the good of all. Locating natural resources and monitoring other conditions on Earth's surface is the task of the Landsat series of satellite spacecraft (see fig. 34).

Placed in polar orbit, one Landsat can examine conditions on Earth's total surface every 18 days. Two satellites reduce this task to 9 days.

The Landsat satellites constantly measure and record the radiant energy that is either reflected or generated by features and objects on Earth's surface. These radiant energy levels occur in different wavelengths. Landsat's sensors scan the radiant energy in four different bands (ranges of wavelength) and by electronically putting the information into picture form, many uses can be made of it.

Agricultural conditions are monitored by Landsat and thus provide very important data to farmers, researchers, and governments. Information relayed back to Earth can show the rate of crop growth and allow accurate predictions of crop yield. Healthy crops radiate at a known wavelength and produce a certain pictorial image. Any change in this image signals disease or damage and corrective measures can be taken early. Similarly, grass lands

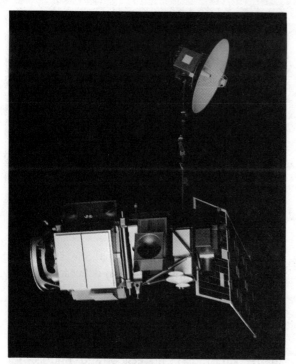

Figure 34. A Landsat satellite (Courtesy of General Electric Co.)

by Landsat-type satellites will play larger and larger roles in future land development programs.

Federal and state governments find Landsat imagery particularly useful in the management of coastal resources. Effects of the tides, the status of industrial and waste pollution entering coastal waters, and many other conditions are readily monitored. This allows corrective action to be taken at the proper time.

Fresh water is essential to life and the availabilty of fresh water has diminished over the years. The problem lies in the fact that the demand for fresh water increases yearly with a higher standard of living and an increasing population. Landsat has been used to discover new sources and amounts of water. Its "pictures" of snowfall amounts provide specialists a measure of the fresh water which will result when the snow melts. In turn, very accurate estimates can be made of how much water will be in reservoirs before the dry seasons begin, how much will be available for growing crops, and so forth. This allows planners to prepare for any water shortages that may develop in certain areas of the country.

The extent of information on natural resources coming from present-day and future satellites is difficult to imagine. Yet, it is possible and probable that the complete management of all natural resources and pollution control will become satellite oriented.

Navigation Satellites. The use of satellites as navigational devices for earth-bound vehicles is a relatively new venture. The system now being deployed in phases is known as the Navstar Global Positioning System (GPS). This is a United States military navigation satellite system. Now, we realize that we promised to discuss only civilian spacecraft in this chapter. On the other hand, anyone with the proper receiving equipment can use the Navstar system. Perhaps this will be the case in the future, or perhaps a civilian system will be orbited.

The Navstar GPS (see fig. 35) eventually will consist of at least 18 satellites located at a distance of about 12,000 miles from Earth and with different orbital directions. Aircraft receiving signals from just four of these satellites will not only be able to determine where they are but they will also be able to

for cattle can be monitored for overgrazing or to locate grazing areas which could provide more nutritious food for cattle. Worldwide soil conditions can and have been evaluated. Thus, better use of available soil is made possible. New mineral resources have been, and continue to be, discovered by Landsat imagery.

Land use information is important to governments at all levels. For example, the study of Landsat imagery can point out the best areas for the future development of cities or the expansion of existing cities. Urban planners can use land areas which are the least suitable for crops. Laws can be passed that forbid construction of new homes or businesses on land that would be more valuable for some other use. Concern for the proper use of land and concern for the environment in general have resulted in the rather common requirement that a written "master plan" be developed before building projects are started. Such plans are intended as a forecast of exactly how the project will affect the surrounding land, water, atmosphere and human habitation environments. No doubt the information provided

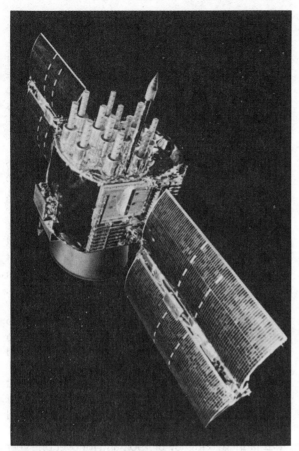

Figure 35. A Navstar satellite

find their true altitude above sea level along with their ground speed.

It is necessary to make corrections in the orbital track to keep the system accurate. This is done by a ground control segment which sends signals to the satellite's on-board attitude and velocity control subsytem. Changes or correction in the satellite orbit are accomplished through the firing of reaction control thrusters. There are eighteen of these thrusters on each satellite, and there is enough fuel on board to last at least seven years.

For a number of years, civilians have been using military-type navigational satellites. Commerical ship owners and yacht owners have used the Navy's polar-orbiting Transit satellites. Equipment needed to use the Transit system costs between $3,000 and $5,000 dollars.

The projected use of satellite navigation systems extends to common surface vehicles, such as automobiles and trucks. For example, the system would show an automobile's location on a map as displayed by a cathode ray tube. The location shown would be accurate to within 900 feet.

Environmental Satellites. Environmental satellites are most closely associated with the pictures we see on television as "weather pictures," but weather is only a part of the total Earth environment. However, the satellites which monitor this environment and help meteorologists with forecasts are generally called weather satellites.

There are currently two systems of this type satellite—the polar orbiters and the geostationary orbiters.

NOAA. Named for the National Oceanic and Atmospheric Administration, two NOAA satellite spacecraft provide environmental observations of the entire Earth four times each day. Their orbital altitude is over 500 miles, and their orbits are of the sunsynchronous type.

The NOAAs are also called meteorological satellites (metsats) in that data provided by their sensor is applied to meteorological uses. But this information gained from NOAAs can be used in several areas. For example, satellite data have been used to help fire fighters control forest fires and to provide analyses of sea ice conditions to the U.S. Coast Guard. The NOAA satellites have detected volcanic eruptions in remote areas. Their ability to detect "hot spots" also makes them useful at detecting waste-gas flows from oil wells and steel plants. Thus, meteorology or weather is but one of many applications of environmental satellites.

GOES. Working with the polar orbiters are the Geostationary Operational Environmental Satellites. The pictures you often see on television of Earth's surface and cloud cover are transmitted from the GOES system.

Aboard the GOES spacecraft are instruments which provide cloud cover pictures in visible light and in infrared. The infrared pictures are very useful to the process of determining the intensity of storm systems. An instrument known as VAS, [for VISSR (Visible-Infrared Spin-Scan Radiometer) Atmospheric Sounder] collects data on the water vapor content and the temperature of the atmosphere; what is very noteworthy about this is that the VAS provides such data according to various altitudes within the atmosphere. As you can see, this type of information is needed by meteorologists for weather forecasting.

Other instruments aboard the GOES spacecraft monitor the enviroment in which they travel. The information gathered by each spacecraft's Space Environment Monitor is transmitted to Earth where it is used by scientists in their various studies.

Search and Rescue Satellites. New to the area of applications satellites are those which help locate people in distress. This is an international effort and it applies to the global society.

Emergency locator transmitters (ELT) are available to any person who desires one. An ELT is a radio transmitter which, when activated, broadcasts a continuous signal on a special frequency. These transmitters are installed in U.S. aircraft and are turned on automatically if the airplane crashes. This special transmitter can also be installed on any type vehicle, or it can be carried by an individual.

Very briefly, the ELT signal can be received by a special satellite. The satellite in turn automatically notifies search and rescue personnel of the signal and the general location of its source on Earth. Rescue units can then be sent to the area and the person's or vehicle's exact location can be determined.

The Soviet Union's COSPAS satellite is a part of the new system and SARSAT is the unit developed by Canada, France, and the United States. (The SARSAT is not a special satellite; it is a unit which is placed aboard an environmental or other type of satellite.)

SCIENTIFIC SATELLITES

We regard scientific satellites as those that are orbited for the sole purpose of gaining information. The information gained is then used by scientists in several fields in the effort to better understand the total aerospace environment.

There have been many scientific satellites orbited since the capability to do so was developed. Each series or individual satellite has had more or less a specific "job" to do. This is how it was in the beginning and we see no reason for the approach to change, except the growth of technology now allows satellites to conduct multiple missions from one spacecraft.

The Explorers. The first of this series of satellites was orbited in 1958. Explorer 1 discovered the Van Allen radiation belts. The Explorer 3, also orbited in 1958, provided more information about radiation in space and investigated the presence of micrometeoroids in its flight path. In 1959, Explorer 6 gave us the first photograph of Earth from space. Subsequent Explorer satellites have examined conditions from Earth's atmosphere to thousands of miles in space, and radiation and solar flares of the sun.

The Explorers were particularly essential to understanding the space environment prior to sending astronauts into orbit and to the moon and back.

Solar Observatories. The sun has been and continues to be studied by different types of scientific satellites. One early group was called Orbiting Solar Observatories (or OSOs). The OSO-1 was launched in May of 1962 and for over one year transmitted data on 75 solar flares which occurred during the satellites "lifetime." (It remains in orbit.) Subsequent orbital flights of the OSO series made further studies of the sun's production of X-rays, gamma rays, and other radiations. The OSO-4 gave us the first pictures of the sun in the extreme ultraviolet wavelength.

Astronomical Observatories. Orbiting Astronomical Observatories (OAOs) have broadened the scientific community's understanding of the universe. The first of the series was orbited in 1968 to study the stars in the ultraviolet, infrared, gamma, and X-ray wavelengths. The OAOs were able to extend scientists' knowledge of interstellar gases. One, the OAO-2, discovered the existence of huge hydrogen clouds around comets. Astronomers had predicted such clouds but could not confirm this and many other theories until the flights of the OAOs.

Figure 36. High Energy Astronomy Observatory satellites (Courtesy of TRW Inc.)

High Energy Observatories. Named for their special mission, the High Energy Astronomy Observatories (HEAOs) were orbited to investigate the sources and intensities of high energy radiations—which are at the very far end of the electromagnetic spectrum. Among the many discoveries of this satellite family were the bursts of gamma rays and "jets" of X-rays coming from the galaxy *Centaurus A*. From within our own galaxy sources of gamma ray bursts were discovered. Pictures of a pulsar, or rotating neutron star, were made from the X-radiation generated by the star.

The why and how of the data received from each HEAO satellite may occupy astronomers for years. But each question answered through study of the data invariably generates more questions. For this reason other satellites with HEAO capabilities have been and will continue to be sent into space.

Dynamic Explorers 1 and 2. These craft were launched in 1982, with the mission of investigating the complex interactions of energy coming from the sun and Earth's magnetic forces. Attention is given to such interactions within Earth's ionosphere and upper atmosphere. Both of these satellites were orbited by one launch vehicle.

Solar Mesosphere Explorer (SME). The mission of this satellite is to study the reactions between sunlight and Earth's atmosphere. Of particular interest to scientists are reactions between sunlight and the ozone layer of the atmosphere and other chemicals.

Infrared Astronomy Satellite (IRAS). A continuation of earlier studies, the IRAS observes the universe as it is seen in the infrared area of the spectrum. This satellite is to complement the observations of the Space Telescope because the Space Telescope's primary mission is to observe in the visible light portion of the electromagnetic spectrum. The IRAS will study the cooler regions of the universe, the dust clouds that are the birthplaces of stars, and the core of our Milky Way galaxy where intense energies are hidden by dust.

LUNAR AND PLANETARY PROBES

There have been numerous spacecraft sent to investigate our moon and various planets within our solar system. Each flight deserves a full explanation, but we can only provide a brief summary here. Similar to the families of satellites discussed above, the planetary probes were, or are, grouped by name:

The Rangers. This was an early series of probes intended to investigate the moon by taking pictures of the moon as the spacecraft approached on a direct impact course. An instrument package aboard each spacecraft was planned to withstand impact and send data back to Earth. Several of the craft failed but three of them provided the first close-up pictures ever seen of the moon's surface.

The Surveyors. Attention to the moon became more concentrated when the series of Surveyor probes landed on its surface during the period 1964-1968. These were *soft landers* in that they carried retrorockets which slowed them sufficiently to land undamaged. Of the seven launched, five landed as intended on different areas of the moon's surface. The probes sent hundreds of pictures back to Earth. They also sampled the lunar soil for its chemistry and other characteristics.

Planners of the then upcoming Apollo landings depended very heavily on the information gathered by the Surveyors. They had to know what the Lunar Excursion Module would encounter upon its descent to the moon's surface.

Lunar Orbiters. In approximately one year, 1966-1967, five orbiter-type probes were launched to the moon. All of the probes were successful and they did their job of providing high-quality photographs of the moon's entire surface. From these photographs, maps of the moon were made.

This effort, like those of the Ranger and Surveyor programs, was in preparation for the Apollo landings. To make certain there would be no danger of collision with the Apollo vehicles near the moon, each of the orbiters was sent crashing into the moon's surface after it completed its mission.

The Mariners. This family of probes was used to investigate the inner planets. Mariner 2 made a flyby of Venus in 1962, confirming that Venus had a very hot atmosphere near its surface and that it had neither radiation belts nor a magnetic field. Mariner 5, in 1967, provided confirmation of the first flyby's findings and provided more information about the planet's atmosphere. Mariner 10 flew by Venus and Mercury in 1973, giving us the first pictures of the circulation pattern of the Venusian cloud cover, and the cratered surface of Mercury.

The Pioneers. Both the outer and inner planets have been probed by Pioneers. The Pioneer 10 gave us the *first* close-up pictures of Jupiter in 1973. The craft continued past Jupiter on its journey out of the solar system.

Pioneer 11 was the second probe of Jupiter. It flew past the Jovian system in 1974 and began a

trajectory to Saturn. The first pictures and data from Saturn were received at Earth in 1979.

The Vikings. In 1975, NASA launched two space probes to explore the environment of Mars, the Viking 1 and Viking 2. Each probe consisted of an orbiter and a lander.

Objectives for the Viking mission included analysis of Mars's atmosphere and the photographing of the planet's surface, but the primary emphasis was the search for life. Each of the landers took samples of the Martian soil and submitted the samples to various tests for evidence of life processes within the soil. The experiments were not conclusive so the final answer will have to wait until another mission is flown.

Although life was not found, scientists did obtain enough information to make several conclusions about the status of Mars, such as the polar ice caps are largely made of water ice. Thousands of photographs were taken of the Martian landscape from orbit and from the lander's positions on the surface. In appearance and in content the surface was found to be somewhat like desert soils on Earth.

Voyagers 1 and 2. The Pioneers opened the way to outer-planet investigations, but the Voyagers gave us greatly improved pictures and data. Both craft were launched in 1977. The Voyager 1 was launched *after* the Voyager 2 because it was placed on a faster trajectory to Jupiter.

Voyager 1 reached Jupiter in March of 1979 and flew on to Saturn, arriving there in November of 1980. From Saturn, Voyager 1 continued flight without any further planetary missions.

We can look forward to further investigations by the Voyager 2 craft. The Voyager 2 flew by Jupiter in 1979 and continued on to Saturn. It flew within 63,000 miles of the planet and headed toward an encounter with two other planets. If everything goes well with the spacecraft, it will give us pictures and data from Uranus in 1986 and Neptune in 1989.

PLANNED SATELLITES AND PROBES

What is accomplished by satellites and probes in the future will depend on the economics of

Figure 37. Artist's concept of Shuttle Orbiter deploying Space Telescope

individual nations and that of the global society. Flights which were planned years ago have been either cancelled, postponed, or had their missions changed because of costs.

The satellites discussed in this section are those which we believe have survived the long reviews of spaceflight budgets.

The Space Telescope (ST). Earth's atmosphere limits the usefulness of our best astronomical telescopes. The atmosphere interferes with light rays by scattering, bending or blocking some of them out before they reach a telescope lens. Another problem is "light pollution." Light pollution results from the interaction of the atmosphere and man-made lights. You can experience light pollution by looking for stars in the sky while in a city at night. Only the brighter stars can be seen.

Space Telescope will operate from an altitude of about 310 miles. At this altitude it will be free of atmospheric interference. Astronomers will then be able to detect objects that are 50 times fainter than those possible to see from Earth-based observatories. The astronomers will also be able to see objects much more clearly; the clarity will be about seven times better than ground observations.

When the Space Shuttle Orbiter takes the telescope into space in 1985, the payload bay will be almost filled. The length of the Space Telescope is 43 feet and its diameter is 14 feet. Figure 37 gives an idea of the relative sizes of the two craft.

There are three main parts which form the complete telescope: The Optical Telescope Assembly, the Scientific Instruments, and the Support Systems Module.Each of these parts has a very sophisticated job to do for astronomy.

Current plans are to operate the Space Telescope for about 15 years. This time may be extended because the satellite can be repaired while it remains in orbit. It can also be retrieved by the

Space Shuttle and returned to Earth for major repair work. After being repaired, the Space Shuttle would return it to orbit.

Advanced X-ray Observatory. This will be a continuation of the great strides already made in x-ray astronomy through the use of satellites. Astronomers are particularly interested in x-ray emissions coming from galaxies. They believe that the study of such x-ray emissions from groups of galaxies will help them understand how giant systems of galaxies form.

Scheduled to be launched in 1989, the observatory will be able to detect x-ray sources that are 50 to 100 times weaker than those sources detected by earlier searches.

Gamma Ray Observatory (GRO). In 1988, further studies will be made of gamma rays generated by pulsars, quasars, and galaxies. Instruments to be carried by the GRO will study how gamma rays are produced and where they come from.

It is hoped that this observatory will help astronomers learn more about quasars. The word *quasar* stands for "quasi-stellar radio sources." The name was given to the mysterious quasars because, in the 1960's, they seemed to be stars and they were discovered by radio telescopes.

Astronomers do not know what quasars really are or why they exist. The astronomers do know that quasars emit tremendous amounts of energy from relatively small volumes of matter. Another puzzling characteristic about quasars is that some of them are going away from us at a rate which approaches 90% of the speed of light.

Galileo. This is the *only* United States Outer-planet probe scheduled to be flown within the next several years. Named for the discoverer of Jupiter's inner moons, the Galileo spacecraft will be launched from the Space Shuttle in 1986. If the launch is made according to schedule, the craft will reach Jupiter in 1988.

Shown in figure 38, the Galileo spacecraft consist of two units joined as an assembly. The larger Orbiter will release the Probe when the spacecraft is about 68 million miles out from Jupiter.

Figure 38. The Galileo spacecraft (Courtesy of Jet Propulsion Laboratory)

The Probe will enter Jupiter's atmosphere and, after being slowed by atmospheric friction, will activate its parachute system. This parachute will allow the Probe to float slowly downward through Jupiter's clouds. All the while, instruments on the Probe will measure the clouds' temperature, chemistry, and electrical activity. Atmospheric pressure will also be a part of the measurements taken. Scientists estimate that the Probe's instruments will operate for about sixty minutes during this descent. As the Probe descends the Orbiter will be receiving the Probe's transmissions of information. The Orbiter will then relay the information back to Earth.

Upon completing this phase of the mission, the Orbiter will begin a series of 11 orbits about Jupiter and its "Galilean satellites." The 11 orbits will require about twenty months to complete.

MANNED SATELLITE SPACECRAFT

Let us remember that a satellite is an orbiting spacecraft. This means that all manned and unmanned space flights, even those to the moon, have been at one time or another during their flight a *scientific* satellite. Every United States manned flight from the first orbiting Mercury capsule (Freedom 7) to the Space Shuttle Orbiter can be called a manned scientific satellite—at least by our definition.

SKYLAB

Until the Space Shuttle became operational, the Skylab program was the most noteworthy of the United States' manned satellite programs and deserves further discussion here. Let us hasten to say that we do not count the spectacular Apollo venture here because its mission was not that of a "pure" satellite.

Skylab was constructed partly of off-the-shelf hardware. Its main compartment, called the orbital workshop module, was constructed from a *Saturn* V rocket section. Within this section were the astronauts' living quarters, a work area, and many of the vehicle's scientific experiments. A second special module was an air lock device used to exit and enter the spacecraft when necessary to perform work outside the craft. This particular module proved very necessary when the astronauts had to erect a sunshade at the location of a micrometeoroid shield which had been torn off during the launch phase. (A secondary function of the micrometeoroid shield was to serve as a sunshield to keep the laboratory/living quarters from overheating.)

The accident which tore away Skylab's micrometeoroid/thermal shield also stripped the vehicle of one of its solar-cell panels and jammed the other so that it would not fully open. The air lock module was used many times as the first astronauts sent up to Skylab worked outside the craft to repair the damage.

A third Skylab structural element was the multiple docking adapter. This portion was especially designed to accept the Apollo command module in airtight linkup so that the astronauts could transfer safely into the laboratory and back to the command module for return to Earth. The fourth module was the Apollo telescope mount. This portion of the vehicle had its own power source in the form of four large solar panels. The telescope mount was an independent unit which could not be entered by the astronauts, although they were responsible for controlling its activities. When the mission schedule called for work with the telescope,

the astronauts had to enter the multiple docking adapter where the telescope's controls were located.

The Skylab utilization program began with liftoff on the 14th of May, 1973. It ended with the return of the *third crew's* splashdown (ocean landing) on the 8th of February, 1974. The vehicle remained in orbit, becoming progressively "weatherbeaten" by the sun's radiations. In addition, its orbit began to deteriorate because of the small amout of drag of Earth's very thin atmosphere at the craft's orbital altitude. As the craft came lower, it began to "tumble" slowly, further increasing drag. Efforts to stabilize its flight by ground controllers were only partially successful, so Skylab was lost.

But what went on in Skylab, did it achieve its objectives? Certainly. The knowledge and data gained from the program could not have been obtained by any other means. This is true because people were there to guide and/or perform experiments.

One of the major scientific benefits of the Skylab program was the information gained about solar activity. Thousands of telescopic images of the sun in visible light and in ultraviolet and x-ray bands were recorded for later study. Such information is expected to help scientists better understand solar processes and to help predict solar cycles which affect the Earth environment. But the sun was not the only cosmic phenomenon studied. Skylab's instrumentation gave even more information about other celestial processes. For example, the comet Kohoutek made its circuit about the sun while Skylab was in service. Photographic records of the comet have convinced scientists that the comet was on its first trip to our sun because it lost more matter as it approached the sun than it did at perihelion.

Experiments in growing larger and more perfectly formed crystals due to zero gravity showed that the process was feasible. The idea that the formation of metal alloys in space would produce a stronger alloy because of increased purity also proved correct. Skylab observations and photography of the Earth below gave startling proof that the mapping of oceans and land masses can be done from space in a matter of days instead of the years required by conventional means. Such mapping is also much more accurate.

We cannot itemize all the Skylab program's accomplishments here because of limited space. But it could be that the program's greatest contribution was in showing that people can live and work in zero gravity for extended periods without permanent physiological effects. This information alone, we believe, was worth the effort because it helped pave the way for future manned spacecraft devoted to providing usable products for Earth society.

Apollo-Soyuz

This was a Joint US/USSR space effort named after the two spacecraft used—the US Apollo and the USSR Soyuz. Some observers looked upon the joint flight as a more or less public relations excercise designed to better relations between the two countries involved. No doubt there was some effect along these lines, but the primary benefit was proof that two or more nations capable of manned space missions *could* develop a means of safely joining two different space craft designs. The basics for future joint ventures in space had been demonstrated. It was also shown that in-space rescue of the "other" nation's astronauts in distress could be effected.

Mechanical and "public relations" were not the only Apollo-Soyuz accomplishments. Both groups of astronauts performed experiments separately and jointly. The program, among other things, detected a new stellar (star) source of extreme ultraviolet radiation. The astronauts and cosmonauts also measured anomalies in Earth's gravitational field, measured atomic oxygen and nitrogen existing between the undocked spacecraft, and observed biological effects of high-energy particles on human body cells.

Cost of the Apollo-Soyuz program was minimal in terms of space efforts. The United States used one of its two remaining Apollo capsules and upper stages of the *Saturn* launch vehicle. The USSR's Soyuz vehicle was their standard manned spacecraft design. In 1975 dollars, the United States spent somewhat less than 240 million on the flight and estimates were that the USSR spent about the same amount. The returns on this investment, however,

cannot be assigned a dollar value. We will never know how much future "revenue" will be realized from application of the knowledge gained, nor can we predict with any accuracy how much improvement will result in the living standards of future generations. Of course, this is the same costs vs. benefits question associated with any space venture.

SPACE SHUTTLE

The United States had no astronauts in space from 1975 until 1981, when the first orbital flight of our Space Transportation Systems' *Columbia* was successfully accomplished. Astronauts Robert L. Crippen and John Young flew for 54 hours and 22 minutes, proving that the system would function as the planner had envisioned.

Since that first flight, the Space Shuttle has become fully operational. It is now taking payloads into orbit on a regular basis. As the years go by, the Shuttle will be refined and its usage will no doubt increase.

Astronauts and Payload Specialists. Prior to the Space Shuttle program, all United States astronauts were highly qualified pilots, and many were not only qualified as pilots but were specialists in other fields as well. The Shuttle, or Space Transportation System (STS), has numerous diversified missions which require the knowledge and skills of several scientific fields. Hence, the pool of STS Astronauts contains individuals with special skills but not necessarily those of a pilot.

When the National Aeronautics and Space Administration asked for volunteers in 1976, over 8,000 applications were received. From this number, 208 were selected as finalists. The finalists were interviewed and given medical examinations at the Johnson Space Center in Houston, Texas. Thirty-five of the finalists were chosen to undergo a two-year training program, after which they would join the existing pool of "older" astronauts.

The new astronaut candidates included women and men, pilots and non-pilots, and civilian and military personnel. There were 21 military officers and 14 civilians. All were grouped for assignment as either Mission Pilots or Mission Specialists. The pilots, of course, were to be trained to fly the STS Orbiter while the mission specialists were to be trained according to the needs of programmed missions. However, with systems as complex as the Orbiter's there has to be a certain amount of cross-training.

Imagine the amount of training astronaut candidates must experience to qualify as a full-fledged astronaut. They all have to understand the organization and structure of their employer (NASA); they certainly must be familiar with the systems and structural aspects of the spacecraft; they have to keep physically fit; they have to understand the aerospace technology associated with the Space Shuttle in order to support technical or scientific assignments, and, among many other things, they must be taught what to expect physiologically and psychologically while in orbital flight.

Mission pilot astronauts keep their flying skills sharpened with a lot of flight time in jet aircraft.

Mission specialists are trained in navigation, communications, and other subjects related to aircraft flight. They also get flight time. Their flights in the jet aircraft are as "rear seaters" to help the pilots with planning, navigation, and communications. Of special benefit to mission specialists with little flight experience is that of becoming accustomed to high altitude and the unusual sensations of various flight attitudes.

Once they are fully qualified, the astronauts continue their training according to need. For example, after an astronaut team is selected for a flight, each person receives intensified training for the flight's mission. The missions differ for every flight and there are numerous other what we might call "sub-missions" to be accomplished. Thus, you can see that learning occupies a large segment of an astronaut's time.

Astronauts not on flight status for a mission have other duties to perform. These duties may include assignments in mission control or other support functions. Some of the astronauts assist public understanding of Space Transportation System flight missions by appearing with news media personnel and providing expert commentary. When missions are not being flown, it is also the astronauts' duty to respond to requests for public appearances. Their knowledge of present systems and plans for future manned space flights is in considerable demand by various national and international organizations.

We cannot imagine an occupation and life more interesting than that of an astronaut. Neither can we imagine an occupation and life being more mentally and physically demanding than that of an astronaut.

Next to being a full-time astronaut, the life of a *Payload Specialist* probably is most interesting. Payload specialists are not astronauts, although they are essential to certain flights.

The payload specialist is a specially trained person who is the expert for a particular payload. Most of the payload specialist's training is received from the payload developer and pertains to a highly technical or scientific project. However, every payload specialist does get some training from the National Aeronautics and Space Administration. This training is conducted at the Johnson Space Center and involves about 150 hours of "classroom" time. The training is sufficient to familiarize the payload specialist with the spacecraft and payload support equipment, crew operations, and emergency procedures.

The Craft. The Space Shuttle has been described as a "space-going truck" which hauls cargoes into Earth orbit and back. In a sense this is true, but the Orbiter is the most sophisticated "truck" ever devised, and it is large! The Orbiter has a wingspan of 78.06 feet. Its total fuselage length, to include its engines and vertical stabilizer, is 122.2 feet. The Orbiter's payloads can weigh a total of 65,000 pounds on a single flight, and, with lighter-weight payloads, the craft can reach an orbital altitude of 690 miles.

Like a conventional aircraft, the Orbiter's fuselage is constructed in three major sections: the forward fuselage, the mid fuselage, and the aft fuselage.

Astronauts and payload specialists occupy the forward fuselage. While the forward fuselage is further subdivided into smaller units, two "decks" form the cabin of working and living quarters. The *flight deck* is where control of the craft and manipulation of most payloads occur. Below the flight deck is the *mid deck*. Here we find the astronauts' living quarters.

The mid deck has storage space for food, a galley where the food is prepared for consumption, sleeping stations for four crew members at one time, multiple storage lockers, a toilet, wet trash storage, and an airlock. The airlock is used to transfer from mid deck into the payload bay area when required. The airlock is where Extra Vehicular Activity (EVA) suits are stored. It is a cylinder which is about 7 feet high and slightly more than 5 feet wide.

An astronaut going for EVA enters the airlock and puts on the very complex suit, which contains its own life support system. Once the suit is checked out, pressure inside the airlock is reduced slowly until a space environment is achieved. The hatch leading into the payload bay is then opened for EVA. Astronauts completing an EVA return to mid deck in reverse manner, storing their EVA suits within the airlock.

The *center fuselage* section contains the purpose of each flight mission because this section consists mostly of the payload bay. The payload bay is about 60 feet long and has a diameter of about 15 feet. Its doors are opened and closed by a mission specialist working on the flight deck.

A most important unit located within the payload bay area is the Remote Manipulator System's *manipulator arm*. This arm is also controlled from the flight deck, and it is the action portion of a very complex system which can deploy, retrieve, or otherwise affect a payload without the need of an EVA. The arm has a special light and TV camera so that its human operator can see the detail of what is taking place as the system is operated. It is possible for two manipulator arms to be located in the payload bay if required by a mission. However, only one arm can be operated at a time.

The Orbiter's aft fuselage primarily contains or has attached to it units for orbital propulsion and aerodynamic flight control. The craft's main propulsion system engines, orbital maneuvering system engines, and aft reaction control system engines are found within the aft fuselage. The vertical stabilizer is attached to the topside of the aft fuselage, and the body flap is attached to the bottom-side of the aft fuselage. The vertical stabilizer's attached rudder is sectioned so that it can be "spread" and serve as a speed brake in atmospheric flight. The body flap also serves as a speed brake during the return flight to Earth.

The craft's wings are attached to the center and aft fuselages, with the major portions joined to the center fuselage. The wings' function does not begin until the upper atmosphere is encountered upon reentry. The primary function of the wings, of course, is to provide aerodynamic lift for the craft. However, they first serve as a brake and energy dissipater to slow the craft to aerodynamic flight speed.

In addition to acting as a speed brake and lift producers, the wings house the craft's main landing gear. To provide the craft a means of aerodynamic control, the wings are fitted with *elevons*. These elevons are located along the wings' trailing edges and function as either elevators or ailerons, according to how they are moved.

Mission Profile. Each Space Shuttle mission flight begins with the complete vehicle positioned vertically on its launch pad—either at the Kennedy Space Center in Florida or Vandenberg Air Force Base in California. As a note, equatorial orbits are flown from Florida while polar orbits are launched from California.

At this time, the flight assembly consists of the Orbiter, two solid-fuel rockets which are called Solid Rocket Boosters, and a huge external tank which contains cryogenic propellants (liquid oxygen and liquid hydrogen). Propellants from this external tank are fed to the permanently installed main engines at the aft end of the Orbiter.

Start of the launch begins with ignition of the Orbiter's main engines. When it is verified that the main engines are functioning properly, the solid rocket boosters are ignited. Almost simultaneously, hold-down bolts are fired (blown apart) to release the assembly for flight.

A total of five engines are operating at the time of lift-off and they produce a combined thrust of almost 7 million pounds. This amounts to an excess of more than 2 million pounds thrust over the

Figure 39. Separation of solid rocket boosters

assembly's total weight. The Orbiter and its key components take off rather quickly, but the crew never experiences more than 3Gs of body stress during their flight to orbit.

Two minutes after lift-off the craft is at 28 miles altitude and the solid rocket boosters have consumed their propellant. A signal generated in the Orbiter separates the boosters. Small rocket motors on each booster fire and thrust the boosters safely away from the Orbiter and external tank. Then boosters descend into the ocean by parachute to be picked up and prepared for another flight.

The Orbiter's three main engines continue operation for another six minutes, quickly draining propellant from the external tank. At the eight minute point, the Orbiter and external tank have reached an altitude of approximately 68 miles and are almost at the velocity required for orbit. Main engine cutoff is given and the external tank is separated. From here until the next launch, the Orbiter's main engines will not and cannot function because their propellant supply has been exhausted.

Still gaining altitude and flying at 17,400 + miles per hour, the now "clean" Orbiter needs more velocity to achieve orbit. This velocity is provided by its two *orbital maneuvering engines* which receive

their hypergolic propellant from tanks *inside* the craft. For orbit, two firings of these engines occur. The first gets the craft into orbit and the second firing circularizes the orbit into a virtually constant altitude above Earth.

The spacecraft's flight attitude and "station keeping" are maintained by its *reaction control system.* This system consists of numerous small rocket engines which also use a hypergolic propellant (nitrogen tetroxide and monomethyl hydrazine). There are 28 such engines in the aft section and 16 in the forward section.

Upon completion of their in-orbit duties, the astronaut crew prepares to deorbit. The payload bay doors are closed and latched, and all items are stored and secured for the return flight. The Orbiter's reaction control system is used to align the craft in a tail-first attitude in the direction of orbit. The two orbital maneuvering system engines are then fired to slow the spacecraft to below orbital velocity.

Dependable gravity again takes charge of the spacecraft and starts to pull it toward Earth. In the meantime, the reaction control thrusters are used to again point the craft forward. The descent continues as the craft encounters "atmosphere." Its flight attitude is governed automatically and through firing of the reaction control thrusters, or engines.

At lower altitudes the reaction control system is turned off in stages, according to when the craft's aerodynamic controls begin to function. The body flap provides thermal protection for the three main engines during the "hot" stages of atmospheric entry; afterward, it is used to help control the flight to landing.

The heat energy generated by entry into the atmosphere is dissipated by rolling or banking the craft. This maneuver increases drag and the craft's sink rate but it also increases the energy dissipation rate. If angle of attack only were used, the craft would be heated to temperatures above design specifications. All of these energy control maneuvers are governed by the Orbiter's automatic *guidance, navigation, and control system.* This system continues to govern the vehicles flight path from the "entry" through the "terminal phase" of flight. The astronaut pilots can manually control the craft, but all of their flight commands are processed through the guidance system's computers before being activated by the actual flight control system.

As with any flight, the mission is completed upon landing. The Orbiter makes a smooth but hot landing. Its touchdown speed is somewhere between 213 and 226 miles per hour, but it soon rolls to a full stop.

The astronauts and payload specialists cannot depart the Orbiter immediately. They must wait until Launch Operations team members go through a series of system checks to see that the vehicle and the area around it are safe for exit.

Preparations for the next mission begin immediately after the flight crew departs. There are too many steps involved for us to discuss here, but the time required to prepare and launch each succeeding mission, or turnaround, is programmed to be 160 hours.

Payloads. Expendable launch vehicles will continue to be used in the future. The reasons are many, but time is one reason. For example, the owners of a satellite system might need to replace a unit quickly or launch a new model much sooner than it could be taken up by the Orbiter. Even the additional cost of an expendable launch vehicle could thus be justified. But we believe that the versatility of the Orbiter's payload capabilities will eventually make the larger expendable launch vehicles enter the "rare bird" category.

Hundreds of payloads have been scheduled for orbital flights already. Some of them will remain in the Orbiters payload bay. Others will be launched from the Orbiter and boosted into higher orbits or along trajectories leading to other planets. The possibilities and payloads are studies in themselves, but we will briefly discuss a few.

Spacelab. This is a shortened term for the European built space laboratory. It is what its name implies—a laboratory in space where many experiments can be conducted.

The system includes a module (long or short) which is the type of laboratory we usually think of as a laboratory. It is large and it has a shirt-sleeve environment where payload specialists and/or scientists work unencumbered by an EVA suit. The module is entered through the Orbiter's airlock and a tunnel attached to the airlock.

Pallets are also part of the Spacelab system. These pallets are special, modular containers in which experiments can be placed. They are specifically designed for those experiments which need direct exposure to space.

The Spacelab system was designed to offer what we might call a broad-spectrum approach to learning. Some of the work to be done in Spacelab will apply to astronomy as studies of the sun, comets, novas, and other phenomena are conducted. Experiments in biomedicine and industrial technology will be extensive, since the knowledge gained can be applied relatively quickly. Life science studies will continue to probe the extent and effects of metabolic changes that occur due to the absence of gravity. And the planet Earth will be surveyed rather extensively. Earth surveys are expected to provide information that will be useful to urban planning, farming, weather forecasting, and numerous other areas which affect our lives.

Long-Duration Exposure Facility (LDEF). The maximum duration of a Space Shuttle mission is 30 days. Some experiments will require much longer exposures to the space environment. The LDEF was designed to provide this service to researchers who need it.

The vehicle is constructed of aluminum and contains room for 72 *experiment trays.* Its shape is that of a 12-sided regular polygon which has a diameter of just over 14 feet. Its length is 30 feet. Bays formed by the vehicle's "longerons" and "ring frames" hold the experiment trays.

Flight operation of the LDEF will begin with it secured in the Orbiter's payload bay. In orbit, the manipulator arm will be used to remove the vehicle from the bay. Before releasing, it is taken through a series of orientation so that it will be positioned correctly in a circular orbit at an altitude of approximately 340 miles.

Servicing of experiments will be conducted from the Spacelab. That is, some experiments will be checked by the laboratory and their conditions recorded. After the vehicle is retrieved, the same experiments will be checked for changes that have occurred.

How long each LDEF orbital flight lasts will vary according to the desires of experimenters who have payed for the service. The duration has to follow an exact schedule because each flight of the Orbiter is planned years in advance of launch date.

Getaway Specials. Users interested in orbiting small experiments get a bargain with the Getaway Special. For about $10,000, a scientific or technological experiment can be flown on the Orbiter if the experiment package is within size and weight limits.

Servicing of the Getaway Special-type payloads is very limited. The crew will activate and deactivate a maximum of three switches for each payload of this type. Other than this, the crew is not expected to have sufficient time to provide any other services.

OSTA-1. This is another payload that remains in the Orbiter's payload bay throughout a flight. It is a scientific unit which consists of five experiments installed on a pallet. The pallet is 10 feet long and is U-shaped. It's name comes from NASA's *Office of Space Terrestrial Applications.*

Experiments conducted by OSTA-1 include using spaceborne imaging radar as a means of geological and mineral exploration. Measurements of Earth's surface radiance (the giving off or reflection of energy) should reveal whether or not instruments can be developed to discriminate between geological formations through measurement of the radiance.

Another experiment will measure the concentration of carbon monoxide in the troposphere over tropical areas. The distribution and condition of marine algae will be mapped: among other things, this will help determine the effects of pollution in bodies of water. And another experiment will be toward developing technology which will "recognize, acquire and track Earth surface features, spectrally sensing and classifying quantitatively the surface of the Earth into cloud cover, water, bare Earth and vegetation."

Solar Optical Telescope. Like the Spacelab, this special telescope will remain in the payload bay throughout successive flights. The telescope is scheduled to begin a series of one-week missions in 1987. Its purpose, as revealed by its name, is to continue studies of the sun. The telescope will be used to observe the sun in visible light, and in the infrared and ultraviolet regions of the spectrum.

Upper Stages. We will admit that the following does not describe true payloads, but upper stages are important *parts* of payloads. What is an upper stage? It is a propulsion carrier unit—rocket, if you prefer—that has been specially designed or modified for use with the Space Shuttle. Without these upper stages, many payloads could not be launched by the Space Shuttle.

Spinning Solid Upper Stage (SSUS). There are two models of this solid-propellant rocket. The SSUS-A and SSUS-D were both designed to propel payloads to geosynchronous orbit. The A model can place spacecraft which weigh up to 4,400 pounds into geosynchronous orbit while the D model can do the same for spacecraft that weigh 2,300 pounds or less.

Both models of this upper stage are derivatives of the third stage of the Minuteman Missile.

IUS. This, the Inertial Upper Stage, was designed for civilian and military payloads. The IUS is a more powerful propulsive unit than the SSUS models. It can propel a spacecraft which weighs more than 5,000 pounds into geosynchronous orbit. It can also propel spacecraft into planetary trajectories.

Other Components. In addition to the Orbiter and its propulsion elements, other components are necessary before the *Space Transportation System* (STS) is complete.

The Space Tug is still in the design stage, so we cannot predict when it will be ready for use. However, this component of the system will be used to boost very large payloads to higher orbits. These payloads will be those which are beyond the capabilities of the upper stages discussed earlier.

Once the last of the Tracking and Data Relay Satellites (TDRS) is in place, the communications portion of the STS will be complete. There will be four of these satellites in orbit when the communications system is fully operational. The fourth TDRS is scheduled for placement in orbit during 1984.

Figure 40. Satellite being deployed from Orbiter's payload bay (NASA photo)

THE SOVIETS' SOYUZ/SALYUT PROGRAM

We do not have much information about the Soviet Union's manned satellite programs because the Soviets' are not completely open about their activities and intentions. Another questionable area is how much of their activities is within our concept of "civilian spacecraft." This question is founded on the fact that all Soviet space efforts are conducted by the government, which does not readily distinguish between civilian missions and those of a military nature.

Since the conclusion of the Apollo/Soyuz Test Program in 1975, the Soviets have continued a very active manned satellite program and have conducted too many flights for us to discuss here. But we will provide some information about what is known about their efforts and plans for the future.

Soyuz. This is the name given to the Soviet's rocket and payload unit which transports Cosmonauts (Soviet astronauts) to and from space. The Soyuz spacecraft has been improved over the years and now has more capabilities and transports up to three cosmonauts.

Salyut. The Salyut is a permanently orbiting unit to which the Soyuz craft are docked. Cosmonauts transfer from the Soyuz into the large Salyut where various experiments are conducted.

The Soviets' latest orbital station is the Salyut 7. This improved model is capable of docking with other spacecraft which are larger than the Soyuz. Other improvements include items which will make the station more comfortable for the crew. The new ventilation system absorbs dust and is quieter; even the interior color scheme was changed to provide a brighter and more pleasant working environment for the cosmonauts.

Among the experiments conducted aboard the Salyut are the study of sources of X-rays in space, and experiments which pertain to Earth resources. The long-term effects of the space environment on the human body have been studied by the Soviets throughout their manned satellite program. Because of the intensity of these studies, the Soviets currently lead all other nations in time spent in space.

Progress. Resupply of the Salyut station is accomplished by a special craft called the Progress. This vehicle is also launched by the Soyuz launcher and transports over 5,000 pounds of supplies to the Salyut. Unpiloted, it contains an automatic guidance system which directs the craft to rendezvous with the Salyut. Progress attaches itself to a special docking module which is located at one end of the cylindrical Salyut. (The docking module for the Soyuz is at the opposite end.)

Cosmonauts enter the Progress from the Salyut to obtain supplies. Such supplies are in the form of bulk cargo—food, etc—and liquids. The known liquids are water and propellants which are pumped from Progress to Salyut. This technique of resupplying a manned satellite has enabled the Soviets to break all records of sustained manned spaceflight and, for the foreseeable future, will keep them ahead of the United States and all other nations.

New Vehicles. It is highly probable that the Soviets will expand their fairly recent program of inviting foreign "astronauts" to share flights with Soviet cosmonauts. Such flights have taken place already, but with new vehicles more mixed crews could be orbited.

The Salyut 7's modified docking unit, which can accept craft larger than the Soyuz, indicates that their planned modular space station is about to become a reality. Exactly how this development or

activity fits with two other special efforts is not clear, but the Soviets are working on a new launch vehicle and a unique "space shuttle."

We do not know the full capabilities of the new launch vehicle, but indications are that it will be larger than our Saturn V. What remains a mystery is whether the new vehicle is to launch modules to be mated with the Salyut 7 or is to launch another of the Soviet's goals, a new very heavy space station that can be home to as many as twelve cosmonauts. Perhaps the launch vehicle will be used for both projects.

The second vehicle, their space shuttle, is in test flight status. Sources believe that the shuttle weighs from 20 to 30 thousand pounds and can transport up to three cosmonauts. It was orbit-tested in June of 1982. On this flight, the shuttle made one and one-third orbits before coming down south of the Cocos Islands.

FUTURE MANNED SATELLITES

We have no way of knowing what the future developments in the field of manned spacecraft will be. The Space Shuttle program will continue for several years. This we can say with some authority. Beyond Space Shuttle, developments will depend upon national and international objectives. However, it seems that United States efforts will first concentrate on the construction of large units, or antennas and platforms, from which direct benefits can be obtained or economies realized. The construction of units in space certainly will involve manned spacecraft on an extensive scale. Right now people are working on various designs and methods of constructing such units. But, other than the makeshift sunshade on Skylab, U.S. astronauts have not actually done any "construction" work in space. A lot of thought must first go into the process and then, on a very small scale and using the Space Shuttle, all the designers' ideas will have to be tested.

As we pointed out earlier, very intense space construction efforts will have to have some type of heavy lift launch vehicles to get the construction materials into orbit. The fact that space workers will not be able to "go home" at the end of a shift means they will require some type of living quarters.

Designers for the future have thought of the workers, and living quarters have been given appropriate attention.

Antennas, Platforms, and Space Stations. We have said that the Soviets seem to be concentrating their manned spaceflight activities on space stations— manned satellites. But what are the fairly near term plans for U.S. efforts in this area?

The Space Shuttle will be the work-horse vehicle for eventual placement of huge antennas and, afterward, platforms in space. Large antennas are planned as the first space construction projects. These antennas will reach the size of a football field and they will be placed into various orbits according to their intended function.

The concept of using a large antenna was proven years ago when the ATS-6 satellite's almost 30 foot-wide dish antenna relayed TV signals down to small receivers in remote areas. The new large antennas will provide this type service for all the nation's people. Millions of home rooftop dish antennas will be able to receive satellite signals now picked up by only the large and powerful ground stations.

Another benefit of the large antenna structures will be in the area of economics. A few of the "super-antennas" placed in geosynchronous orbit will replace countless smaller satellites, while improving the type service formally provided by the smaller satellites.

Multipurpose space platforms are now being designed for deployment. These platforms are intended to host several types of units which today have to be flown as individual satellites. The space platforms will not be identical in appearance but their functions will be similar. They will provide the electrical power needed to operate the units they host. In addition, they will contain station-keeping systems, heat dissipating systems, and a centralized on-board computer system to direct all functions of an individual platform.

Beyond construction of these antennas and platforms, U.S. space stations are the next logical step. We can see the eventual need of constructing large power generation stations in space. To construct and maintain such large units will require

space stations to serve as homes and fabrication shops for the workers.

All of these space station and space power system developments are projected for sometime in the next century—somewhat later than earlier projections. On the other hand, unforeseen factors could speed up the process.

Space Colonies. Far beyond the concept of space stations is that of permanent colonies for some of Earth's people. It will be a long, cautious road to the eventual construction of space colonies, and there seems to be no reason to doubt that the colonies will become a reality. But why should they be built? One of the primary reasons is that extensive materials processing and manufacturing can take place without pollution of Earth's environment. Another is that more unique and better products can be developed in space. Still another more far-reaching promise is that the space colony approach could lead to mankind's existence in other solar systems that do not have habitable planets. However, the overpowering reason probably is that space is indeed a new and different frontier and the history of mankind shows that new frontiers have always attracted explorers and settlers.

Very serious work has been done and is continuing toward determining the best locations

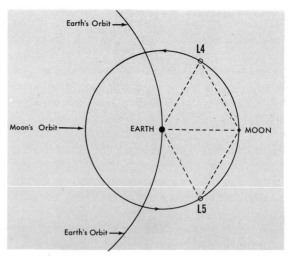

Figure 41. Diagram of Lagrangian libration points 4 and 5

and missions for space colonies. Summer workshops of scientists, engineers, and others concluded as early as 1975 that colonies in space are feasible and could be a great boon to human life.

There are two points in space which seem to be the best locations for eventual, sophisticated space colonies. These points are designated L4 and L5. The "L" of the designation signifies Lagrange, after Joseph Louis Lagrange. In 1772, Lagrange pointed out that there are points in relation to two large planetary masses where a body will be in gravitational equilibrium. The Lagrangian libration points, diagramed in figure 41, would be a precise location around which space colony structures could orbit. (This "orbit within an orbit" is necessary because of the gravitational influence of the sun.)

When will space colonies be in orbit at L-5? No one really knows. The exact date does not matter, just knowing that advances in space construction techniques and propulsion systems will eventually lead to the colonization of space should reinforce our hopes for the future.

PART THREE

THE AEROSPACE COMMUNITY

In the previous Parts of this text we looked at the history of aerospace, both here and abroad. We also examined a wide variety of aircraft and rockets and their uses. In each of these Parts we briefly talked about the important part aerospace plays in our lives. In this Part we will look at the importance of aerospace in more detail.

Most Americans have some idea of how aircraft and missiles are used in a war. They are also starting to realize the role that aerospace is playing in improving communications and in the way that we travel. They probably do not understand as well the political, social and economic importance of aerospace or its impact on our daily lives.

Aerospace is a new field of study, yet its advances have already started to change our thinking. In the short period of only 20 years, man has gone into space, walked on the moon, and has explored distant planets. New aerospace developments will continue to alter the course of history just as they have already altered it. Aerospace offers a challenge to our youth far greater than any earlier generation has known. Whether or not they meet this challenge depends on the education and training they receive to prepare them for their future in aerospace.

The main learning objective for this Part is for you to Know the Composition of the Aerospace Community. Upon completing your study of all six chapters in this Part, you should:

1. know the meaning of aerospace power,
2. know military aerospace activities that help determine U.S. aerospace power,
3. know the economic and sociological aspects and problems of the civilian aerospace programs that help determine U.S. aerospace power,
4. know the governmental agencies and services provided to civil aviation and the importance of our civilian space exploration program to U.S. aerospace power,
5. know the economics and the problems of the aerospace industry,
6. know the aerospace education and training factors that help determine U.S. aerospace power.

3-2

Chapter 3-1

THE MEANING OF AEROSPACE POWER

Since the end of World War II, all areas of aviation and space exploration have developed very rapidly. Many people have called this growth rate explosive, and perhaps it is. Today aerospace has spread to the point that no part of our society is unaffected.

All areas of science have been changed by the new knowledge which our aviation and space programs have produced. Where people once could only wonder and question, they now can go and observe. Scientists are able to view the heavens and the Earth from a new perspective never before available to them. The social scientist, the philosopher, the historian, and the humanist also are affected by the ever growing knowledge.

Aerospace vehicles, aircraft and spacecraft, are really time machines which bring all people of the world closer together. We can travel from any spot on Earth to any other in just a matter of hours. We can talk with any spot on Earth by telephone, using communications satellites, in only minutes. These things have happened because of aerospace developments.

The general learning objective for this chapter is for you to know the meaning of aerospace power. To reach this objective, you must pattern your study of the material according to the *specific learning objectives* listed in the Appendix of this textbook.

THE SCOPE OF AEROSPACE

Today we live at a time and in a nation where aerospace has become a vital part of our everyday lives. Of course, aviation and space travel today affect all nations and all people of the world—but none so much as the people of the United States. No other nation in the world is as air minded as the United States. Nearly half of all passengers that fly on commercial airliners in the free world board their aircraft in the United States. There are more general aviation aircraft and pilots in the United States than in all the rest of the world combined.

In 1981 aerospace sales in the United States totaled more than 61 billion dollars. More than eighteen billion dollars worth of aerospace products (aircraft, engines, instruments, satellites, etc.) were exported by the United States. In recent years this is the one area, other than agriculture, where we have had more exports than imports. They are becoming more and more important as our balance-of-payments problem increases because of oil imports.

Our world leadership in aerospace is due greatly to the freedom made possible by our democratic form of government. This includes the free enterprise system which allows competition by many industries. This competition in aerospace insures that the products manufactured are of the highest quality. United States aircraft, both civil and military, are widely regarded as the best produced anywhere in the world. Competition also means that the customers will get the most for their money.

When discussing the scope of aerospace, we cannot overlook the numbers and the variety of jobs that aerospace provides. There are about 1,220,000 people employed in the aerospace industries in this country. There are probably that many more who are employed by government and education in the aerospace area. These employees range from highly trained scientists and engineers to production workers. They are considered to be highly skilled and are some of the highest paid workers in this country. It has been estimated that an additional 700,000 jobs are created indirectly by aerospace in the areas needed to support the industry. The total payroll for all of these employees approaches 50 billion dollars.

However, let's not fool ourselves by thinking that aerospace does not have problems. The same freedoms which make us the world leader in aerospace also produce the most serious problems. Among the most serious problems facing aerospace in the U.S. today is the lack of understanding of its importance by the American public. This is important because lack of understanding leads to lack of support. We will discuss this concept and its importance in the last chapter of this Part.

AEROSPACE POWER

In today's world, any nation that wants to be a world power is interested in a strong aerospace-oriented economy. This increasingly means both a strong military aerospace program and a strong civilian aviation and space program. Examples of this are seen in the United States and the Soviet Union. Both of these nations are superpowers, and both have reached that position partly because of their strong military and civilian aviation and space programs

Immediately after World War II, both the United States and the Soviet Union pledged themselves to the role of leadership of the smaller nations of the world. They did this by building an image based on strong modern military forces and efforts in civil aviation and space exploration, as well as by establishing economic ties and providing economic and military assistance. Many of the lesser developed nations were looking for a strong nation with which to be allied. The nation which showed them the strongest military forces, the most impressive modern aviation and space program, and which offered the most assistance was likely to be the one with whom they became allied.

When we talk about a nation's total commitment in aviation and space, we call it a nation's *aerospace power.* When most people see the word power, they immediately associate it with an aggressive or hostile action. To them, the term aerospace power means only bombers and missiles, the use of aerospace for warlike purposes.

This is because one definition for the word power is "possession of control or authority over others." Some synonyms for power when this definition is used are might, force, or strength. In many cases, the person or organization in authority uses force or aggression to control others. This use has become so widely practiced and accepted that the word power has come to have a very negative meaning to many people.

There is another definition for power which is the one we will use. It is "the ability to act or to produce an effect." This definition has no positive or negative meaning, all it refers to is an action. You can see that we use this definition of power in our definition of aerospace power. Aerospace power is a *nation's total capacity to act in the aerospace environment* (the expanse beyond the Earth's surface). Using this definition, aerospace power is not limited to military uses. It also includes all civilian aerospace activities. Anything that increases a nation's capability in aviation and space exploration adds to that nation's aerospace power. Likewise, any factor that limits or decreases this capability reduces a nation's aerospace power. This is an important concept to understand because it is the cornerstone of our entire aerospace program. Let's look at a couple of examples.

Many types of raw materials, such as copper, aluminum, rubber, gasoline, etc., are necessary to build and fly airplanes. If, for any reason, any of these materials become scarce, our ability to fly is reduced. This is what happened when the OPEC (Organization of Petroleum Exporting Countries) nations cut back on their oil production. Since we must import 50 percent of our crude oil, this reduction caused a shortage of gasoline in our country. The result of the gasoline shortage was higher prices and allocation of fuel to priority users. If these fuel shortages had become severe enough, we may have had to shut down some of our airlines.

One of the greatest developments in aviation was the invention of the turbine engine which made our jet aircraft possible. This invention and any improvements in jet engines greatly increases our nation's aerospace power.

AEROSPACE POWER FACTORS

There are three factors that determine the aerospace power of the United States. First, our *civilian aerospace programs* including all commercial, private, and other nonmilitary aerospace activities; second, all *military aerospace activities;* and third, the *aerospace education* of our people.

The first two factors are more commonly accepted than the third, aerospace education. Keeping strong military and civilian aerospace programs is necessary to maintain peace and to provide a vital transportation system. They also insure that we will have a strong aerospace industry, and the research and development needed to continue to progress. The airports and airways and other facilities necessary to support these programs will also be provided. They will also insure that we will have the trained scientists, engineers, and the technical people required to continue our progress in aerospace. The third factor, aerospace education, is as important as the other two factors because without public support we would not have any civilian or military aerospace programs. Books such as this one help prepare our citizens to understand the role of aerospace in the growth of the United States.

Figure 1.

Figure 2. General William "Billy" Mitchell

This definition, and the concept of aerospace power, was understood by many of our early aviation leaders. Of course, they used the term air power instead of aerospace power because space exploration had not yet begun.

Perhaps the earliest of those who understood this concept was General William "Billy" Mitchell. In his 1925 book *Winged Defense,* he wrote:

"Air Power may be defined as the ability to do something in the air. It consists of transporting all sorts of things by aircraft from one place to another . . ."

In 1946, General H.H. Arnold, Commanding General of the Army Air Forces, wrote:

"Air Power is not composed alone of the war making components of aviation. It is the total aviation activity—civilian and military, . . ."

He went on to say:

"It is the American people who will decide whether this nation will continue to hold its air supremacy. Air power will always be the business of every American citizen."

General Carl A. Spaatz wrote in *Air Force Magazine* in November 1974:

"The third component, public support, is as essential to effective Air Power as industries, airplanes, and airmen. Public support determines the rate of translation into action of the airman's faith—the conviction that ability to control the air is essential to victory in time of war, and equally essential to prevent war in time of peace."

This, then, is our definition of aerospace power. The three factors, military aerospace programs civilian aerospace programs, and aerospace education are all of equal importance and indivisible. You cannot do anything in one area without affecting the other two. Now, if you understand the definition of aerospace power, let's press onward and expand the concept.

ELEMENTS OF AEROSPACE POWER

The total capacity of a nation to act in the aerospace environment depends on two major elements—the *capability* to act, and the *right* to act. Capability should not be confused with right. Both elements are necessary to aerospace power, but they are separate and different.

CAPABILITY

Our nation's aerospace capability includes all of the social, political, economic, industrial, and educational factors that make aerospace programs possible. Some of these, such as airports, airplanes, and pilots, are very obvious. Others like colleges, laboratories, and political parties are not as apparent. The elements necessary to possess the capability to fly, both in the air and in space, can be grouped into five categories as follows:

A Strong Aerospace Industry. The aerospace industry includes those companies that produce the aerospace vehicles as well as all of the support equipment needed to operate and maintain them. This industry must be able to keep up with the needs of the nation and also capable of immediate expansion when necessary. The aerospace industry is the backbone of our nation's security. It is also a dominant force in maintaining a strong national economy. The aerospace industry includes the more commonly known aircraft and rocket manufacturers like Boeing, Lockheed, Cessna, Piper, etc. It also includes the less known manufacturers like Lycoming and Pratt and Whitney (aircraft engines); King and Collins (avionics); and IBM and Control Data (computers). Lesser known, but equally important, are the component manufacturers. They make the small parts which go into the instruments and engines and guidance systems. Much of the nation's highest technology can be found in this industry. It is often called on to solve other non-aerospace problems like pollution control, rapid transit systems, communications, and industrial management. The area in the aerospace industry which is growing the most rapidly today is sales of these non-aerospace-related types of equipment.

A Strong Civil Aviation System. The civil aviation system includes all of the civilian aircraft in service, the pilots who fly them, and all the support equip-

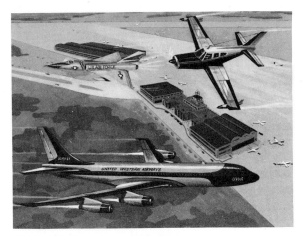

Figure 3. Airports and Air Bases

ment necessary to operate them. As with the aerospace industry, this too has a dual function. In peacetime it provides an important part of our national transportation system. In time of emergency, it provides a reserve of airplanes, experienced personnel, communications systems and navigation systems.

A Strong Military Establishment. This includes all military aircraft and missiles. It also includes the required support equipment and supplies in use and in reserve. In order to be strong the military must be equipped with modern equipment. New equipment must also be supplied as necessary.

Airports and Airbases. This element includes the landing areas as well as all necessary support facilities for both military and civilian aviation. Military airbases are entirely self-contained communities. They include living areas, schools and training institutions, stores, hospitals, and everything found in a small city. Large modern airports also include much more than the average airline passenger sees. They have restaurants, shops, fuel depots, fire departments, aircraft sales offices, computer centers and much more. In times of national emergency these civilian airports can be used for military operations.

A Continuing Research and Development Program. Research is the key to superior quality in all areas of aerospace. There must be enough money

available to government, industry, education and the military services to insure continued progess in areospace. In the world of aerospace vehicles, progress is very rapid, and the nation that fails to keep up soon becomes a second rate nation. There are three essential steps in producing superior modern aerospace vehicles: (a) research (producing new knowledge); (b) development (producing new equipment); (c) evaluation (operational testing and evaluation). All three steps are expensive and all three are essential to continued aerospace power.

The five elements set forth above, in turn, depend on various other things. Skilled personnel, for example, are an essential ingredient of both civil and military aerospace operations. They are equally as essential in industry and in research and development. It takes years of training to become skilled as a pilot, astronaut, mechanic, electronics engineer, or any of the hundreds of other specialists and technicians who are vital to both a stable aerospace industry and a modern aerospace force. These skilled personnel must be retained within aerospace because of the time and the expense of retraining new personnel.

The Federal Government's role in aerospace is significant. Legislation and policies must be strong but flexible to create healthy competition and growth in civil aviation and in the aerospace industry. These conditions are vital to a strong national

Figure 4. Aerospace Research and Development

economy. National policies in domestic and international trade and commerce, travel, and transportation also affect aviation and space programs. The Federal Government also plays a leading part in safety regulation through research services, air traffic control, airport construction, weather information, and many other services.

Aerospace power also depends on a strong national economy. A strong national economy makes it possible to pay the bills security demands. A strong economy means a healthy domestic and international exchange of commerce; expanding trade and manufacture; discovery of new materials, of new uses for old materials, and of new markets; and a stable, well paid, expanding labor force. These are the things that nourish our national economy. Both civil and military aerospace programs contribute significantly to the development of these things.

On the other hand, when the national economy is not strong, cuts in spending for defense programs, research and development, and other aerospace programs receive early consideration.

All of the elements listed above provide a yardstick for the measurement of the present status of our aerospace power. In addition, there are several elements which measure the potential aerospace power of any nation over a longer period. These conditions or elements will contribute to or limit the future of aerospace in a nation during peace or war. When all else is gone, these elements are the vast assets which will allow a nation to rebuild. An example of how these elements can restore a nation's aerospace power can be seen in Germany and Japan. Both of these nations were nearly destroyed during World War II. Their industries had been devastated and their air forces destroyed. However, in less than 15 years, each nation's industry had recovered, and their military and civilian aviation was back in existence.

Included in the measurements of a nation's potential aerospace power are resources, population, industrial development, political conditions and geographic conditions.

Resources: This includes both economic and natural resources. The availability of natural resources needed for aerospace operations is a limiting factor to a nation's aerospace power. Included are materials necessary to build aircraft and spacecraft and those required to fly them. An example would be fuel. In order to operate aircraft a nation must have fuel. This fuel must be available either within a nation or imported from another country. It is easy to see that a country which does not have its own petroleum resources and whose money to buy fuel from another country is limited will also have its aerospace capability limited. Then, too, if a country must rely on another nation for its fuel, there is always the possibility that the supply will be cut off.

Population. The size and education level of a nation's population will determine its future in aerospace. The largest underdeveloped nations of the world are not aerospace leaders now and probably will not be in the future because of the population factor. The population of these countries is so large that their national economies are overburdened with the problems of simply keeping the people clothed and fed. There is little money available to develop an aerospace industry and the other things that are necessary to have the capability to fly on a large scale. In addition, the general education levels are too low to provide the skilled people necessary for a successful aerospace program. Before these nations can develop aerospace capabilities they must, among other things, control their population problems and improve their educational institutions.

Industrial Development. This includes the technological level of the nation as well as manufacturing, engineering and research available or adaptable to aerospace. The aerospace industries are at the top of the technological ladder and require a strong research and development capability and a general manufacturing and engineering industry to support them. It is difficult to imagine a country able to manufacture highly technical jet aircraft or missiles without first developing the ability to manufacture automobiles, electrical appliances, etc. This is very closely related to the above item (Population). The industrial development is tied directly to the population and educational level of a nation.

Political Conditions. This includes government policies and national incentives. It is easy to see how this has an effect on a nation's future in aerospace by looking at the example of the United States and the

3-8

Soviet Union. The Soviet Union is an autocratic government, with the rulers making the decisions and the citizens having no say as to national priorities. The Soviet Union has decided it will be the world leader in aerospace power, particularly military aerospace power. It is spending whatever money is necessary to accomplish this and making great progress.

The United States, on the other hand, is a democracy with the citizens making the decisions as to national priorities. The political climate in such a nation is closely related to the nation's potential and actual aerospace power, especially in the military area. If the citizenry puts a higher priority on other problem areas, less of the nation's resources will be allotted to increasing military aerospace power. Continuing political conflict over such issues is inevitable.

There is no completely reliable yardstick for measuring aerospace power in terms of the amount spent on national defense. However, many yardsticks are used. Standards used include such terms as percent of gross national product*; or simply a comparison of dollars in various years adjusted for inflation; or a percentage of the total federal budget spent on defense in a given year as compared to prior years.

A frequent technique in political debates is also to compare percentages of the total federal budget spent on health, education and welfare with the percentage allotted to defense in a given year. With this approach it can be shown that there have been very clear decisions by our citizenry, through their elected representatives, to increase the percentage of the fiscal year budget allotted to health, education and welfare in comparison with defense. Those who favor this would not admit that the lowering of the defense percentage meant a decrease in our relative strength in comparison with the USSR. They contend that defense expenditures beyond a given point are meaningless, or for unnecessary overkill capability. They may also question the terms of comparison with the USSR, perhaps contending that U.S. weapons are of a higher technology and effectiveness—and the debate goes on.

The Soviet Union's efforts to augment its aerospace power are not just in military aerospace programs, but in the areas of civil aviation and space exploration as well. The Soviets have a large air carrier business with one government-owned airline—Aeroflot. Aeroflot is the largest in the world in terms of passengers carried.

In the area of space exploration, the Soviet Union launches about seven times as many satellites as the rest of the world combined. For example, in 1981 the Soviet Union launched 110 satellites, the United States launched 12 (7 military, 5 by NASA), and 3 were launched by other countries.

Geographic Conditions. This includes the size, location, climate and weather of a nation. Any or all of these factors control the aerospace developments of any nation. Sweden and Switzerland are both very modern industrial nations with highly educated populations. However, their small physical size, and to some extent their location and climate, limits their development as aerospace powers.

All of these five elements interrelate in various ways to produce varying levels of aerospace power. Obviously the two superpowers must be fairly well-blessed in all of the areas. It is difficult to say who has the advantage in what areas, although the number one position in one or all areas is sometimes attributed to one or the other, usually with over-simplified arguments. It might be interesting for you to think

Figure 5.

*Gross National Product—The total value of goods and services produced in a nation in a given time period (usually a year).

Figure 6. The airspace over any nation is sovereign

about a comparison in these terms.

Other nations such as Germany, Britain, France, and Japan are behind the United States and the Soviet Union, even though they do have quite good aerospace programs. Consider each of these four nations and see if you can tell which of the five elements might be limiting their aerospace power.

We have looked at how strong aerospace industry, military establishment, and research and development programs contribute to the present capability of aerospace power. We also outlined how resources, population, industrial development and political and geographic conditions impact on the future of a country's place in aerospace. These are all parts of the first major element—a nation's "capability to act." Now let's look at the second element—"the right to fly."

RIGHT TO FLY

A nation's right to fly, whether within the atmosphere or in space, is always political. It has nothing whatsoever to do with capability. It is not related to the number or type of aircraft that a nation possesses or to the skill of its pilots. The right to fly relates to the *ownership of the air space over a nation, and the nation's ability to guarantee its sovereignty.**

Aviation. Prior to 1909, the questions of who owned the air and the sovereignty of the air space within the boundaries of a nation were mainly theoretical.

*Sovereignty refers to absolute control over something with complete freedom from outside control.

There had been a few balloon flights in Europe that crossed over another nation's border, but all heavier-than-air flights had taken place entirely within one country. On July 25, 1909, this ended because Louis Bleriot flew a heavier-than-air aircraft across the English Channel from France to England.

With Bleriot's flight these questions became practical ones. For centuries, nations recognized the sovereignty of another nation's land. Borders between countries were established and recognized. They could be defended by the nation's armies to prevent others from crossing. Now, suddenly, a nation's borders were not sovereign. They could not be protected by armies because an aircraft could fly right over them.

In 1910, France held the world's first international aviation conference in Paris. The United States was not among the nations which were invited to the conference. The conference was held to discuss other matters, but the right to fly soon became the major topic of discussion. The Germans proposed that an international right to fly freely between countries be granted to all nations. It would also allow all aircraft, regardless of nationality, the right to takeoff and land freely in all nations. The British delegation could not accept this proposal because national boundaries would become meaningless. The conference ended without any agreement being reached.

Less than a year later the British Parliament passed the first Aerial Navigation Act. This law was amended in 1913 to give Britain the complete power to regulate entry of foreign aircraft into England and to establish zones over which no foreign aircraft could fly.

In 1913, France and Germany signed an agreement which required that aircraft from one nation could never cross the other nation's border except by invitation. Civil aircraft could cross only after asking for and receiving a permit from the other nation. The agreement also allowed each nation to establish restricted zones. Very soon both nations had restricted all their airspace except for narrow corridors running between large cities.

These early laws and agreements were the first statements of what was to become the major premise of the right to fly —*every nation has absolute control of the airspace over its own territory.* Every nation can fly within its own airspace as it sees fit and can allow all others to enter as it sees fit or exclude them entirely.

At the end of World War I, the Peace Conference was convened in Paris. There were two aviation-related issues which were discussed during this conference. One had to do with prohibiting all military aviation in Germany, and the other addressed an international agreement on civil aviation.

Several proposals were made concerning the right to fly through another nation's airspace. One proposal considered the air to be "free" territory and would allow absolute freedom of air travel by any nation over another nation. Another would provide sovereignty of a nation's airspace up to a certain altitude and absolute freedom to fly above that altitude. A third proposal was to provide absolute sovereignty to all airspace above a nation's territory.

Figure 7. Paris Convention of 1919

The proposal which was selected and which formed the international agreement was officially called the Convention Relating to the Regulation of Aerial Navigation and was signed on October 13, 1919. Unofficially, this agreement has come to be known as the *Paris Convention of 1919.* The foundation for all other international agreements relating to sovereignty over airspace, including the principle of the right to fly, was provided for by this agreement. It reads as follows:

"ARTICLE 1. The High Contracting Parties recognize that every power has complete and exclusive sovereignty over the air space above its territory. For the purpose of present Convention the territory of a State shall be understood as including the national territory; both that of the mother country and of the colonies, and the territorial water adjacent thereto."

"ARTICLE 2. Each contracting State undertakes in time of peace to accord freedom of innocent passage above its territory to the aircraft of the other contracting States, provided that the conditions are observed."

The right of a nation to establish areas over which no foreign aircraft can fly was provided in Article 3 of the agreement.

The agreement was adopted and signed by all of the World War I Allied nations except the United States. However, in 1926 the United States did declare sovereignty over its airspace in the Air Commerce Act of 1926.

Every international aviation agreement since 1919 has reaffirmed the sovereignty of a nation's airspace. Of particular importance is the Convention on International Civil Aviation which was held in Chicago in 1944. Article 1 of this convention reaffirmed the sovereignty of national airspace. "The contracting States recognize that every State has complete and exclusive sovereignty over the air-space over its territory." This convention established the International Civil Aviation Organization (ICAO). The International Air Transport Agreement was also signed during the "Chicago Agreement" and established what are called the "five air freedoms." These apply only to civil aircraft in time of peace and are recognized by all nations who signed this agreement. The "five air freedoms" are:

1. The freedom to fly across a nation's territory without landing.
2. The freedom to land for non-traffic purposes.
3. The freedom to put down passengers and cargo originating in the nation of the aircraft.
4. The freedom to take on freight and passengers destined for the nation of the aircraft.
5. The freedom to take on or put down passengers and cargo destined for or coming from a third nation.

An example of the first freedom would be a United States aircraft flying from New York to Rome. It would be allowed to fly over Great Britain, France and Switzerland provided they had signed the agreement. The second freedom would allow the above flight from New York to Rome to land in London for refueling or repair (but not to pick up or discharge passengers).

The third freedom would allow this airline to pick up passengers and cargo in New York and disembark them in Rome. The fourth freedom would then allow passengers to board in Rome for a return flight to New York.

The fifth freedom would allow the Rome to New York flight to land in Madrid, Spain, to load and unload passengers provided Spain had signed the agreement.

The "five freedoms" are recognized by most nations of the world today. However, rather than a single agreement covering all nations, there are

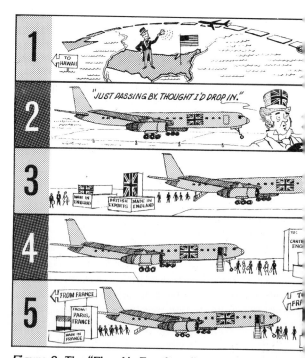

Figure 8. The "Five Air Freedoms"

FREE OUTER SPACE

SOVEREIGN AIR SPACE

EARTH

Figure 9. Space is free and open to all

hundreds of small agreements which have been signed between two or more nations.

Under all of these international agreements covering the right to fly, it has been recognized that no one has control over flight above the "high seas." The "high seas" are internationally recognized as being the oceans outside a nation's territorial waters. Freedom of travel on the high seas was recognized for centuries before flight occurred. This freedom to travel on the seas was extended to the freedom to travel over the seas.

Space. The right to fly in space has been determined in a different fashion from flight through the air. None of the international agreements concerning the sovereignty of airspace ever placed an altitude limit on airspace. It was assumed, and agreed upon, that airspace continued upward to the top of the air (atmosphere). Of course, no one knew where that was. Most people in those days thought that the atmosphere had a top, and no one imagined anyone flying above it. What we are saying is that no one ever worried about anyone flying over their territory in space. Therefore, they ignored the sovereignty of space. On October 4, 1957, this aspect became a practical concern when the first satellite was launched into space.

On December 13, 1958, the General Assembly of the United Nations established a committee on the peaceful uses of outer space. Among the things considered by this committee was the question of sovereignty of space over a nation's territory. Since no nation objected to the flights of the first United States and Soviet Union satellites over its territory, the committee's finding was that "there may have been initiated the recognition or establishment of a generally accepted rule to the effect that in principle, outer space is, on conditions of equality, freely available for exploration and use by all . . ." What they were saying is that since no nation complained about satellites flying over its territory, it must not be claiming sovereignty over the space over its territory. This finding is the basis for international recognition of the right to fly in space. Space has the same status as the high seas—free and open for all to use.

We have examined the right to fly, both in air and space, in quite some detail. Let us not lose sight of the fact that the right to fly is a political right. This means that it is subject to change as national and international politics changes. It also means that the right to fly, like all political rights, must be defended.

All of the international agreements we have discussed are based on civilian activities in times of peace. For military activities in times of war, these agreements are meaningless. If one nation enters another nation's airspace without permission, this is an act of aggression. The nation whose airspace was violated has international organizations to which it can appeal. However, if the first nation entered the airspace specifically for the purpose of aggression, the nation attacked has only its own military strength or its allies to rely upon for protection.

As an example, the political agreements between the United States and Japan provided no protection against the Japanese attack on Pearl Harbor. The attack was a violation of our airspace and led to our entry into World War II. The same holds true today. Our right to fly in the air or in space is guaranteed only by our ability to defend it. This requires a strong military capability.

We have looked at Aerospace Power as a nation's total capacity to act in the aerospace environment. This capacity requires both the *capability* and the *right* to act. Before you continue on to the

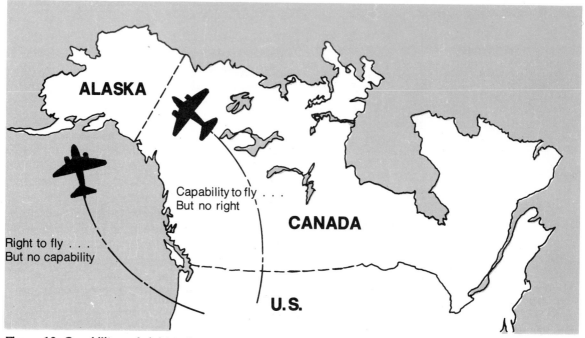

Figure 10. Capability and right to fly

next chapter, let us provide one more example to show the difference between capability and right.

The United States has the exclusive right to fly in the airspace over the United States including Alaska, Hawaii, and Puerto Rico. To fly from the lower 48 states to Alaska there are two routes an airplane can take. One is out over the ocean and the other is an inland route over Canada. For many years we did not have aircraft which could fly non-stop to Alaska over the ocean route. We did have airplanes which could reach Alaska by flying over Canada, but we did not have an agreement with Canada which allowed us to fly over her territory. In this case we had the *right* to fly the ocean route but not the *capability*. For the inland route we had the *capability* but not the *right* (see fig. 10).

Another example would be in space exploration. All nations on Earth have the right to fly into space, but only the United States, Russia, Japan, Australia, and several European countries have the capability (the capability to act in space—not necessarily manned flight which capability is limited to the U.S.

and USSR). The other nations of the world lack either the desire or the resources to explore space, and therefore lack the capability.

The factors of capability and right which are essential to achieving aerospace power superiority give rise to some burning questions. Just how strong is our aerospace power right now? Is it ready to perform its functions? If not, what is needed to get it ready? What does the future hold for aerospace power in the United States?

Time is a prime essential in our defense preparations. It is also vital to maintaining our world leadership in civil aviation and aerospace manufacturing. Time is consumed by the complex problems that accompany each technical advancement in the development of aerospace power.

Today, the Congress, the military, the industrial world, the airlines, and the people are attempting to get answers to these questions. We will look at the various elements of aerospace power in the remainder of this Part in an attempt to find some of these answers.

Figure 11. All nations have the right to fly into space

Chapter 3-2

MILITARY AEROSPACE POWER

I n the last chapter we mentioned that the right to fly both within the atmosphere and in space is always political. Since it is political, it is subject to change, either peacefully or through force. The only way that we can guarantee our right to fly is to be sufficiently strong to prevent anyone from taking it away. This really requires several types of strength. We must be economically strong so that we can afford both the military programs necessary for security and the non military programs which provide us with our current life-style. We must be morally strong to insure that the freedoms envisioned by our founders are maintained. And, of course, we must be militarily strong to prevent anyone from challenging our right to fly.

Aerospace power is a formidable weapon of war. A single aircraft today can carry weapons capable of unleashing more destructive power than that of all weapons used in World War II. The Intercontinental Ballistic Missile (ICBM) makes the weapons and techniques used in wars of yesterday obsolete. Today's aerospace weapons include not only the mighty armaments of modern fighters, bombers and ICBMs, but also the missile-launching capabilities of nuclear-powered submarines. The Army has also entered the aerospace age with its battlefield missiles and armed attack helicopters.

Many people would like to completely ignore the military aspect of aerospace. To them the military means war and war is distasteful. In our nation and our form of government, the military also means peace and is regarded as an effective and essential way to preserve it. George Washington said it best when he stated, "To be prepared for war is one of the most effectual means of preserving the peace."

The general learning objective for this chapter is for you to know military aerospace activities that help determine U.S. aerospace power. To reach this objective, you must pattern your study of the material according to the *specific learning objectives* listed in the Appendix of this textbook.

NATIONAL POLICY AND THE MILITARY

The national policy of the United States is the broad course of action adopted by the United States Government. This course of action includes the foreign and domestic programs established to promote the vital interests of the United States. Our representatives in Congress, the Judiciary, and the

President and his administration formulate the national policy. Many parts of the national policy are established by the Constitution and therefore are constant. These include our Bill of Rights and many of our basic laws. Other parts of the national policy change from year to year and from administration to administration. As changes occur in the world, our national policy must change to accommodate them. An example of this would be our energy policy. As fuel becomes more scarce and therefore more expensive, our national policy toward energy must change. This may include rationing, higher prices, or shortages.

Included in our national policy are economic, political, social, scientific, technological, and military programs. The military programs are grouped together into what is generally termed our national security policy.

National security policy has as its basic task to *guarantee the security of the United States and its vital interests.* To do this, the military forces of the Army, Navy, Marine Corps, and the Air Force are coordinated and controlled by a single civilian agency—the Department of Defense. The Department of Defense (DOD) was established by the National Security Act of 1947. Prior to this act, the Army and the Navy were under separate control, the Marine Corps was part of the Navy, and the Air Force was part of the Army.

The basic objectives of the United States military forces are to:

(1) Prevent military aggression or action which threatens the security of the United States or its allies.
(2) Defend United States territory, waters, and air space.
(3) Engage in all necessary military operations and other duties assigned.
(4) Quickly and effectively end hostilities on terms favorable to the United States.

Figure 12. The "Great White Fleet"

These four objectives and the special capabilities required to accomplish them are the subjects of this chapter.

To be a useful part of our national policy, the military must be able to react to many types of involvement. These can range from just a show of military strength to an all-out involvement in total nuclear war.

A display of military strength as a method of implementing our national policy has been used for many years. In 1908, President Theodore Roosevelt had a fleet of ships painted white to increase its visibility (the "Great White Fleet" fig. 12) and sent it on a round-the-world cruise to demonstrate our naval strength to the world. In those days a nation's navy was its first line of defense. In 1962, during the Cuban Missile Crisis, President John F. Kennedy placed our active-duty forces on alert and our reserve forces on standby. This was a show of strength to get the Soviet Union to remove her nuclear missiles from Cuba, and it worked.

THE NATURE OF CONFLICT

Conflict between nations has always been a part of international relations. To resolve conflict before it results in armed or military action is the purpose of *diplomacy.* Usually, conflicts are resolved by negotiation or by some type of political, economic, or psychological action. We often see conflicts settled by a nation or group of nations putting economic pressure on one or both members of the conflict. In

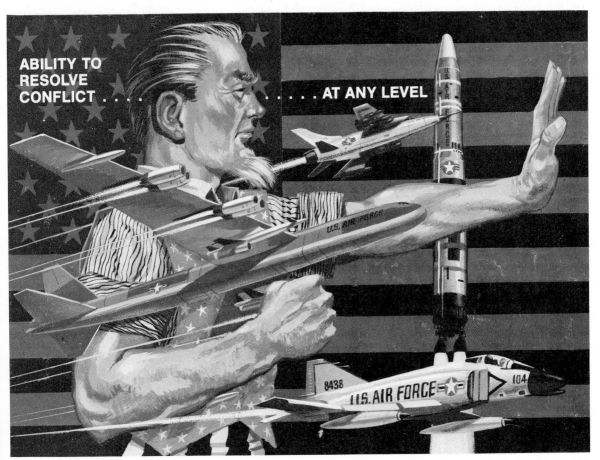

ABILITY TO RESOLVE CONFLICT . . . . AT ANY LEVEL

Figure 13. National Security Policy

Figure 14. F-100 in Vietnam

some extreme cases, other nations may impose an economic boycott in order to stop the conflict. When this is done, the other nations refuse to buy anything from, or sell anything to, the conflicting nations until the disagreement is settled. Another technique which is often used to settle international conflicts is to offer one or both conflicting nations a political or economic reward for resolving the conflict. All nations of the world today recognize that they are not completely self-sufficient. They all rely on other nations for certain resources. To cut off or even threaten to cut off these vital resources can usually settle most conflicts. Fortunately, it is rare that military action is required to resolve international differences. Many people think that wars happen very frequently or maybe even continuously. But just consider, every time one nation has a difference of opinion with another nation there is a chance of war occurring. If you think this way, wars are actually quite rare.

Alliances between nations, such as NATO (North Atlantic Treaty Organization) or the Warsaw Pact, are another way to reduce the chance of armed conflict. In these alliances, several nations band together for their common defense. This is less costly than for each nation to maintain a large army, and at the same time provides more strength than each country would have standing alone. In these alliances, all nations have the same basic political philosophy, and the alliance is led by one large powerful nation. In the case of NATO this leader is the United States. The leader of the Warsaw Pact nations is the Soviet Union.

The United Nations is an international organization which was formed to reduce the chance of war. This body includes nations of all political philosophies enabling them to meet and discuss problems which affect the entire world. The United Nations has no military forces of its own and must resort to political, economic, and psychological action to solve international differences. Sometimes, like in Korea during the 1950s, the member nations of the United Nations will provide military forces to a unified command to fight a war. Also, the United Nations often serves in a peacekeeping role, using troops from member nations to patrol demilitarized zones and to act as "international policemen."

LEVELS OF ARMED CONFLICT

Occasionally, the conflict between nations is not resolved peacefully and military action occurs. There are many possible levels of warfare. Generally the types of armed conflict are placed into two categories—*limited war* and *general war*. The national policy of the U.S. is to prevent any war. General war is total all-out warfare using the most modern military weapons, including nuclear weapons. Limited war is a war conducted at any level below that of general war. The degree of United States involvement in any war will vary according to the national priorities of the United States. If a limited war breaks out in an area where the United States has a great deal at stake, we would become more involved than in an area where we have little interest. Our national interest will determine the size of the military force we send, the amount of destruction allowed, and how long the war will last.

At the lowest end, our involvement would be to provide assistance in the form of weapons as we have done in the Arab/Israeli conflicts. At the other extreme we would commit many troops and other types of support as we did in the Korean and Vietnam Wars.

One of the problems in fighting a limited war is to keep the conflict at as low a level as possible. There is always the possibility of the war escalating* to a level which cannot be controlled in the small war. If nuclear powers are involved, the danger of escalation to a general (nuclear) war is a real threat. In Korea and Vietnam the threat of Russia or China being drawn into the war was one factor which limited the level of warfare and the weapons used.

The United States must be able to react quickly to any level of limited warfare as well as to an all-out

*Escalating—to expand or grow more intense.

general war. This requires a military capability which is flexible and provides a wide range of options in case of military conflict. It also requires a mobile force, one which can be moved rapidly to the war zone with all of its equipment. These factors, together with the fact that our military strength provides security in some degree to most of the free world, are the reasons why our defense budget is so high.

LIMITED WARFARE

Since World War II, the United States has been involved in several limited wars. The most notable have been the Korean War (1950-1954), and the Vietnam War (1964-1975). As we mentioned earlier, limited wars are fought at a level below that of general (nuclear) war. The limited war usually ends with a negotiated settlement rather than a victory by one side or the other. Our involvement in limited wars is determined by our national interest in the nation or nations involved. This means that as our national interest and our national policy changes, our level of involvement in a limited war will also change. This was very evident in Vietnam where our involvement went from a few advisors to more than 500,000 United States troops, to a complete withdrawal of all United States support. In general, the strategy followed in limited warfare is to: (1) strike rapidly to end the conflict as soon as possible, and (2) keep the conflict from spreading. Both of these require the unique capabilities of our military aerospace forces.

AEROSPACE FORCES IN LIMITED WAR

The United States Army, Navy, Air Force, and Marine Corps each has a separate role or set of roles to perform in insuring the security of the United States and our allies. If a limited war breaks out between two countries which requires the United States to commit military forces, the number and type of forces used will depend on how large the conflict is. Often the conflict can be ended rapidly with a very small force. On other occasions, what starts as a small conflict which seems easy to settle will grow into a large, long-duration war. This is what happened in Vietnam. The military forces of the United States are organized and can be used to stop the conflict early before it grows. However, you must remember that the decision as to when to commit troops and how many is a political decision, not a military one. To wait too long before sending troops, or to send too few, is often worse than committing troops too early.

United States Readiness Command. In 1972 a unified command of United States Army and United States Air Force units was established. This command is called the United States Readiness Command and its purpose is to have a reserve of combat-ready forces based in the United States which can be moved anywhere in the world on short notice. They will be used to reinforce United States commands throughout the world or to respond rapidly to other emergencies anywhere on the globe.

Figure 15. Airborne Troops

The United States Readiness Command headquarters staff includes officers and enlisted men and women from the U.S. Army, Navy, Air Force, and Marine Corps; and Air Force civilian personnel.

The commander in chief is an Army general; and the deputy commander in chief, who also serves as chief of staff, is an Air Force lieutenant general.

Army forces assigned to Readiness Command include the XVIII Airborne Corps and III Corps, with headquarters at Fort Bragg, N.C., and Fort Hood, Texas, respectively. The two corps' forces include airborne, air assault, mechanized, armored, infantry, and special forces units. Air Force forces assigned

to the command include the Ninth Air Force and the Twelfth Air Force, with headquarters at Shaw Air Force Base, S.C., and Bergstrom Air Force Base, Texas, respectively. These forces include tactical fighter, tactical reconnaissance, special operations squadrons, and technical command and control elements. Tactical airlift is provided by Military Airlift Command squadrons with C-130 aircraft. Strategic or long-range heavy airlift is provided by Military Airlift Command C-141 and C-5 aircraft. In-flight refueling for overseas deployments of combat and transport aircraft is provided by Strategic Air Command KC-135 jet tanker aircraft.

U.S. Navy and Marine Corps forces are not assigned to United States Readiness Command. However, these forces can be provided if required. A small number of Navy and Marine Corps staff officers are assigned to headquarters to assure that they understand how they might be used by Readiness Command if required.

A Joint Special Operations Support Element also is located at MacDill Air Force Base. It is staffed by officers and enlisted men and women from the U.S. Army, Navy, Air Force and Marine Corps.

Under the operational command of Readiness Command, the Joint Special Operations Support Element provides unconventional warfare experts to help the staffs of other U.S. unified commands when needed for joint readiness exercises, contingency operations, or in the event of major conflicts.

United States Air Force. In addition to providing airlift and tactical support to the United States Readiness Command, the United States Air Force has other responsibilities in limited wars. As a limited war escalates and lasts longer, the United States Air Force provides continuing airlift and tactical air support.

Tactical air support is comprised of four basic tasks, all aimed at supporting the ground troops in the battle area (see fig. 16). These four basic tasks are: (1) *counter air operations,* which are designed to gain air superiority over the battlefield; (2) *interdiction,* which is designed to deny the enemy use of supply routes and communications; (3) *close air support,* which delivers aerial firepower against enemy positions within the battle area; and (4) *tactical air reconnaissance,* which obtains information about the activities and resources of the enemy.

The priority assigned to these four basic tasks will vary according to the type and duration of the

Figure 16. Close air support

conflict. In a very short and limited engagement, the tactical air support may involve only close air support. In a larger and longer-duration conflict, priority would be given to counter air and interdiction, although reconnaissance and close air support would also be provided. Also, the number of aircraft assigned to each task will vary. If the enemy has a very small air force, there would be no need to assign a great many of our aircraft to the counter air mission.

In the airlift mission, the United States Air Force supplies both strategic and tactical airlift support. Strategic airlift is the continuous movement of personnel and equipment into the battle zone. These missions may involve airlift from the United States to the overseas battle zone, or from another overseas command to the overseas battle zone. An example of strategic airlift was the airlift of the 101st Airborne Division from Kentucky to Vietnam in November of 1967.

Tactical airlift support involves the movement of men and material within the battle area. Tactical airlift can deliver these troops and equipment faster and into areas where other forms of transportation cannot go. The men and equipment can either be air dropped or, if there is an airfield available, they can be landed.

United States Army. As our nation's main land force, the Army is responsible for defeating the enemy in land combat and occupying the territory captured. In recent years the methods of accomplishing this have changed dramatically. The Army still has its infantry, artillery, and armored divisions, but it also has its own aerospace capability. The *airmobile division* (fig. 17) is a rapid assault division equipped with over 400 helicopters and fixed-wing observation aircraft. The helicopters include

Figure 17. Airmobile Division members

heavy-lift transport helicopters, light observation helicopters and armed attack helicopters. The airmobile division moves rapidly, using its helicopters to move men and equipment into the battle area. The helicopters are then used for resupply and reinforcement and to evacuate the wounded. The airmobile division has no armor, but it is equipped with light artillery and its own close air support from the attack helicopters. United States Air Force tactical air support is also available if needed.

In addition to the airmobile division, the United States Army also is equipped with many and varied missiles to support its ground operations. We have already discussed the battlefield missiles, antiaircraft missiles, and antitank missiles in Chapter 4-6.

United States Navy. The Navy's overall mission in time of war is fourfold: (1) to seek out and destroy

Figure 18. F—14A carrier landing

enemy sea forces; (2) to destroy or interrupt enemy shipping; (3) to maintain control of the sea; and, (4) to conduct land and air operations necessary to accomplish these objectives.

In limited wars, the Navy provides both aviation support and gunfire support to the troops engaged in battle. Naval aviation has a built in flexibility and speed because it operates from a movable, self-supporting air base—the aircraft carrier. The aircraft carrier has several valuable characteristics. It can move rapidly to the battle area, and since 70% of the Earth's surface is covered with water, it can reach almost any land area with its aircraft. Air strikes from aircraft carriers can be made more rapidly and more frequently, over a shorter range, and from unpredictable directions. The aircraft carrier also eliminates the need to build expensive airfields. However, let's not lose sight of the limitations of aircraft carriers. They are vulnerable to being sunk, either by aircraft or by submarines.

United States Marine Corps. The United States Marine Corps is organized as a naval force which functions as a highly mobile air-ground team. However, the Marine Corps is not a part of the Navy as many people think. It is a separate military service within the Department of the Navy. The mission of the Marine Corps is to seize and defend advanced naval bases and conduct operations essential to naval campaigns. The Marines can be and often are given missions not associated with naval campaigns.

The Marine Corps is organized into Fleet Marine Forces, each of which consists of one or more Marine divisions and one or more air wings. Marine divisions and air wings are always located together and form an air-ground team. Marine Corps air wings are equipped with fighter, reconnaissance and attack aircraft as well as helicopters and transports. The air wings can operate from United States Navy aircraft carriers or land airfields. The Fleet Marine Forces are highly mobile, self-contained combat units with their own tactical air support.

The military forces of the United States are highly organized, well equipped, and able to react quickly to any level of limited warfare. Within the military structure they can react to small, guerrilla type raids or to large, long-duration conflicts.

GENERAL WARFARE

The national security policy of the United States is to prevent all military actions which threaten the security of the United States and areas considered vital to its interests. It has been determined that, of all levels of conflict, the most serious in terms of the survival of the United States is general warfare. With the advent of nuclear weapons, there can be no winner in a general war between nuclear powers. Therefore, number one priority has been given to *deterrence* of general war. Deterrence means *prevention through fear, anxiety, or doubt.* This concept is based on convincing any potential enemy that an attack on the United States, or our allies, will lead to *retaliation** which would be so destructive to their homeland that the cost of victory would be unacceptable. Strategic deterrence has been our defense policy for more than thirty years and it is vital that the concept be understood.

Deterrence is a state of mind which causes an enemy to question or doubt their ability to win if they attacked us. In order to create this doubt in the mind of a potential enemy, we must convince them that we possess two things—(1) the military capability to destroy them, and (2) the strong determination to use our power if necessary.

Capability. When World War II ended, we were the only nation in the world that possessed nuclear weapons. We also had a bomber (B-29) which could deliver those weapons anywhere in the world. At that point there was absolutely no doubt in the minds of the Soviet leaders, or anyone else in the world, that we had the military capability to win any general war we entered.

Since that time, we have lost our monopoly in nuclear weapons. At least five** other nations are known to possess them. Technological advancements have also led to other methods of delivering the weapons such as missiles. These new developments make it more difficult to maintain the military capability necessary to insure deterrence.

The "arms race" between the United States and Soviet Union has been caused by the need to maintain our military capability during a period of rapid technological advancement. This has been a very costly process because each new advance by the Soviet Union must be counter-balanced by a similar advance by the United States. By the time new weapons become operational, new technology has usually made them obsolete in terms of what is possible, and more advanced ones are begun to ensure the maintenance of a lead over the potential enemy.

As advances in knowledge and technology were made, the problems of deterrence became more difficult. At first, our bombers alone were enough of a threat to deter war. Then the missile was developed, making deterrence even more difficult. The end result of all of these developments is that deterrence has become very expensive. Since World War II we have developed such strategic bombers as the B-50, B-36, B-47, B-58 and B-52. We have also developed ICBMs like the *Atlas, Titan,* and *Minuteman.* None of them have ever been used in general warfare and many people look at this as a big waste of money. The fact is that all of them have fulfilled their purpose—*to prevent general warfare.* Ideally, they were developed never to be used, but also to be effective if used. If any of them had been used, the national policy of deterrence would have failed. If we look at them from this perspective, these weapons are the most *successful* ever developed. *Since prevention of war is the goal, the most successful weapons are those that are never used* (fig. 19).

*Retaliation—to return like for like; to pay back injury for injury.
**Soviet Union, Great Britain, France, India, Peoples Republic of China.

CAPABILITY . . . WE MUST HAVE THE MILITARY STRENGTH TO WIN ANY WAR.

SINCE PREVENTION OF WAR IS THE PURPOSE, THE ONLY SUCCESSFUL WEAPONS ARE THOSE THAT ARE NEVER USED.

Figure 19. Capability

Determination. Equally as important as capability to the concept of deterrence is the courage or the determination to use our military strength if necessary. It is easy to see why this strong determination is necessary. Regardless of how much military strength you have, if an enemy believes you will not use it, the enemy will not be deterred. In fact, with the very survival of the United States resting on deterrence, we must be careful not to give a potential enemy any reason to question our determination. If the enemy is not absolutely certain we will use our military strength, it might lead to nuclear war by mistake (fig. 20).

An analogy to this policy of deterrence might be two boys of equal ability on the school playground. As long as both of them are unsure of who would win, a fight probably will not occur. If one of the boys obtains something that gives him an advantage, the other boy must match him or risk the chance of an attack. This stalemate will continue only so long as

DETERMINATION . . . WE MUST HAVE THE COURAGE TO USE OUR STRENGTH IF NECESSARY.

Declaration of Independence

When in the course of human events it becomes necessary for one people to dissolve the political bands which have connected them with another and to assume among the powers of the earth, the separate and equal station to which the laws of Nature and of Nature's God entitle

THE MILITARY AND THE CITIZENRY MUST BE UNITED TOWARD THE GOAL OF KEEPING THE PEACE.

"SO THAT GOVERNMENT OF THE PEOPLE, BY THE PEOPLE, FOR THE PEOPLE, SHALL NOT PERISH FROM THE EARTH."
A. LINCOLN

Figure 20.

both boys remain convinced that the other will fight if necessary. If, for some reason one of the boys begins to think that the other may be "chicken," it will increase the likelihood of a fight.

Today our deterrent policy is founded on *equivalency* and *second strike.* The policy of equivalency means that rather than trying to maintain a military force which is always superior to that of the Soviet Union, we will maintain one equivalent (equal force) to the Soviet Union. Second strike means that our national policy is never to attack first, but wait until attacked and then retaliate. These policies make our maintenance of a deterrent force even more complex. It means that our nuclear forces

must be able to survive a first strike by an enemy and still be able to deliver a blow so destructive to the enemy that he will not want to attack us. Of course, our nuclear forces must also be able to penetrate the enemy's defenses. If the enemy believes his defenses are strong enough to prevent our second strike, again deterrence is questionable. In order to be effective, our nuclear forces must be able to *survive* and *penetrate.*

Triad. The flexibility required to survive and penetrate the enemy's defenses is provided by the Triad. Triad is based on having three completely independent delivery systems—(1) Intercontinental Ballistic

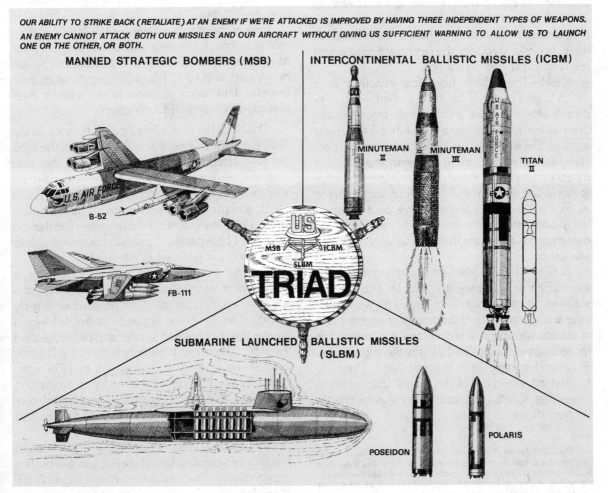

OUR ABILITY TO STRIKE BACK (RETALIATE) AT AN ENEMY IF WE'RE ATTACKED IS IMPROVED BY HAVING THREE INDEPENDENT TYPES OF WEAPONS. AN ENEMY CANNOT ATTACK BOTH OUR MISSILES AND OUR AIRCRAFT WITHOUT GIVING US SUFFICIENT WARNING TO ALLOW US TO LAUNCH ONE OR THE OTHER, OR BOTH.

MANNED STRATEGIC BOMBERS (MSB)

B-52

FB-111

INTERCONTINENTAL BALLISTIC MISSILES (ICBM)

MINUTEMAN II

MINUTEMAN III

TITAN II

US
MSB — ICBM
SLBM
TRIAD

SUBMARINE LAUNCHED BALLISTIC MISSILES (SLBM)

POSEIDON

POLARIS

Figure 21. The Triad.

Missiles (ICBMs), (2) Submarine Launched Ballistic Missiles (SLBMs), and (3) Manned Strategic Bombers (MSBs).* (See fig. 21).

Triad's strength and flexibility lie in the independence of the three systems which eliminates an enemy's ability to destroy all three systems with a single first strike. For example, if an enemy concentrates on destroying our ICBMs, we still have the SLBMs and MSBs with which to retaliate. The Triad also reduces the likelihood that a future technological breakthrough will make all three systems obsolete. This also further complicates a potential enemy's defensive problems because he must now defend against three types of delivery systems. Basically, the Triad creates *doubt* in an adversary's mind and it is this doubt which serves as a deterrent.

Each system of the Triad has certain advantages and certain shortcomings. The combination of all three, however, provides the flexibility and strength required to provide deterrence.

ICBM—The ICBMs have *fast reaction time* which means that they can be launched within minutes of attack and will arrive at their targets within one-half hour. They are also very *difficult to defend against.* Because they are buried in hardened (concrete) silos, they can survive an enemy attack unless a near or direct hit is made on a silo. However, there is increasing concern that new technology relating to improved accuracy and explosive force of attacking missiles are making them more vulnerable and new methods to ensure their survivability are being worked on.

SLBM—The one great advantage possessed by the SLBMs is that they are mobile. The nuclear submarines can remain submerged for weeks at a time and can roam over thousands of square miles of ocean. With present technology, it is impossible for an enemy to locate and destroy the submarines. SLBMs also have *fast reaction time.* They are located off the coast of the Soviet Union (much closer than ICBMs), and the flight time of the missile is often 15 minutes or less.

*The ICBMs consist of the Minuteman and Titan missiles buried in concrete silos across the north central portion of the United States. The SLBMs consist of Polaris and Poseidon missiles aboard our nuclear submarines. MSBs consist of the B-52 and FB-111A which are either in the air or positioned at Strategic Air Command bases.

MSB—One major advantage of the manned strategic bomber is that it has a man aboard which enables it to react to unforeseen circumstances and even change targets while in flight. Both ICBMs and SLBMs have a pre-programmed target and this cannot be changed after the missile is launched. The MSBs also are equipped with electronic devices which assist in penetrating an enemy's air defense.

An additional advantage of the MSBs is that they can be recalled. If we suspect an enemy attack, the B-52s and FB-111As can takeoff and start toward their targets. If we discover that the warning was a false alarm, the bombers can be recalled to their bases. This cannot be done with the ICBMs and SLBMs. Once they are launched, we are committed to a nuclear war.

One of the disadvantages of the MSBs is *slow reaction time.* It can take as much as one-half hour to get the bombers airborne if they are not on airborne alert, and 10-12 hours for them to reach their targets. This slow reaction time reduces their chance of surviving a sneak attack.

The MSB leg of our Triad currently rests on the B-52 bomber. During the war in Vietnam, the B-52 did an outstanding job both as a nuclear deterrent and as a conventional bomber. However, this aircraft was designed in the 1940's, the first one flew in 1952, and the newest one came off the assembly line in 1962. Many of our military leaders feel that the B-52 must be replaced in order to have an MSB that could carry out its mission effectively.

The Air Force wanted a new bomber as a replacement for the B-52. The B-1 was developed as a supersonic aircraft using the most modern technology. The Air Force argued that the B-1 would have a better chance to survive and penetrate than the B-52. The major argument against the B-1 was its cost (up to $100 million each). In 1977, after much debate, President Carter stopped production of the B-1 bomber. However, he authorized continued flight testing using the four B-1s which had been built.

In October 1981, President Ronald Reagan reauthorized construction of the B-1 bomber but in a changed form. The new bomber, designated B-1B, will no longer be a supersonic bomber and will carry

Figure 22. Rockwell International's B-1

either conventional and/or nuclear bombs or cruise missiles.

The differences between the original B-1 and the B-1B will be difficult to identify by outward appearance. Structurally, the B-1B will be strengthened to increase the gross takeoff weight from 395,000 pounds to 477,000 pounds. It can carry up to 14 air-launched cruise missiles or additional fuel along the fuselage. The forward weapons bay will be modified to carry cruise missiles or fuel internally.

The B-1B has several other significant advantages over the B-52. The B-1B will fly lower and at a faster low altitude speed than the B-52, while carrying a larger payload. The B-1B is much more economical than the B-52. The B-1B has a longer unrefueled range and thus is less dependent on aerial refueling. It also has fewer crew members (four vs. six on the B-52).

The first aircraft delivery to the Strategic Air Command is expected in late 1985, with an Initial Operational Capability (IOC) of 15 aircraft in late 1986.

STANDOFF BOMBERS AND CRUISE MISSILES

During the controversy over the B-1 bomber, discussion began on two additional weapons systems, the standoff bomber and the cruise missile. Neither of these systems is new. In fact, the Soviet Union has had cruise missiles for many years, just as we have, but they have been for tactical and not air-launched strategic use.

A standoff bomber differs from the B-52, and all other bombers we have built, in that it would never fly over the target it is bombing. All bombers we have developed to date fly over the targets and drop bombs. This requires them to penetrate into the enemy's territory and fly through antiaircraft defenses. They are all classed as *penetrating* bombers. A standoff bomber flies outside the enemy territory and launches missiles. The missiles then penetrate the enemy's defenses and hit the target. Several proposals have been made for a standoff bomber including the Boeing 747 and the Lockheed C-5A.

Cruise missiles are small turbojet-powered missiles which fly at subsonic speed to their targets. An early example of a cruise missile would be the V-1 developed by Germany during World War II. Modern technology enables the cruise missile to fly at very low altitude (under the enemy's radars). They are extremely accurate and have a range of up to 1,500 miles. This allows them to be launched from a standoff bomber, a submarine, or a mobile land based launcher. They are relatively inexpensive (one-half to one million dollars each) when compared to an MSB, an ICBM, or an SLBM. President Carter gave the go-ahead to develop both an air-launched cruise missile and a submarine-launched cruise missile when he canceled the B-1.

Other Air Force Missions. In addition to the strategic and tactical missions we have already discussed, the Air Force also is responsible for space operations.

On September 1, 1982, a new Air Force command called Space Command was formed. Its mission is to control U.S. Air Force space programs including launch and recovery of satellites; support

Figure 23. ALCM (Air-Launched Cruise Missile)

and tracking of military spacecraft in orbit; control of surveillance satellites; navigation, communication and meteorological support using satellites; and space defense.

Space has always been "off limits" for military uses, but we must be prepared to defend ourselves in space if necessary. Some of the space defense operations are to detect, track and identify all objects in space; provide warning of hostile acts in space; and be able to nullify hostile acts in space.

The USAF Space Command will probably eventually become a unified command with responsibility for all military space operations (U.S. Army and U.S. Navy).

Political Limitations.

Our national security policy is developed jointly by professional military leaders and elected and appointed civilians. National security policy must fit within the entire national policy of the United States and therefore is limited by political considerations. For example, our military leadership wants the best possible weapons with which to defend our country. They also want as many of these weapons as they can get. Modern day aerospace weapons systems are very expensive and other national priorities limit the defense budget. The defense budget must compete with federal spending in the areas of welfare assistance, social programs, and all other national programs. Often the defense budget is the one that is cut.

International politics also affects our defense establishment. The first Strategic Arms Limitation Treaty (SALT I), which was signed in 1972, limited the number of strategic missiles which the United States and the Soviet Union can possess (see fig. 24). It did not address manned bombers or cruise missiles. A later agreement signed in Vladivostok, Russia, in 1974, placed a ceiling of 2,400 on all nuclear delivery systems (ICBMs, SLBMs, "heavy" bombers, and cruise missiles).

The Soviet Union and the United States have spent a number of years negotiating a SALT II agreement. This treaty was signed in 1979 by President Carter and Soviet Premier Brezhnev. However, the United States Senate refused to ratify the treaty. The SALT II treaty, therefore, never became "law" although we have been abiding by the accord since it was signed by President Carter. Three major elements in the SALT II treaty discussions were as follows:

(1) The total number of nuclear delivery systems (ICBMs + SLBMs + "heavy" bombers) which each nation can have reduced from 2,400 to between 2,100 and 2,250. Of these, only 1,200 to 1,250 with MIRV warheads, and only 820 of the MIRVed weapons could be ICBMs.

(2) Limitations placed on mobile ICBMs, cruise missiles, and new types of ballistic missiles. A ban placed on deployment of mobile ICBM launchers. All cruise missiles limited to a range of about 1,500 miles and cruise missiles launched from the sea or land limited to a 375 mile range.

(3) The treaty will establish the principles and guidelines to be followed for any SALT III talks.

One of the big reasons the SALT II Treaty was not ratified was the problem of verifying compliance with the treaty. Neither side will allow the other to make on-site inspections of its missile sites or submarines. Any verification must be done by some

1972 SALT I AGREEMENT		
	USSR	US
FIXED LAND BASED ICBMs	1608	1054
SLBMs	950	710
MSBs	NOT LIMITED	NOT LIMITED
CRUISE MISSILES	NOT LIMITED	NOT LIMITED

Figure 24.

other method. Another problem was the definition of a "heavy" bomber. The Soviets do not want the *Backfire* counted in their total number of delivery systems because they claim it does not have sufficient range to bomb the United States. The United States wants the Backfire counted because they claim it can be refueled while in flight and this capability gives it enough range to reach the United States.

There is a constant struggle to balance our national security needs with our needs for international understanding. However, when the stakes are our very survival, we must be willing to negotiate.

The national policy of the United States is to prevent all levels of armed conflict in any area of the world. It is much more difficult to do this for limited

wars than it is to deter general war. There are many emerging nations in the world and they all have conflicts with their neighbors. Our policy is to prevent these conflicts from becoming wars by using political and economic pressure. Only as a last resort, and only if it is absolutely necessary for the national interest, will military forces be committed. This policy is often referred to as *realistic deterrence* and was formulated by the Nixon administration in 1969. Briefly this strategy proposes:

(1) Negotiate for arms control and a gradual reduction in strategic forces.

(2) Avoid future commitment of military forces unless absolutely necessary.

(3) Support all allies and honor all treaties by providing technical and economic aid; the

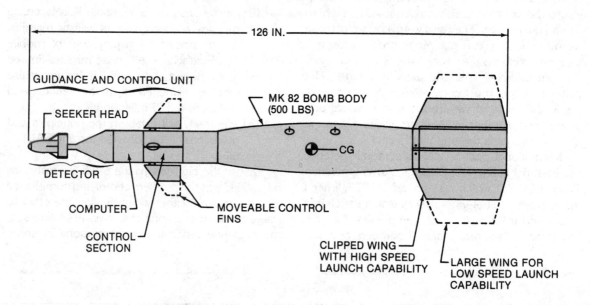

Figure 25. Diagram of a laser-guided "Smart" Bomb

Figure 26. RPV (Remotely Piloted Vehicle) mated to a C-130 aircraft

At the other end of the spectrum would be the commitment of United States forces, such as during the Vietnam War. The United States Army, United States Navy, United States Marine Corps, and United States Air Force all participated in that conflict in a coordinated use of military aerospace power. Bombers, fighters, attack aircraft, helicopters, transports, and reconnaissance aircraft were all used to support the operations of the ground troops. At the peak of the conflict the United States had more than one-half million men and women involved in the war.

Although the Vietnam War ended in defeat for South Vietnam, there can be no doubt that aerospace power played a major role in keeping the South in the war as long as they were. There were also many technological innovations produced by the war. They included guided bombs (TV and laser) which can be delivered to targets with pinpoint accuracy. Remotely piloted vehicles (RPVs) were used for the first time in Vietnam. These small unmanned aircraft are air launched from another aircraft and flown by radio control. They were used as reconnaissance aircraft but can also carry weapons. During this conflict the gunship and helicopter came into widespread use. Although neither was a new development, they became an important part of close air support.

The importance of these new technological developments cannot be overemphasized. Each of them not only strengthens our military aerospace power, but they also permit us to maintain our defense capability with a smaller active duty armed force. Our smaller but better trained and better equipped military force must balance the much larger armed forces of the Soviet Union and its allies.

ally being threatened would furnish the manpower for its own defense.

Within the framework of this policy, our military aerospace capability may be employed at many levels.

During the 1973 Yom Kippur war between Israel and the Arab nations, our involvement consisted of providing military equipment to Israel. These military supplies were airlifted into Israel by United States Air Force C-5A transports. In addition to delivering the supplies rapidly, this airlift demonstrated to the world the strategic airlift capability of the United States Air Force.

Chapter 3-3

CIVILIAN AEROSPACE PROGRAMS I

The civilian capacity to act in the aerospace environment covers all of civil aviation including the commercial airlines and general aviation. Included are: (1) the aircraft, airports, air traffic control facilities, maintenance facilities and the personnel required to support them; (2) the governmental agencies which regulate civil aviation; (3) our civilian space program with all of its scientists, engineers, launch facilities and tracking stations; and (4) the public and private institutions that participate in and regulate our space efforts. In this chapter we will examine the civil aviation aspect and look at the impact it has on our daily lives. We will discuss the government support and control of aviation and our space exploration program in the next chapter.

Civil aviation has become a dominant part of our society in the United States. Today, commercial air travel is a multi-billion dollar business which carries more passengers than all of the buses and railroads combined. With the new reduced air fares, it is sometimes cheaper to travel cross-country by air than by rail or by bus and air transportation compares favorably with other modes as a safe way to travel.

It is not unusual to find that the largest business in a large city or even in an entire state (in terms of money) is a large metropolitan airport. These modern facilities are almost self-contained cities and hundreds of thousands of people pass through them each day. Passengers spend millions of dollars each year in these airports and in the cities served by them. Even the airports which serve smaller communities generate a great deal of revenue and whether or not a community has an adequate airport is becoming a major factor in whether it will be selected as a location for large businesses.

Most of us take all of these contributions of civil aviation for granted. We do not understand how important it is to the continuance of our way of life. It is necessary, however, that we begin to understand and appreciate these contributions.

The general learning objective for this chapter is for you to know the economic and sociological aspects and problems of the civil aerospace programs that help determine U.S. aerospace power. To reach this objective, you must pattern your study of the material according to the *specific learning objectives* listed in the Appendix of this textbook.

AIR TRANSPORTATION

Elsewhere in this text we mentioned that civil aviation includes both air carrier aviation and general aviation. Air carrier aviation is that portion of civil aviation which deals with transporting passengers and/or cargo on a regularly scheduled basis, and is often referred to as "commercial airlines." General aviation is also involved in transportation, but not on a regularly scheduled basis. General aviation also deals with the use of aircraft for a great many uses other than transportation. Our discussion of the social, political, and economic aspects of air transportation in this chapter will deal first with the air carriers and then with general aviation.

HISTORY OF TRANSPORTATION

Some archeologists and anthropologists believe that man has inhabited the Earth for about two million years. For the first 1,990,000 years, walking provided the only form of transportation. For centuries, people spent their lives within one or two days walk of where they were born. They were superstitious, afraid of the dark, and rarely traveled farther than 10-15 miles from the home cave. It is easy to see that this limited the spread of knowledge. Most of these early people remained isolated, never meeting anyone from another tribe or area of the world. In fact, in most cases they were not even aware that people other than themselves existed.

The domestication of animals about 8,000 years ago led to the first big revolution in transportation. The horse permitted travel at a speed only slightly faster than walking. As figure 27 shows, this first development in transportation increased the average speed of travel from two miles per hour to about two and one half miles per hour. It also increased the outward range from ten miles to about fifty miles. In addition to providing mankind with something to ride, horses could carry heavier loads than people could carry on their backs or drag along behind them while walking.

In addition to just increasing the speed and carrying capacity, the domestication of the horse also resulted in an increase in the spread of knowledge. People from different regions began to meet each other and a new development that occurred in one region was seen by others and copied by their tribe. However, there were still barriers (mountains, oceans, rivers, etc.) which many could not yet cross.

About 5,000 years ago, the wheel was invented which again revolutionized transportation. This invention allowed mankind to build wagons which

COMPARISON OF TRANSPORTATION SYSTEMS

FORM OF CARRIER	AVERAGE MILES 1 HOUR
HUMAN WALKING	2
PACK ANIMAL	2.5
WAGON AND TWO HORSES	2.5
CARGO SHIP	22
RAILROAD (U.S.)	30
MOTOR TRUCK	40
AIRPLANE (DC-3)	150
AIRPLANE (707/DC-8)	500
AIRPLANE (747)	600

Figure 27.

could be pulled by beasts of burden, increasing cargo hauling capability many times. However, again, it did little to increase his speed of transportation. The horse trails improved and became crude roads. Towns and cities grew up along these roadways, especially where several of them crossed each other. Civilization was well underway, and knowledge again spread and increased.

At about the same time the wheel was invented, the building of small boats and ships opened the rivers and oceans for transportation. These water vehicles were propelled either by the currents of the rivers or by oars or sails. It wasn't until the early 1800's that steam power came into wide use. The entire structure of civilization was changed by the development of water transportation. The population centers moved from the crossroads to the seacoasts, particularly at the mouths of large rivers. We still see the effect of this today in cities like New York, New Orleans, London, Tokyo, etc.

As the railroads began to dominate land transportation in the late 1800s, civilization followed them. The large cities which built up after 1900 were located along the railroads and are associated with railroads as a form of transportation. Some examples of these in the United States are Kansas City, Chicago, Denver, Dallas, etc.

Highways were developed to carry goods from the rail centers to outlying areas. This development caused civilization to spread outward from the rail centers and other smaller cities began to spring up. These highways carried the first crude automobiles and trucks which were invented in the early 1900s, and suddenly we were in the age of the automobile.

This "thumbnail" history of transportation, and how closely civilization is tied to transportation, takes us from mankind's first appearance on Earth up to the early 1920s. During these 1,999,950 plus years, man's average speed increased from 2 miles per hour to almost 40 miles per hour. In the next fifty years, the development of aviation would increase this average speed to 500 miles per hour for some aircraft. In the one hundred fifty years that railroads have been in existence in the United States, the average speed of a train has increased by only about 10 miles per hour (50%). In the sixty years that trucks have been used for transportation in the United

States, their average speed has increased by only 20 miles per hour (100%). However, in the fifty years that aircraft have been used to carry passengers and/or cargo, their average speed has increased by over 400 miles per hour (over 400%). The effects of these increases in speed on civilization have been revolutionary.

It took George Washington about twelve hours to travel from Philadelphia to New York City. Today, President Reagan can fly from Washington, D.C. to Moscow in less than twelve hours (fig. 28). In 1878, it took about seven days to travel from New York to San Francisco. Today that same trip can be made by air in just five hours. Between 1840 and 1880 (40 years), about 500,000 people traveled over the Oregon Trail by wagon train. This 2,000-mile trail ran from Kansas City, Missouri, to about what is now Portland, Oregon. The trip took four to six months. Today, that same trip would take less than four hours by air, and the commercial airport in Kansas City now boards this same number of people (500,000) every fifty-eight days.

Air transportation affects all of our civilization today because it touches all aspects of our daily lives, either directly or indirectly. It affects the way we live and work and the way we play (leisure time). It also influences our relationships with other nations. It eases world travel and allows cultural exchange. (When the United States normalized relations with mainland China, one of the first acts was for a number of U.S. airlines to request authority to establish routes between the United States and China, and, perhaps coincidentally, China purchased three long-range Boeing 747s on the day of the announcement.) The importance of air transportation can be classified into three areas of impact: (1) economic; (2) social, and (3) political.

Economic Impact

In the United States we have become so dependent on air transportation that our society as we know it could not exist without it. The United States is probably the most air minded nation in the world. In 1981, scheduled air carriers in the United States carried a total of about 286 million passengers. This

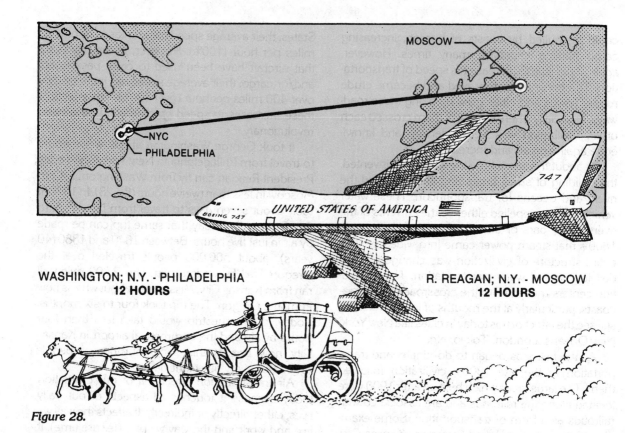

WASHINGTON; N.Y. - PHILADELPHIA
12 HOURS

R. REAGAN; N.Y. - MOSCOW
12 HOURS

Figure 28.

was about 49 percent of the 594 million total passengers carried by the 135 nations of the world which comprise the International Civil Aviation Organization (ICAO).* The United States has only five percent of the world's population, but it carries 49 percent of the world's airline passengers (see fig. 29).

In 1971, the United States scheduled airlines earned $10 billion in total revenue. Ten years later, in 1981, those earnings had grown to over $36.4 billion. This is an increase of over 300 percent. Even if you figure an inflation rate of 10 percent per year, this growth in earnings was over 250 percent. However, this growth in earnings does not tell the entire story and does not mean that the airlines' profits increased by this much. The airlines' operating expenses in 1971 were about $9.7 billion, leaving a net operating income of about $300 million. In 1981, the airlines' operating expenses were over $36.9 billion and this resulted in an operating loss of

$420.7 million. While the airlines' earnings had increased by over 300 percent between 1971 and 1981, their net operating income had decreased by over 200 percent.

A great deal of the increase in operating expenses was accounted for by increases in fuel costs. In 1968, jet fuel cost about 10 cents per gallon as compared with $1.04 cents per gallon in 1981 (see fig. 30). Fuel now accounts for 30.4 percent of the direct operating expenses of the airlines and is expected to increase further. It is interesting to note that the airlines used 306 million fewer gallons of fuel in 1981 than in 1971. This is a decrease of about three percent. During this same period they carried 65 percent more passengers. Since the energy crisis began (1973), the airlines have become increasingly more efficient in their use of fuel. This has been

---

*Does not include the Soviet Union or the People's Republic of China.

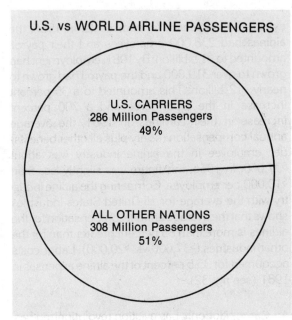

U.S. vs WORLD AIRLINE PASSENGERS

U.S. CARRIERS
286 Million Passengers
49%

ALL OTHER NATIONS
308 Million Passengers
51%

Figure 29. U.S. vs.World Airline Passengers

accomplished in several ways, including flying fewer flights but with more passengers on each flight. The number of full seats on an aircraft divided by the total number of seats on the aircraft is called the passenger load factor. In 1973, the load factor for the entire airline industry averaged 52 percent. This means that nearly half (48%) of all airline seats were empty. By 1981 the load factor had grown to 59 percent. Preliminary figures indicate that the 1982 load factor was about 62 percent. Each increase of one percent in load factor generates about $400 million in revenue.

Other methods employed by the airlines to increase fuel economy are (1) the use of simulators for pilot training, (2) better flight planning using computers. (3) reducing aircraft speed and, (4) using newer technology. Flight simulators are large computer-operated devices which allow a pilot to practice many aspects of an airline flight without ever leaving the ground. They are now used in much of the pilot training by the airlines. This enables the airlines to save millions of gallons of fuel annually.

Using computers in flight planning enables the airlines to select altitudes which are the most economical from a fuel standpoint. This is accomplished by taking advantage of the winds aloft and by avoiding weather and delays en route wherever possible. We will discuss (4) new technology in the fifth chapter of this Part.

In the operation of a Boeing 737 aircraft on a

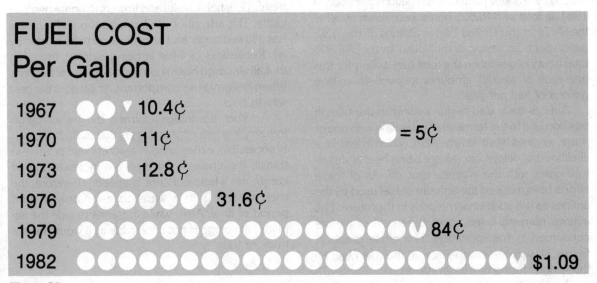

FUEL COST
Per Gallon

1967	●● ▼	10.4¢
1970	●● ▼	11¢
1973	●● ◖	12.8¢
1976	●●●●●● ◖	31.6¢
1979	●●●●●●●●●●●●●●●● ◡	84¢
1982	●●●●●●●●●●●●●●●●●●●●● ◡	$1.09

● = 5¢

Figure 30.

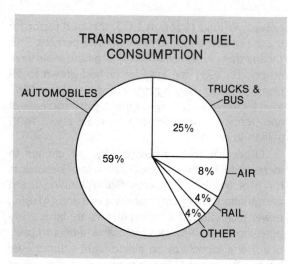

TRANSPORTATION FUEL CONSUMPTION

AUTOMOBILES

TRUCKS & BUS

25%

59%

8% — AIR

4%

4% — RAIL

OTHER

Figure 31.   Source: Department of Transportation

expenses is increases in labor costs. In 1966, the airlines had 238,000 employees and their payroll amounted to $1.5 billion. By 1981, employment had grown to over 319,000 and the payroll had grown to nearly $12 billion. This amounted to a 35 percent increase in the labor force and a 700 percent increase in their earnings. In 1981, the average annual compensation (salary plus all other benefits) per employee in the airline industry was about $37,000. In 1966, this figure was slightly less than $10,000 per employee. Comparing the airline industry with the average for all United States industries shows that the average annual compensation for the airlines is more than 85 percent greater than for the other industries ($37,000 vs. $20,000). Labor costs accounted for 35.5 percent of the airline expenses in 1981 (see fig. 32).

Air Cargo. Not only has aviation revolutionized passenger travel, it also has had a significant impact on moving cargo. In 1977, 3.8 billion ton-miles* of cargo (freight, mail, and express) were carried by the scheduled airlines. By 1981, this had grown to over 7.1 billion ton miles (see fig. 33). This added over $2¼ billion to the airline revenues in 1981, an increase of 150 percent over the $850 million income from air cargo in 1977.

The type of cargo carried by air varies from highly perishable fruits and flowers to entire herds of cattle. The advent of the large jumbo jet freighters has allowed larger and heavier cargo to be carried by air. Regardless of what is being airlifted, the thing that all air cargo has in common is speed of delivery. When delivery time is important, air cargo is the best way to ship.

Another advantage claimed by the air cargo industry is a reduction in losses due to theft. If cargo is accessible, either while in a warehouse or while in transit, the chances for theft are increased. In air cargo, the whole concept is speed. Therefore, the merchandise is in a warehouse for only a short period of time. Also, while in transit (inside the airplane) the cargo is not accessible as it would be in a truck or train.

500-mile flight, reducing the cruising speed of the aircraft from 520 miles per hour to 500 miles per hour will increase the flight time by only three minutes, but it reduces the fuel consumption by seven percent. On a 4,000-mile flight by a 747, if the speed is reduced by only 15 miles per hour, the flight time is increased by only 16 minutes, but the fuel saving would amount to about 900 gallons. This may not seem like much of a saving, but let's look at it another way. This 900-gallon saving on a 4,000-mile flight amounts to about 130 gallons per hour. In 1981, a total of 348,805 hours were flown by all of the 747s in the United States airlines. If this 130-gallon-per-hour saving is multiplied by the 348,805 total hours of operation the total fuel saving for this one type of aircraft amounts to over 45 million gallons of fuel per year.

Airlines have also begun taxiing to the takeoff position and to the terminal after landing with one or more engines shut down. Also, when there is a likelihood of delays, aircraft are being held at departure gates with the engines shut off. All of these efforts have reduced the amount of fuel used by the airlines as will additional methods in the future. The airlines currently used about 8 percent of all fuel consumed in transportation. The circle graph in figure 31 shows a comparison of the fuel used by the various forms of transportation.

Another factor which is increasing the airlines

* Ton-mile is equivalent to carrying one ton of cargo one mile.

A new type of air cargo service which has sprung up in the 1970s is called *small package service* or *expedited air service*. In this type of service, the customer takes the package to the airline ticket counter. The package is checked and handled just like baggage. It is placed on the first flight out and transferred at connecting airports just like baggage. The airlines will guarantee same-day service to any point in the United States which is serviced by that airline.

This special service is limited to quite small packages (120 cubic inches or 70 pounds) and is quite expensive. For example, Eastern Airline *Sprint* service and Delta Airline *Dash* service charge $45.00 to ship a package anywhere on their route system. This cost is the same for any package from one ounce to fifty pounds.

A great many businesses use this small package service to ship important business papers and other important items which must reach a certain place rapidly. This service is also used to ship prescrip-

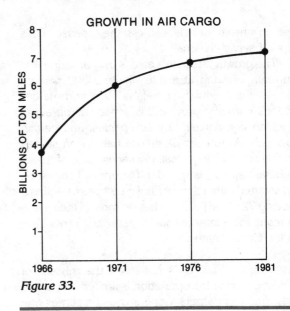

GROWTH IN AIR CARGO

Figure 33.

tions or other vital medicines, eyeglasses, hearing aids, etc. to people. If rapid delivery is vital to a

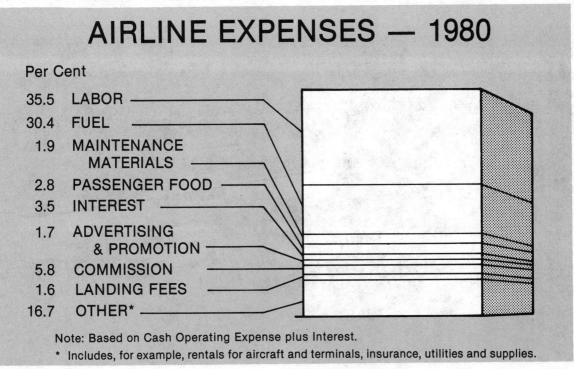

AIRLINE EXPENSES — 1980

Per Cent

35.5	LABOR
30.4	FUEL
1.9	MAINTENANCE MATERIALS
2.8	PASSENGER FOOD
3.5	INTEREST
1.7	ADVERTISING & PROMOTION
5.8	COMMISSION
1.6	LANDING FEES
16.7	OTHER*

Note: Based on Cash Operating Expense plus Interest.
* Includes, for example, rentals for aircraft and terminals, insurance, utilities and supplies.

Figure 32.

Courtesy of ATA

person's health or to a business, the expense of this type of service is small.

The growth rate in this area is truly amazing. It is currently growing at a rate which is 500 percent greater than regular air freight. Most commercial airlines currently provide this service as do some trucking companies, bus companies, and certain railroads. A number of airlines have been started specifically to carry small packages. One of these, Federal Express, is based in Memphis, Tennessee, and started with a fleet of Fanjet Falcons as well as a Boeing 727 (see fig. 34). They do most of their flying at night and guarantee one-day service to anywhere in the United States.

General Aviation. Let's not make the mistake of thinking that air transportation is limited only to the scheduled air carriers. General aviation carries one out of every three intercity air passengers, a total of almost 100 million passengers each year.

Later in this chapter we will discuss airports and their importance to the community. It is important here to point out that only 700 airports in the United States are served by air carriers. The other 14,000 plus United States airports have only general aviation traffic, and the people in these communities use general aviation for their air transporation. Many of these people fly from their home airport into a major metropolitan airport to connect with an air carrier.

There is no requirement for general aviation to report its air transportation earnings to the Civil Aeronautics Board like the air carriers have to. Therefore, it is difficult to measure the economic impact of the 100 million passengers carried annually by general aviaition. Most of these flights are of short length (100-500 miles), and many are taken by businessmen in company-owned airplanes. It is probably conservative to say that this segment of air transportation generates at least five billion dollars in revenue each year. Let's look at only one small segment of this industry in more detail.

The offshore exploration for oil and natural gas has become one of the largest users of helicopters in the nation. In December 1978, there were a total of 479 helicopters being operated along the 500 mile stretch of Gulf Coast between Corpus Christi,

Figure 34.

Texas, and New Orleans, Louisiana. These helicopters are used to carry workers and equipment to more than 1,200 offshore oil rigs. These oil rigs are spread out over a 60,000 square mile area with some being over 150 miles from shore. It would take all day to reach some of them by boat, but the choppers can fly to even the most remote ones in a little over an hour. In 1978, these helicopters flew a total of 434,000 hours and carried more than 2.1 million passengers. This amounts to about 175,000 passengers each month or more than 5,800 per day. In addition, they transported more than 15,000 tons of cargo in 1978.

In 1978, this industry earned an estimated $400 million, and it is still growing. The chart in figure 35 shows this growth since 1955. Bell Helicopter has orders for 90 new helicopters, 80 have been ordered from Aerospatiale, and Sikorsky will deliver 14 new S-76s to the operators along the Gulf Coast. This represents a considerable investment when you consider that the average cost for helicopters is over $400,000.

In 1978 this industry employed about 25,000 people including about 1,000 pilots and over 900 mechanics, and it hires about 200 new pilots and 150 new mechanics each year. Part of this new employment is due to the rapid turnover each year, but part is caused by expansion.

You can see that this one small segment of general aviation is a very large and thriving business. There are also offshore oil exploration programs along the California coast and in the Atlantic Ocean off the coast of New York. Presently, they are not as large as the Gulf Coast program, but as the need for new energy increases, they will surely grow.

So far, we have looked only at the direct economic impact of air transportation, but this is just the tip of the iceberg. In addition to the economy of the air carriers and general aviation, we must also look at all the other business generated because of air transportation. The most obvious of these are the manufacturers of the airplanes used by the airlines and the economics of other businesses, such as motels, restaurants, ground transportation, etc., which have developed to support the air passengers. We will discuss the manufacturing of aircraft in the section dealing with aerospace industries. Here we will look at the economics of an airport and of the businesses supporting the airport.

ECONOMIC IMPACT OF THE AIRPORT

There were 15,476 airports on record in the United States as of December 31, 1981. Of these, 4,814 are publicly owned*, and the remainder are privately owned. Only 774 airports are certificated for service by air carriers; the others have no scheduled airline service (see fig. 36).

The cities served by the air carriers are part of the "air traffic hub" system which was developed by FAA to classify communities according to the number of passengers boarding scheduled airlines. There are four classes of airports in the hub system : large hub, medium hub, small hub, and non-hub airports.

Twenty-six communities are classified as large

*Owned and operated by the federal, state, or local government.

YEAR	NO. HELICOPTERS IN OPERATION	FLIGHT HOURS	NUMBER OF PASSENGERS
1955	16	10,730	21,460
1960	28	35,744	107,232
1965	62	78,464	270,998
1970	153	141,308	706,538
1975	266	272,253	1,503,494
1978	419	434,214	2,150,000

Figure 35. Helicopter Operations Growth (Gulf of Mexico)   *Source: Business and Commercial Aviation*

hubs, including cities like Chicago, New York, Denver, Seattle/Tacoma, etc. In 1979, seventy-one percent of all airline passengers were boarded in the large hub airports. The three tops hubs (Chicago, Los Angeles, and Atlanta) accounted for 20.2 percent of all air passengers in the United States, and almost half (44.5 percent) of all airline passengers who flew in the United States in 1979 were boarded in only ten cities.

The medium hubs include cities like Baltimore, Indianapolis, Nashville, Salt Lake City, San Jose, etc. There are 37 communities in the United States which are considered medium hubs. In 1979, 16.5 percent of all passengers carried were enplaned at the medium hub cities (see fig. 37).

The 83 small hub cities like Montgomery, Alabama; Portland, Maine; Little Rock, Arkansas; etc., accounted for 8.6 percent of the airline passengers in 1979. Even smaller communities like Casper, Wyoming; Bozeman, Montana; Ashland, Oregon; etc., are typical "non-hub" airports. About four percent of the commercial passengers were boarded at the 628 non-hub airports. The fact that only four percent of the passengers are boarded in 81 percent

of the cities with airline service leads to a major problem which we will discuss later.

It should be evident from these figures that there is a great deal of difference in airports. They are different in size, the type and number of aircraft which use them, and in the passenger services available. The thing they all have in common is that they provide access to air transportation for the citizens of their community. They also provide the benefits of air transportation to the community. A look at some of the large hub airports will give some indication of the economic impact the airport has on a large city.

The three airports in greater New York City— Newark, LaGuardia and John F. Kennedy—employ over 80,000 persons with a payroll of almost two billion dollars per year. Fifteen million visitors a year enter New York through these three airports, making tourism New York City's fifth largest industry. This accounts for another 500,000 jobs, and creates almost ten billion dollars worth of employment benefits.

The commercial airports in Los Angeles account for 50,000 jobs, but the secondary employment they generate brings the total to over 200,000. The annual payroll exceeds four billion dollars. In addition to this, spending by businesses based at the airport and by passengers flown into the area adds another fourteen million dollars, per *DAY,* or five billion dollars per year to the Los Angeles area.

These same types of figures are seen for San Francisco—30,000 employees with a payroll of over six hundred million dollars. Atlanta International Airport, employing 19,000 people, is the largest private employer in the State of Georgia.

These same economic impacts are seen at the smaller airports only on a smaller scale. Many large corporations are looking for sites away from large cities to locate their new manufacturing facilities. One of the prime requirements for selection is the availability of an adequate airport. According to a recent study by the Chamber of Commerce of the United States, every 1,000 new factory jobs creates $1,400,000 increased personal income, $675,000 more retail sales, $600,000 more bank deposits, four new retail establishments, and 68 more employees in non-manufacturing jobs.

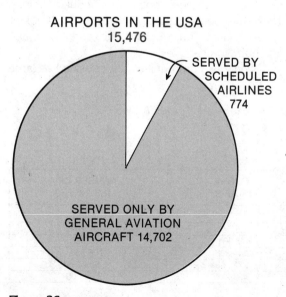

AIRPORTS IN THE USA
15,476

SERVED BY SCHEDULED AIRLINES 774

SERVED ONLY BY GENERAL AVIATION AIRCRAFT 14,702

Figure 36.

AIR CARRIER PASSENGER BOARDING				
	LARGE HUBS	MEDIUM HUBS	SMALL HUBS	NON-HUBS
NUMBER OF AIRPORTS	26	37	83	628
% OF PASSENGERS	71%	16.5%	8.6%	3.9%

Figure 37.

An additional economic consideration which should be looked at is the cost of building a new airport and the jobs generated by this construction. With the advent of the large new jet aircraft, and the "boom" in passenger travel, the size of new large hub airports has grown greatly. Another reason for this has been the environmental considerations imposed by the federal and state governments. It is necessary to provide a buffer zone around the airport to protect the community from the noise of arriving and departing aircraft. This requires the purchase of a great deal of extra land, particularly at the ends of all runways.

The Federal Aviation Administration projects a need for one thousand new airports by 1990 with one hundred of them suitable for combined air carrier and general aviation use.

SOCIOLOGICAL IMPACT

In addition to the dramatic economic impact air transportation has on our lives, there are many social changes which are caused by this industry. One example of this has been changes in population trends toward centers of air transportation. Just as cities in the 1800s and early 1900s developed along rivers, seacoasts, and railroad lines, cities of the later 1900s are developing according to air transportation access. Industries today are moving out of the congested large cities. They are moving to areas where there is a good supply of labor, energy, and a good airport, and they are taking people with them.

Another sociological change seen, particularly in the United States, is the dispersing of the family. Throughout history the family unit has always lived either together or in very close proximity. Today, we are a mobile society and families are spread all over

the country, and yet with our air transporation system they are really only hours away. It is easy and inexpensive to travel over long distances to relatives because of our airlines. Air travel has also changed vacations. Many more people are now traveling to foreign lands. This allows people of different countries to better understand each other. Air transportation has its greatest sociological impact on regions which are undeveloped or underdeveloped. This is true because aviation is not limited by geographic barriers. Underdeveloped areas can be "opened up" quickly and without building expensive highways or railroads. Also great distances do not affect aircraft like they do surface transportation.

An excellent example of this is seen in the State of Alaska. Aviation is the main transportation system in Alaska, and from the lower 48 states to Alaska. This is because of the vast size and remoteness of Alaska. Alaska also has many geographic barriers like mountains and rivers, and it is easier and cheaper to fly over them than to build railroads or highways over them.

This same impact is beginning to be felt in South America and Africa. Many people on these continents have not progressed for centuries, and natural resources have remained trapped behind mountains and jungles. Suddenly, this is all being changed by the airplane and air transportation. These people have gone from the Stone Age to the Space Age in one generation (fig. 38).

Another dramatic change which aviation has had on our lives is the change in our thinking about distances. For hundreds of years distances were thought of in terms of miles or kilometers. Travelers were interested in how many miles it was from New York to Houston or from London to San Francisco. Today, aboard a modern jetliner, distance is measured in terms of hours and minutes rather than

Figure 38.

miles. Air travelers want to know how long it takes to get there rather than how far it is. If you are traveling from Tokyo to San Francisco, you don't care that it is 5,150 miles. What is important to you is that it will take you 13 hours to get there.

NON-TRANSPORTATION ASPECTS

In the field of general aviation, there are a great many aircraft used for purposes other than transportation. These include the nearly 7,300 aircraft involved in aerial applications, and the 3,000 industrial and special aviation aircraft. It is difficult to measure the direct economic or sociological impact of these more than 10,000 aircraft because of the types of services they perform.

There are about 3,000 aerial applicators in the United States who fly the 7,300 specially designed "crop duster" aircraft. In most cases, the application of fertilizers, pesticides, and weed killers from the air is the most economical way it can be done. The aerial seeding of grass on remote grasslands and of forests in inaccessible regions is the only way this seeding can be done. It is impossible to estimate how much more our groceries and clothing would cost if these services were not performed, but it would be considerable.

Frequently, when there is a forest fire, aircraft are used to drop fire-retardant chemicals to slow or stop the spread of the fire. If this could not be done, how much more timber would be lost? How much would this add to the cost of building materials or paper? Again it is impossible to estimate, but again it would have some impact on these prices.

Small aircraft are used to inspect power lines for transformer failures, broken insulators, short circuits or line breaks. Inspection by air is frequently the only economical means of performing such services. How much would our electric bills increase without this service? Who knows?

More and more, general aviation is involved in

weather modification and wildlife conservation. The creation of irrigating rain in arid regions and of snow for ski resorts and the protection of natural resources are valuable, but again difficult to compute in dollars.

PROBLEM AREAS

There are several problem areas facing air transportation, but the major ones seem to be financial in nature. The Federal Aviation Administration forecasts that commercial passengers will have increased by an average of 4.7 percent per year between 1978 and 1990, or a total of 73 percent. This would mean that in 1990, the airlines would be carrying about 454 million passengers per year. This same forecast predicts that the total number of miles traveled by these passengers will increase at an even faster rate (5.3 percent per year). What this means is that there will be more passengers flying and that they will be flying farther. The problem this poses for the airlines is: where will they find the aircraft to accommodate this increase? To meet these needs, the airlines must buy about $10 billion worth of new aircraft in 1982 and an additional $100 billion worth during the remainder of the 1980s. This purchase of $110 billion worth of equipment in a ten year period of time is even more of a shock when compared with the $53 billion spent by all the airlines since the first jets came out in 1958. During these twenty-three years of jet service (1958-1981), the airlines spent an average of about $2 billion per year for aircraft. During the next 12 years, they will have to spend an average of almost $12.5 billion per year (see fig. 40).

The $110 billion will be spent both to buy additional aircraft, which will be necessary to handle the

Figure 39. Aerial application

SPENDING FOR NEW JET AIRLINERS

1958-1981 $53 BILLION	1982-1990 $110 BILLION

Figure 40. Forecast of expenditures for New Jet Aircraft

growth in passengers, and to replace older aircraft. The purchase of replacement aircraft will cost about $45 billion and growth aircraft about $80 billion. The problem is: Where do the airlines get this $110 billion?

Obviously, they will have to borrow the money. This is more than the combined worth of all the airlines and all of the aircraft manufacturers. When borrowing money, the airlines compete with all other businesses, and the banks give priority to industries which show a good profit margin. During the last ten years, the United States manufacturing industry's profit margin has averaged almost 5 percent. During this same period the airlines have averaged about 1 percent according to the Air Transport Association of America. This means that it becomes increasingly difficult for the airlines to borrow money and they also have to pay a higher interest rate. Of course, figures can be used in many ways, and the Civil Aeronautics Board (CAB) would contend that the airlines' return on investment was much higher.

The dilemma that airlines are facing is how to increase their profits without decreasing their passenger service. We have already mentioned their efforts in the fuel conservation area. Another way they could do this would be to drop the routes that are the least profitable. Another would be to increase their fares. In both of these cases, the CAB has historically had absolute regulatory powers. The CAB allocated the air routes, and would only let certain airlines fly certain routes. They also gave unprofitable routes to the airlines and required that they either provide service on these routes or pass them off to a commuter airline. In the area of fares, the CAB set the fares and required that all airlines charge the same fare between the same cities. The only way an airline could raise the fare on a certain route was for all other airlines to raise theirs, and this must be approved by the CAB.

The Airline Deregulation Act of 1978 reduced the regulatory powers of the CAB, and will dissolve the organization by 1985. The long-range effects of this new legislation are not yet known, but it has already increased the load factor on many of the airlines. The Airline Deregulation Act caused changes in regulation in two major areas. One part of the law allows the airlines to increase their fares by up to 5 percent, or decrease them by up to 50 percent without approval of the CAB. Many airlines have already decreased their fares by up to 50 percent on some flights. The effect has been that the load factors have increased on all flights and in some cases they are approaching 100 percent. The airlines' earnings for 1978 increased dramatically, but then, as the economic crisis of the 1980s appeared, their earnings began to drop off.

Another part of the law allowed the airlines to add one new route each year in 1979, 1980, and 1981. These routes must be non-stop between only two points within the United States (excluding Hawaii). This part of the law is called the automatic market entry program and allows additional airlines to provide service to cities which in the past were closed to them. For example, the route between Miami and San Francisco is a well travelled route and, because it is a long route, it is very profitable for the airline which is allowed to fly between these two cities. In the past, only Delta Airlines flew this route and the CAB protected it for them. Now, because of the new law, any other airline can offer service between these two cities.

The new legislation also provided methods of allowing the airlines to reduce or eliminate their service on many unprofitable routes without caus-

Figure 41. This type DC-8 will need new engines to meet noise standards

ing the communities to suffer because of the reduced service. This provision guarantees essential air service to smaller communities by providing "fair and reasonable compensation" to any eligible air carrier who is providing or will provide air transportation to these smaller communities. In effect, what they are saying is that if a route is unprofitable, the government will pay the airline to continue its service. This will help overcome the losses that an airline suffers by providing the service.

Another problem area in air transportation is noise. The FAA established maximum noise standards for aircraft in 1969. These standards were imposed because of the protests of environmentalists. The first generation of commercial jets (707, 727, DC-8, and DC-9) were built before the standards were formulated, and now the federal government is forcing the airlines to reequip the first generation jets with engines which will meet the standards (see fig. 41). This will cost several billion dollars, and the airlines believe the government should pay the cost since the standards were imposed after the airplanes were already in service. Many of these first generation aircraft are only a few years from the end of their service life. The airlines say it is ridiculous to spend three or four million dollars to put new engines on an aircraft which will

be retired in a couple of years.

There certainly is a need for noise standards. Also, there must be a deadline date with which the airlines must comply. The problem lies in how you meet the noise standards without causing the airlines undue financial hardship. Again, there is no simple solution. All parties (airlines, government, and environmentalists) must work together for a fair solution.

Another problem which becomes evident with the increases in both air carrier aviation and general aviation is in the area of building new airports. The development of a new airport has become very difficult today because of the environmental restrictions and because most airports are under the jurisdiction of several different political entities. In order to finance an airport today, a community almost has to apply for federal assistance. This requires that federal regulations be met. Generally, a community also receives state aid, which means that certain state requirements must be followed. The county and the local community governments are also involved in planning and building the airport. The outcome is that the construction is delayed because so many political groups are involved. This becomes even more serious if the airport is controversial from an environmental standpoint. Environmental groups have held up the construction of some airports for years. In some cases they have actually caused an airport project to be cancelled.

As the construction is delayed, the airport becomes more and more expensive due to inflation. If the citizens do not understand and support the airport, they may decide it is not worth the added expense.

GENERAL AVIATION

There are two major problems facing general aviation, namely, the increasing cost of fuel and increased governmental regulation. The increased cost of fuel since 1973 has hit the general aviation pilot even harder than the air carriers. In the case of the business and executive aviation segment, they can and are doing much to conserve fuel. The commercial and industrial aviation businessman can pass on the increased costs to his customers. However, the personal and sport aviation enthusiasts can do little about the increased costs except to fly less. This is what happened during 1977 and 1978. The FAA Aviation Forecast through the 1980s predicts that general aviation will continue to grow, but at a much slower rate than during the 1970s. The majority of the growth will be in areas other than personal and sport aviation. As the general aviation manufacturers build more fuel economy systems into their new aircraft, this problem should be reduced somewhat.

In the area of increased governmental regulation, the general aviation community feels it is really being treated unfairly. As air traffic has become more and more dense at many airports used by both general aviation and air carrier aircraft, the FAA has required that the general aviation aircraft be equipped with more and more expensive equipment. This is done in the name of safety, but the general aviation community thinks that it is just an excuse to get the small aircraft out of the sky.

On September 25, 1978, a midair collision between a Pacific Southwest Airline 727 and a Cessna 172 over San Diego, California, killed 144 persons. At that time this was the worst United States air disaster in history. As a result of this accident and other near misses between aircraft in flight,

FAA proposed that the amount of controlled airspace throughout the United States be increased. The San Diego accident occurred even though both aircraft were under control, and investigations seem to agree that the accident was the result of improper controller procedures. Included in the FAA proposals is lowering the floor of Positive Control Airspace from 18,000 feet to 10,000 feet. This would prohibit most general aviation pilots from flying above 10,000 feet because uncontrolled aircraft cannot fly in controlled airspace, and most general aviation pilots are not instrument rated. Another proposal is to increase the number of airports with terminal control areas and raise the ceiling of the terminal control areas to meet the floor of the positive control airspace. This would further limit the number of airports which general aviation aircraft could use. The general aviation community comprises 98.7 percent of all aircraft flown in the United States, and they insist that they should be able to fly in uncontrolled airspace without being required to purchase the very expensive equipment necessary to fly under instrument conditions.

On the other side of this coin is the concern for passenger safety. There is no doubt that as the numbers of aircraft increase, the chance of accidents also increases. Our present air traffic control system is already overloaded. To require the majority of the general aviation fleet to also use this system will add to the problem, not solve it. How do you insure passenger safety and at the same time not strangle general aviation? How do you provide more control of aircraft in the vicinity of airports without requiring that the average pleasure pilot buy thousands of dollars worth of equipment which will seldom be used? These are some of the difficult questions facing general aviation today.

Civil aviation in the United States is a multibillion dollar business. It has taken years to develop both the transportation and the non-transportation aspects of this industry. No other country in the world has an airline or a general aviation system that comes close to ours. We face many problems today, most of which are financial in nature. These problems must be solved without jeopardizing aviation and this requires the understanding of all the American public.

Figure 42.

Chapter 3-4

CIVILIAN AEROSPACE PROGRAMS II

Previously we mentioned that the airlines are considered to be common carriers. A common carrier is a person or company that provides the *public* with transportation of passengers or goods for hire. The common carriers are considered to include railroads, steamships, buses, taxicabs, motor freight companies, and pipelines. Because common carriers provide a service to the public, they are subject to certain governmental controls. The Constitution of the United States (Section 8) gives the Congress the power "to regulate commerce with foreign Nations and among the several States . . ." Many state constitutions also provide for state regulation.

The federal government and many state and local governments also provide many types of service to civil aviation. We will discuss some of the regulations and services provided to civil aviation in the first part of this chapter. The remainder of this chapter will deal with the importance of our civilian space program.

The general learning objective for this chapter is for you to know the governmental agencies and services provided to civil aviation and the importance of our civilian space exploration program to U.S. aerospace power. To reach this objective, you must pattern your study of the material according to the *specific learning objectives* listed in the Appendix of this textbook.

FEDERAL AVIATION ADMINISTRATION

The Federal Aviation Administration is the United States government agency which is charged by Congress with regulating air commerce to foster aviation safety; promoting civil aviation and a national system of airports; achieving efficient use of navigable airspace; and developing and operating a common system of air traffic control and air navigation for both civilian and military aircraft.

HISTORY

The regulation of air traffic by the United States government began with the passage of the Air Commerce Act of 1926. This law gave the federal government the responsibility for the operation and maintenance of the airway system over the United States, including all aids to air navigation. It also authorized the Department of Commerce to develop a system of regulations which would provide safety in air commerce. The Bureau of Air Commerce was established within the Department of Commerce to carry out these programs.

Among the first safety regulations developed were the requirements for registration and licensing of aircraft and the certification and medical examination of all pilots. The Bureau of Air Commerce did much to improve aviation radio and other navigation aids. It also promoted airport construction throughout the country, but it did not provide financial assistance for building airports.

Civil Aeronautics Act—1938. By 1938, the carrying of airmail and passengers had increased significantly and new legislation was necessary. The new law governing civil aviation was called the Civil Aeronautics Act of 1938. This act placed all air transportation regulation, both economic and safety, under three separate agencies: (1) the Civil Aeronautics Authority, which established policies governing the safety and economics of air transportation; (2) the office of the Administrator of Aviation, which was formed to carry out the safety policies of the Authority; and, (3) the Air Safety Board, which was formed to investigate aircraft accidents.

In 1940, the Civil Aeronautics Act was amended and the three agencies were reduced to two. The Civil Aernautics Board (CAB), a group of five individuals reporting directly to the President of the United States, took over the policymaking responsibility in both safety and economic matters. It also assumed the accident investigation duties of the Air Safety Board. The second agency, the Civil Aeronautics Administration (CAA) was charged with executing the safety regulations developed by the CAB, and with operation of the airway system. The CAA was placed under the Department of Commerce.

Federal Airport Act of 1946. This act provided for the CAA to develop a comprehensive system of airports throughout the United States using federal funds for their development. This legislation was needed because of the tremendous increase in aviation activity after World War II. The Federal Airport Act of 1946 was amended several times but remained in effect until the Airport and Airway

Development Act of 1970 was passed in June of 1970. The Airport and Airway Development Act of 1970 is administered by the Federal Aviation Administration.

Federal Aviation Act—1958. The Civil Aeronautics Act remained in effect for 20 years (1938-1958) before the regulation of civil aviation was again changed by the Federal Aviation Act—1958. The biggest change provided by this act was that the CAA, which was part of the Department of Commerce, became an independent agency—the Federal Aviation Agency (FAA). The Federal Aviation Act—1958 removed from the CAB the responsibility for developing safety regulations and gave this responsibility to the newly formed FAA. In effect, what this did was to give FAA the responsibility for both developing safety regulations and for enforcing them. The CAB retained its responsibility for economic regulation of air commerce and the investigation of aircraft accidents.

Department of Transportation Act. The final change in the status of FAA came with the Department of Transportation Act, which was passed in 1966. This act placed all public transportation under a single manager, the Department of Transportation. The duties and responsibilities of FAA remained unchanged, but the name was changed to the Federal Aviation Administration. During its history, the present-day FAA (Federal Aviation Administration) has been called the Bureau of Air Commerce, the Administration of Aviation, the Civil Aviation Administration, and the Federal Aviation Agency.

DUTIES AND RESPONSIBILITIES

Air Traffic Control. One of FAA's biggest tasks in the area of aviation safety is the control of air traffic. Air traffic control is concerned with keeping aircraft safely separated to prevent accidents. This is necessary while the aircraft is taxiing on the ground, during takeoff and ascent, while en route, and during approach and landing. The FAA also provides preflight and in-flight services to all pilots for air traffic control and safety purposes.

Air traffic control is accomplished by establishing certain parts of the airspace as *controlled airspace* and by requiring that all aircraft flying within this controlled air space follow certain rules and regulations.

There are two types of facilities that control the IFR (instrument flight rules) traffic flying within the controlled airspace. The first are the Airport Traffic Control Towers (see fig. 43) which control traffic departing or arriving at certain airports. The control towers are equipped with complex electronic equipment and are operated by highly skilled FAA Air Traffic Controllers. These facilities also handle (con-

trol) aircraft taxiing on the ground. As would be expected, the busier the airport, and the more different types of aircraft it handles, the more restrictive are the rules and regulations. Certain large metropolitan airports require all aircraft using the facility to be equipped with various types of traffic control equipment. Some of this equipment is very expensive and many general aviation pilots cannot afford it. Therefore, they are restricted from using these large airports.

After the IFR aircraft leaves the immediate area of the airport, the controller in the tower will "hand it

Figure 43.

Figure 44.

off" (transfer it) to another air traffic controller in the second type of facility—the Air Route Traffic Control Center (ARTCC) (see fig. 44). The "center" assigns the aircraft a certain altitude and a specific route to follow to its destination. The pilot must not change the route or the altitude without permission from the center. As the flight continues, the aircraft is transferred from center to center. The flight is under positive control at all times and no other aircraft is allowed to enter that aircraft's "piece of airspace." The ARTCCs follow the flight on radars and are in voice communications at all times. Commercial airliners, general aviation, and military aircraft all use the same traffic control system when flying within the controlled airspace.

The FAA also provides assistance to pilots who do not fly within the controlled airspace. These are mostly general aviation pilots because most airline and military aircraft are required to fly IFR at all times. This assistance is provided by a third type of facility called the Flight Service Station (FSS). The FAA personnel who work in the FSSs provide pre-

Figure 45.

flight information such as weather information, suggested routes, altitudes, etc., to pilots. In addition, the FSS provides inflight information via radio and assistance in the event a pilot becomes lost or is having trouble. From the volume of aircraft traffic handled, the FSS provides by far the most service. But then, this is not surprising since they handle mostly general aviation traffic, which includes over 90 percent of all pilots and aircraft.

The control towers, centers, and flight service stations are all connected by more than a half-million miles of communications lines and work closely together to keep a safe and orderly flow of traffic. The system is currently very heavily loaded, and as traffic increases in the next decade, it may become overloaded. For example: There are 25 Air Route Traffic Control Centers in the United States. In 1981 they handled a total of 29,300,000 aircraft. This is an average of over 3,200 per center per day, or 133 per hour. It is estimated that by 1990, these centers will average 38,900,000 aircraft handled per year. There are 317 Flight Service Stations in the United States which provided flight services (pilot briefings and flight plans) to 62,600,000 pilots in 1981. By 1990, this number is expected to grow to over 92,000,000 services per year. FAA operates 431 control towers at United States airports. In 1981, they handled 61,600,000 aircraft operations (takeoff or landing). This amounts to an average of almost 400 per day for each tower. By 1990, it is expected that the number of operations will increase to over 97,200,000 operations per year.

Airways facilities. The nation's airways are a 250,000-mile system of "highways in the sky" which pilots follow from takeoff to landing. The heart of the system currently is the Very High Frequency Omni-directional Range (VOR) System which covers the United States (see fig. 45). These VORs are used for navigation along the airways system. The FAA is responsible for operation and maintenance of these facilities. They also own and maintain other radars, instrument landing systems, and communications at the various airports. These facilities are checked regularly by specially instrumented FAA aircraft.

Flight Standards. The FAA is responsible for insur-

ing that all pilots and aircraft are safe through enforcement of a system of standards. These standards assure that all aircraft are airworthy, all airmen (pilots, navigators, air traffic controllers, engineers, mechanics, etc.) are competent, and that all regulations and procedures are followed.

All new models of aircraft, engines, instruments, or other components must meet very rigid safety standards before they are certified by FAA. When a manufacturer brings out a new aircraft, FAA works with the engineers and designers during construction of the prototype. It is then thoroughly ground tested and flight tested before being given a *type certificate*. This certificate confirms that this type of aircraft has met FAA standards of construction and performance. A *production certificate* is later provided which shows that the manufacturer can duplicate the aircraft that was type certificated. The production certificate allows the manufacturer to continue to produce that type of aircraft. As each production aircraft is built it must be issued an *airworthiness certificate* which insures that it has been tested and is safe for use.

Even after an aircraft starts flying, the FAA continues to check its safety. They control aircraft maintenance programs, setting times for inspection and overhaul. The FAA also certificates the repair and overhaul facilities to insure that the aircraft receives proper maintenance and repair.

Before a pilot can fly an aircraft, he/she must have an FAA-issued pilot certificate. There are many types of certificates, but in all cases they certify that the holder has passed medical examinations. FAA also requires that a physical examination and a flight check ride with an FAA flight examiner be completed every two years.

Research and Development. The National Aviation Facilities Experiment Center (NAFEC) is the FAA's research and development center. This center, located in Atlantic City, New Jersey, is involved in research to upgrade our airways systems, to improve aircraft instruments and systems, and to reduce the workload on the pilot in the aircraft and the controller on the ground. All of these efforts are expended to make flying easier and safer (see fig. 46).

The NAFEC is currently working on new types of airway navigational systems which will reduce the congestion of our airways in the future. Another area which they are working on is new types of *instrument landing systems* which would allow aircraft to land safely in any type of weather regardless of visibility. They are also involved in research on *collision avoidance systems* for use in aircraft. This would provide a warning to pilots in both aircraft any time two aircraft were on a course which would lead to a collision. The system would also tell the pilots what type of evasive action to take to avoid the collision.

Aeronautical Center. Another facility operated by FAA is the FAA Aeronautical Center in Oklahoma City, Oklahoma. This multimillion dollar facility is the home of the FAA Academy which is the training center for FAA operational personnel. They train the personel that operate the ARTCCs, FSSs, and airport control towers. In addition to training FAA control tower operators, they also train controllers for the military and for many foreign countries at the Academy. The Academy is also the training ground for the engineers and technicians who install and maintain the electronic equipment used for navigation, communications, and air traffic control. Finally, the Academy also provides initial and refresher train-

Figure 46. FAA study on evacuation of jumbo jets

ing for their maintenance inspectors. The Civil Aero-medical Institute (CAI) is also located at the Aeronautical Center. CAI operates the program for medical certification of all airmen. It is also involved in research to identify human factors which cause aircraft accidents and on how to make accidents more survivable. The Aeronautical Center is also the home of the people who write the airmen examinations, develop the airworthiness standards for all civil aircraft, and keep all the records of airmen and aircraft. The pilots and aircraft that fly the inspections of the airways and airport control and communications equipment are also based at the Aeronautical Center.

CIVIL AERONAUTICS BOARD

As we have already seen, the Civil Aeronautics Board (CAB) was established by the Federal Aviation Act of 1958. The Department of Transportation Act of 1966 limited the CAB's authority to the economic regulation of civil aviation. The Airline Deregulation Act of 1978 calls for the CAB to be phased out by 1985.

The CAB is an independent federal agency composed of five members appointed for a six-year term. The board members are appointed by the President with the advice and consent of the Senate. No more than three of the CAB members can be from any one political party. Historically, the CAB has authority over the economic, routing and pricing practices of airline companies operating in the United States.

The passage of the Airline Deregulation Act of 1978 greatly diminished the the CAB's authority over airline fares and routes. Despite this reduction in authority, the CAB still carries out some very important functions. Many of these have to do with ensuring that the airlines provide adequate service and making sure customers receive fair treatment.

Under the Airline Deregulation Act of 1978, the CAB will be phased out by December 31, 1985. The responsibilites of the CAB will be transferred to the FAA, the State Department, the Justice Department and the Post Office Department.

NATIONAL TRANSPORTATION SAFETY BOARD

The National Transportation Safety Board (NTSB) is a five member board appointed by the President with the advice and consent of the Senate. The members of the NTSB are appointed for a term of five years and, like the CAB, there can be no more than three members from any one political party.

The NTSB is responsible for determining the cause, or probable cause, of any transportation accident (see fig. 47). Under the Chairman of the NTSB, the Bureau of Aviation Safety carriers out these duties in the area of aviation. The Bureau of Aviation Safety makes rules governing accident reporting. They also investigate all aircraft accidents (they have delegated this duty to the FAA in the case of general aviation accidents), report the facts relating to each accident and the probable cause, and make recommendations to FAA as to how to prevent similar accidents.

The NTSB maintains its own technology division which provides engineering and technical assistance in areas of aerodynamics, structures, propellers, powerplants, instruments, electronic aids to navigation, human factors, etc. These experts are available to assist in determining the causes of var-

Figure 47. NTSB accident investigation

ious accidents. They also assist the manufacturers in making their aircraft safer.

The result of all of these agencies working together to promote aviation safety is an air transportation system which is as safe as any other form of public transportation (see fig. 48).

OTHER PROGRAMS

There are several programs which have been developed to make use of civil aviation in case of a national emergency. These programs recognize that aviation, both air carrier and general, is a valuable national resource which should be organized so that is can be used in time of emergency.

CIVIL RESERVE AIR FLEET (CRAF)

The Civil Reserve Air Fleet is composed of com-

mercial airliners which have been designated for use by the Department of Defense in time of national emergency. These aircraft are long-range jet transports which have been specially equipped so they can be quickly converted for military use. The CRAF is subject to call on twenty-four hour notice. However, the CRAF is more than just aircraft; it also includes aircrews and maintenance crews which are supplied by the airlines. It has been estimated that this reserve fleet is valued at over a half billion dollars and the added cost of training the crews and the maintenance of the aircraft is worth an additional quarter of a billion dollars. This 750 million dollar asset is ready and waiting twenty-four hours a day at no cost to the government.

If it were ever activated, the CRAF would provide the armed forces with modern, fast airlift aircraft capable of moving troops and supplies to any point on the Earth's surface. The capability of the CRAF continues to expand as more of the newer and larger

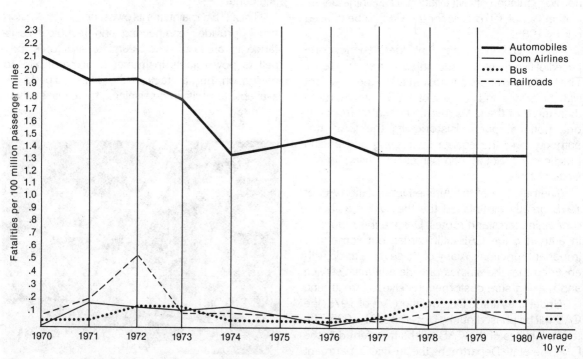

Figure 48. Fatality Rate for Various Forms of Transportation

jumbo jets are added to airline service.

The CRAF was established to assist the military in case of a national emergency, but it is also available for use in case of a natural disaster. In this case only a small portion of the CRAF would be activated to provide airlift assistance to earthquake, flood, or drought victims.

CIVIL AIR PATROL (CAP)

The Civil Air Patrol is a federally chartered, private, nonprofit corporation and is also the official civilian auxiliary of the United States Air Force. The 65,000 volunteer CAP members are all aerospace-minded citizens dedicated to service to their fellow Americans.

Civil Air Patrol has three basic missions— emergency services, aerospace education, and a cadet program.

- Emergency Services—The Civil Air Patrol uses its more than 575 corporate-owned and 7,000 member-owned aircraft to fly various emergency missions. These include search and rescue (SAR) missions for downed aircraft, lost hunters, fishermen, children, etc.; disaster relief missions for natural disaster; and emergency airlift of sick or injured persons as well as blood and body organs (see fig. 49).
- Aerospace Education—CAP conducts an aerospace education program for its membership and for the general public.

Figure 49. CAP Emergency Service

Figure 50. CAP Cadet Activities

This program is to develop an awareness and appreciation of the aerospace world in which we live. CAP's involvement in aerospace education includes sponsorship of workshops for teachers and developing materials to help teach aerospace education at all grade levels.

- Cadet Program—CAP cadets are young men and women, ages 13-18, who are interested in aerospace and in community service. The cadet program is structured to use aerospace as a vehicle to help teach leadership and management skills, moral leadership and physical fitness. The program emphasizes activities and involvement of the cadets (see fig. 50).

Civil Air Patrol was founded in 1941, and for over 40 years the CAP members have been involved in service to their communities and their nation.

STATE AND REGIONAL DISASTER AIRLIFT (SARDA)

This program was developed to make use of the tremendous general aviation resources available in case of an emergency. SARDA is the responsibility of the FAA and each state develops its own SARDA plan. The State Aviation Authority is responsible for organizing the general aviation community within each state to meet these emergencies. These aircraft may be used in time of national emergency or during a natural disaster.

The SARDA plan recognizes the value of general aviation aircraft in time of emergency and they might be called upon to carry out the following types of missions:

1. Airlifting urgently needed personnel and supplies
2. Visual reconnaissance and appraisal
3. Communications assistance
4. Search and rescue
5. Aerial radiological monitoring
6. Air support of essential priority requirements (health, agricultural, industrial, welfare, etc.).

The State Aviation Authority is responsible for

developing the SARDA plan which includes surveying the state to determine the general aviation resources available, providing them with training, developing a method of activating them in case of emergency, establishing a communication network, and then coordinating with all local, state, regional and national agencies about implementing the plan when, and if, required. In many states, CAP is the operational organization around which the SARDA plan is developed.

STATE AGENCIES

Most people are aware of the responsibility the federal government has in regulating and providing support to aviation. On the other hand, very few people know about the level of support provided by state governments.

In 1911, Connecticut enacted the first law governing aviation within an individual state. In 1921, Oregon established the first state aviation agency. By 1931, twenty-five states had aviation agencies. In September of that year, they created the National Association of State Aviation Officials (NASAO). Today, NASAO represents 48 state aviation agencies as well as Puerto Rico's Aviation Department. The information in this section was provided by NASAO.

One of the major functions of the various state agencies is the location, design, construction, and licensing of airports. A recent NASAO survey revealed that 23 states now actually own and operate a total or more than 150 airports. Fourteen of these airports are large air carrier airports. These figures do not include Alaska, which owns over 300 airports, or Rhode Island, where all public airports are state-owned and operated.

Forty-seven of the 50 states now provide financial assistance for airports. Twenty-two states provide funds for maintenance.

Some of the other areas where state aviation agencies are involved are:

- Air Navigation Aids: In areas where FAA facilities are inadequate, states often supply supplemental air navigation aids.

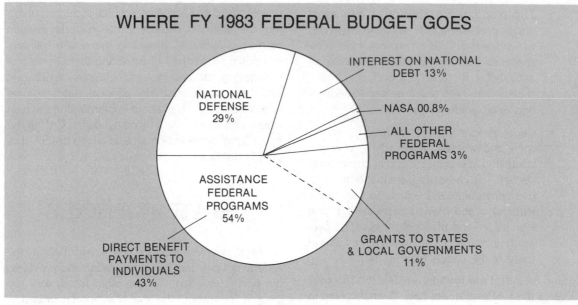

WHERE FY 1983 FEDERAL BUDGET GOES

NATIONAL DEFENSE 29%

INTEREST ON NATIONAL DEBT 13%

NASA 00.8%

ALL OTHER FEDERAL PROGRAMS 3%

ASSISTANCE FEDERAL PROGRAMS 54%

DIRECT BENEFIT PAYMENTS TO INDIVIDUALS 43%

GRANTS TO STATES & LOCAL GOVERNMENTS 11%

Figure 51.

- Aircraft/Airport Noise: State governments are leaders in controlling the use of land in close proximity to airports. They often enact legislation which requires adoption of airport zoning regulations.
- Safety: State agencies cooperate with FAA and NTSB in investigation of aircraft accidents. Many states also publish state aeronautical charts and airport directories to provide information to their pilots.
- Airspace/Air Traffic Control: State agencies cooperate with FAA in local air traffic control. This includes developing standards for land use around airports to prevent construction of towers or other structures which would be hazardous to flight.

This is just a sample of the responsibilities of the various state agencies. They are also involved in promotion of aviation within their states, including many aerospace education projects. The level of support from the states is high and it is expected to continue to grow as civil aviation grows in the next decade.

SPACE EXPLORATION PROGRAM

Today, more than twenty-five years after the beginning of space exploration, many of the people of the United States still do not fully understand the importance of this program. This area, more than any other, holds the potential to solve sociological, economic, and political problems. Ten years ago this same statement was made, and ten years from now we may still be saying it holds the *potential* to solve our problems. If space exploration is ever to realize its potential, it must have public understanding and support.

The average American taxpayer probably has a distorted view of the cost of our civilian space effort. The National Aeronautics and Space Administration (NASA) has a yearly budget of slightly over six billion dollars. This means that the entire annual spending for our space effort is only about 2 to 4 percent of what is spent in major areas like health, education and welfare or defense by the federal government. By comparison, the entire cost of the

Apollo program is spent by the Department of Health and Human Service (HHS) every month and a half. NASA was founded in 1958 and its *total* spending since that time amounts to 81 billion dollars—only 50 percent of what HHS spends each year. Figure 51 shows how the federal budget will be spent in 1983.

The project to put a man on the moon, Project Apollo, was a very expensive undertaking. It cost a total of about 20.6 billion dollars to accomplish this amazing feat. However, this 20.6 billion dollars was spent over a six year time period.

The question the taxpayers often ask is,"What are we getting back for the billions of dollars we are spending in space?" In the first place, let's understand that the money is not spent in space—it is spent here on the Earth. It pays the salaries of the employees who develop and build the equipment. It is used to buy groceries and to pay the rent and purchase automobiles. It sends their children through college, and it is even used to pay taxes. This is the money that fuels our economy and provides us with our high standard of living. This is a simple answer to the question, but this money also buys a lot more. It buys knowledge, technology and capability.

You cannot pick up knowledge and hold it in your hands and weigh or measure it. You cannot see capability or technology, and this is why it is so difficult to understand what is bought with the space program budget.

RESEARCH AND DEVELOPMENT

Knowledge. In today's world, knowledge and technology* are the two things that separate the nations that are world leaders from those that are second class nations. No nation can develop any faster than its national supply of knowledge will let it. This can be compared with a large pool (knowledge pool) into which all new knowledge is poured. In order to develop a new product or solve a problems, you go to the pool for the required knowledge. If the knowledge is there, you take it out and use it. If the knowl-

*Technology is the application of knowledge.

edge is not there, your progress stops and you have to wait until that knowledge becomes available.

Education is the method by which knowledge is passed along to future generations. It does not itself develop any new knowledge. Education prepares you to search and to understand and use what you learn, but new knowledge is acquired only through inquiry or basic research. This is a concept which is sometimes difficult to understand.

Basic Research. Basic research is performed only to answer a question—not to produce anything. It is accomplished only to gain new knowledge, and the new knowledge itself is the end product which justifies the money spent. If this new knowledge can be used to solve a problem or to produce a useful product, that is a bonus.

Applied Research. Applied research works toward finding ways to apply existing knowledge to provide something useful. In this way, applied research and technology are one and the same thing. Let us review this one more time because it is important to understand the differences. Basic research is performed to answer a question or to gain new knowledge. For example, basic research would be done to answer the question, "How does a cell divide?" The end product of this research is the new knowledge gained about cell division. Later, this new knowledge may be applied to looking for the relationship between cell division and cancer. The basic research was not aimed at discovering a cure for cancer; it was looking only for new knowledge about cells. The applied research took that new knowledge and applied it to the search for a possible cure for cancer. It is easy to see the value of applied research when it leads to the cure for a dreaded disease.

Development. Development takes what is learned from basic or applied research and uses it to produce a new product. In the example we used above, development would be the end product of the basic and applied research such as a new medicine or device used to cure cancer. It is easy to see the value of the development phase, because it results in a product which you can pick up and carry or at least see and use. What is difficult to see is the value of the basic research which was done to provide the knowledge necessary to cure the disease or develop the new product. Even the newest of our modern day products (pocket calculators, transistor radios, etc.) are the result of basic research which was conducted five to ten years ago.

When a brand new field of study opens up like space exploration, a great deal of basic research is needed. In fact, most of the research done to date in our space program has been basic research, and it is very difficult to judge its value. A "storehouse" of new knowledge has been developed, and only now is this knowledge being applied. The real value may not be seen until many years in the future.

Another reason why the usefulness of basic research is difficult to understand is that there is often a long time between the gaining of new knowledge and its useful application. If this time lag is too long, people forget that the money spent on basic research years ago is what finally led to the development they are now seeing. Part of this time lag is caused by slow communications between the scientists and technologists. This often takes years and NASA has made a diligent effort to shorten this type of delay. Another reason for the time lag is often the lack of immediate need. New knowledge may be gained for which there is just no immediate use. Many years later a need arises and the knowledge is used.

How much new knowledge has been developed by the space program? How much would have been developed even without the space program? These questions are very difficult to answer. It has been said that the total accumulation of scientific knowledge developed from the time of man's creation until 1700 doubled the first time 200 years thereafter (by 1900). It doubled again between 1900 and 1960 (only 60 years) and again from 1960 to 1970 (only 10 years). Now, it is doubling every seven years—this is almost impossible to comprehend and results in a growth curve as shown in figure 52

Of course, we cannot say that all of this new knowledge is due directly to space exploration. However, we can say that the space program provided the national incentive which led to much of it. How much is the new knowledge provided by our space program worth? There is no way to measure the value of new knowledge until a need arises for it and then it is often invaluable.

Technology. It is in this area that we begin to see the impact of the new knowledge developed by our space program. Technology uses new scientific knowledge to bring forth ideas, inventions, materials and processes. Applying space technology to Earth problems sometimes provides a method of doing a job better or, in some cases, in a way that could not otherwise be done. An example of this would be the use of satellites for weather monitoring. Not only do these satellites do a better job of keeping track of our weather, they do it in a way not otherwise available.

Another way that technology benefits us all is through "spin-off." This is a term used to explain a secondary use of technology or the use of technology for a purpose other than that for which it was originally developed. We will look at a few examples of both the direct use of technology and the spin-off area in this section.

Prior to the advent of satellites, weathermen had to rely on ground-based or aerial weather monitoring. Weather forecasting was never better than the information they received from their monitoring stations. The biggest problem was to get enough monitoring stations to provide a look at the weather over a large portion of the Earth. A simple look at a globe

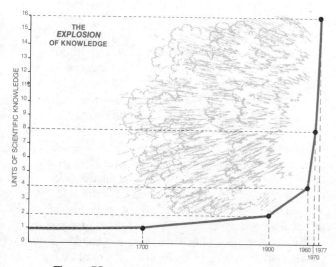

Figure 52.

shows the problems faced by the weathermen. Three-fourths of the Earth's surface is covered by water and it was impossible to provide enough weather ships or planes to give a continuous reading of what was happening over the oceans. Another problem was a political one. Much of the weather affecting the United States develops over Siberia, and the Soviet Union would not permit us to build weather stations there. As a result, weather forecasting was very poor. It was difficult to forecast more than a day or so in advance with any accuracy. This caused many hardships—for farmers, for transportation industries, and for citizens in general.

We launched our first weather satellite, Tiros II (see fig. 53), in 1960, and suddenly our weathermen got a look at the weather from an entirely new perspective. Our weather satellites are not restricted by large stretches of ocean or by political barriers. For the first time weathermen could see what the weather was doing over the entire Earth. Weather forecasting began to improve, particularly in the area of providing warnings of severe weather like hurricanes, typhoons, etc. By 1966 we had an operational weather satellite system providing continuous monitoring of the weather throughout the world. Since that time, no major storm has gone undetected at any point on the globe.

The savings in terms of lives and dollars just from our improved weather forecasting is probably enough to pay for our entire space program; but it has another important impact. Weather affects all people throughout the world probably more than any other single factor. The technology provided by our weather satellite program is available to all nations large or small. By construction of a simple and inexpensive ground receiving station, any nation can receive weather information from our satellites on a continuous basis. This provides the United States with a political bonus. Many of these small developing nations are looking for a leader to follow, and allowing them to share in this technology may cause a more friendly feeling toward the United States.

Another field of technology which is just beginning to be used is in the area of Earth survey satellites. Two *Landsat* satellites (fig. 54) are currently circling the globe scanning the Earth with a number

Figure 53. Tiros weather satellite

Figure 54. Landsat satellite

3-67

of cameras. The pictures taken by Landsat show a large portion of the Earth—over 13,000 square miles in each picture. They allow us to see large geographic features that are impossible to see from Earth or from an airplane (see fig. 55). The pictures allow the survey of such things as natural resources, agriculture, pollution, urban growth and the fishing industry.

Already the pictures returned to Earth have led to the development of new oil and natural gas fields on three continents. Mineral deposits have been discovered including a copper deposit in Nevada estimated to be worth $10 billion. The pictures are being used in agriculture to identify crops, predict the probable yield, and identify plant diseases or insect damage. They are used to inventory forest lands, discover fires, detect diseases in trees and help conserve our timber resources. They are being used to map ocean surface temperatures and fish movements to help fishermen. They allow us to

Figure 55. Northeast Utah from 560 miles out. A & B-mountain ranges, C-cumulus clouds, D-Duchesne River, E-Green River, F-Ouray, Utah, G-Price, Utah, H-Provo, Utah, I & J-reservoirs

3-68

monitor from space in a few days what would take years to monitor by airplane.

What is the value of this? Two of the most serious problems facing all people of the Earth today are food problems and the growing shortages of natural resources, such as oil. Of what value would the solution of these two problems be to mankind?

Two other areas of space technology which we will mention only briefly are communications satellites and computers. In each of these areas there

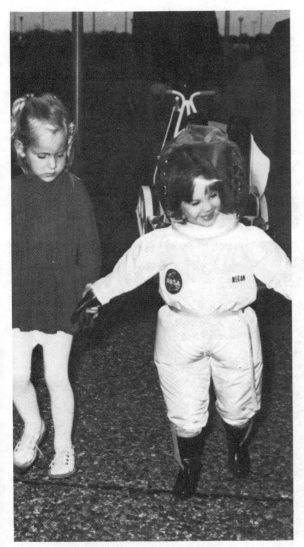

Figure 56. Biological isolation garment

have been great developments and many economic, political and sociological benefits. Outside of the obvious things like worldwide telephone communciations and live television from all over the world, communications satellites are also used for:

1. Educational television to remote areas where other educational methods are either not available or very expensive. This has been tried experimentally in India to provide education to remote villages. In these cases rather than teaching reading, writing, and arithmetic, the natives are taught things like good nutrition, proper hygiene, and even birth control methods.

2. Medical diagnostic services to remote areas. This allows health services to be provided to areas that are without doctors through two-way communication between a nurse in the field and a doctor in a hospital thousands of miles away. This type of service also allows a doctor in one country to consult with a recognized specialist in another country.

3. Libraries in different parts of the world are connected via satellites to share information. It is possible to transmit, via satellite, copies of pictures, articles or even entire books.

4. Law enforcement agencies in different states or countries share information including photographs, fingerprints, and descriptions via communications satellites. This allows instantaneous, worldwide communication of information to help fight crime/terrorism nationally and internationally.

The use of computers has grown so rapidly in the past twenty years that it is impossible to imagine our society existing without them. Our entire business community is dependent on computers for keeping records and storing information. Most companies have all their billing done by computers. Computers also keep track of their inventories, and employee, and payroll records. Airplanes are flown by computers, traffic flow on city streets is controlled by computers and we even have computers in our homes and automobiles. Computers are used to design buildings and automobiles, they diagnose illness in people, they write music, play games, and they even talk to each other.

We cannot say that these developments would not have taken place without our space program. We can say, however, that without our space program the development would not have been so rapid. Without the demands of the space scientists, for better, smaller, and cheaper components with which to build their satellites, the electronic revolution would have been slower in developing.

Spin-off. Our space program did not directly develop such things as solid state televisions, vest pocket calculators, or microwave ovens, but these items and thousands more are spin-offs of aero-space technology. Other things we can list are sun-glasses that darken as the light becomes brighter, quartz wristwatches, and tiny nickel cadmium batteries. Small hearing aids in the bow of your glasses and artificial pacemakers for heart patients are also spin-offs of aerospace technology.

The field of medicine has probably benefited the most from space program spin-off. Figure 56 shows an isolation garment modeled after our astronauts' space suits. This garment is useful to people who

Figure 57. Boeing hydrofoil, built using aerospace technology

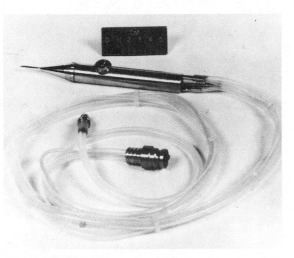

Figure 58. Cataract surgery tool

the patient's eye, and then the tool "pumps" it out of the eye. This procedure is faster, easier, and safer than surgery. It should also prove less expensive.

In the area of materials we have new temperature-resistant metals, extra strong plastics, bonded lubricants, super insulations, and composite materials which were developed for our space effort and are now being used in aircraft, automobiles, sporting goods, housing, etc. How do you judge the value of these spin-off products? The answer will vary for each individual. If you are one of the more than 1,000,000 people being kept alive by an artificial heart pacemaker, your answer will probably be "very valuable." Others will probably see little or no direct benefit and will answer that they are of no value.

As mentioned earlier, our space program holds the potential for solving many of the problems of the Earth whether they be social, economic or political. If we are to achieve this potential we must continue to support our space program at least at the current level of funding. Public understanding and support are vital because without them the budget for space exploration will continue to erode. We have spent twenty years *exploring* space and only now have we reached a point where we can begin *using* space for peaceful purposes and for the benefit of all mankind.

lack the ability to produce antibodies. They have no natural immunity to diseases and thus must be isolated from all germs. Before this isolation garment was developed, they were restricted to living inside a plastic "bubble." Now, protected by the suit, they can get out and move around. Another medical marvel is shown in figure 58. This is a tool which is inserted into the eyeball of a patient with cataracts. A high frequency vibration dissolves the cloudy lens of

THE AEROSPACE INDUSTRY

The aerospace industry is composed of hundreds of companies, large and small that are involved in some form of manufacturing related to aircraft, missiles, spacecraft, and their parts and accessories. Sixty of these industries belong to a professional organization—the Aerospace Industries Association (AIA). Some of the industries that belong to AIA are the Boeing Company, Grumman Corporation, Bell Helicopter Textron, Hughes Aircraft, Lockheed Corporation, RCA, Honeywell Inc., International Business Machine Corporation (IBM), General Electric, and McDonnell-Douglas Corporation. Many of the manufacturers of general aviation aircraft like Cessna, Piper, Beech, etc., are not members of AIA, but have their own professional organization—GAMA (General Aviation Manufacturers Association). There are about 29 manufacturers which belong to GAMA including many that build engines, instruments, radios, and other equipment for general aviation aircraft.

The industries which are involved in aerospace manufacturing are considered high technology industries. This means that the areas they work in are involved in the most modern, up-to-date areas of applied research. Because of the highly technical nature of the work in the aerospace industries, the personnel tend to be very skilled and more highly trained than in the average manufacturing industry. This is true for the production workers, the managers, and the scientists and engineers. One result of this is that salaries average generally higher in the aerospace industries.

The data we are using in this chapter are supplied by the Aerospace Industries Association and the General Aviation Manufacturers Association. The general learning objective for this chapter is for you to know the economics and the problems of the aerospace industry. To reach this objective, you must pattern your study of the material according to the *specific learning objectives* listed in the Appendix of this textbook.

AEROSPACE INDUSTRY ECONOMICS

In 1981, the aerospace industry employed more than 1,200,000 people directly. These people include highly trained scientists and engineers as well as many thousands of production workers. This amounts to over five percent of the total manufacturing labor force in the United States. The

AEROSPACE EMPLOYMENT AND PAYROLL

Year	YEAR-END EMPLOYMENT (In Thousands)			ANNUAL PAYROLL (Millions of Dollars)		
	Total	Production Workers	All Others	Total	Production Workers	All Others
1978	977	476	501	19,501	7,873	11,628
1979	1,019	562	547	24,243	10,247	13,996
1980	1,187	598	589	28,795	12,087	16,708
1981	1,207	593	614	32,105	13,088	19,017

Source: A.I.A.

Figure 59.

average salary for aerospace production workers is about $22,000 per year, and for the others (management, scientists, engineers, etc.) it is about $30,000 per year. The total payroll for the industry in 1981 was about $20 billion. This is $32 billion which comes directly into our economy to buy houses and groceries and to pay taxes (see fig. 59). However, if we use the multiplier effects* on other businesses and industries, it is estimated that the aerospace industry also accounts indirectly for an additional 800,000 American jobs. The annual payroll for these jobs adds another $10 billion to the economy.

Another unique feature of the aerospace industry that can be seen in the chart in figure 59 is the high percentage of the work force who are not production workers. In most manufacturing industries, the production workers make up a very high percentage of the work force (up to 75 percent). In the aerospace industry this figure is only about 49 per-

cent. This is also a reflection on the highly technical nature of aerospace. Included in the "all other" category, in addition to the scientists and engineers and management, are designers, draftsmen, computer operators, technicians, and sales and promotion people. There are more of these types of careers in the aerospace industries than in other types of manufacturing.

SALES

Aerospace sales totaled $63.5 billion in 1981, an increase of 15 percent over 1980 (see fig. 60). The profit on these sales was about $2.9 billion, or about four and one-third percent. It is important to point out that inflation accounted for over five percent of the dollar increase in sales during 1981.

One area in which aerospace sales have always been of great economic benefit to the nation is the area of exports. In 1981, there were $13.3 billion

*It is estimated that for every three people employed by an industry, there are two additional jobs created outside of the industry.

AEROSPACE INDUSTRIAL SALES BY PRODUCT GROUP
(Millions of Dollars)

YEAR	AIRCRAFT			MISSILES	SPACE	NON AEROSPACE	GRAND TOTAL
	TOTAL	MILITARY	CIVIL				
1978	21,617	8,222	13,395	4,792	5,717	6,813	38,939
1979	24,659	13,227	11,432	5,291	6,545	7,715	44,210
1980	30,144	16,285	13,859	6,041	7,892	8,819	52,896
1981	36,625	17,392	19,233	6,807	9,472	10,586	63,490

Source: A.I.A.

Figure 60.

AEROSPACE SALES BY CUSTOMER
(Millions of Dollars)

| Year | Total Sales | Aerospace Products and Services | | | Non-Aerospace | |
| | | U.S. Government | | Other Customers | U.S. Gov't | Other Customers |
		DOD	NASA and Other Agencies			
1978	38,939	16,770	3,151	12,205	3,860	2,953
1979	44,210	17,708	3,453	15,334	4,087	3,628
1980	52,896	20,994	4,106	18,977	4,762	4,057
1981	63,490	25,896	4,688	22,320	5,822	4,764

Source: A.I.A.

Figure 61.

worth of civil aviation exports from the United States. An additional $4.3 billion worth of military aircraft and missiles were exported in 1981. Total aerospace exports for 1981 were $17.6 billion. During 1981, aerospace imports ran about $4.5 billion. This led to a balance of trade surplus in the aerospace industry of $13.1 billion in 1981. For the first time, the aerospace industry exceeded agriculture as the leading exporter in the Nation. This is a significant factor in our economy, particularly when we are importing so much oil from the Middle East. For example, every time we sell an F-15 fighter (worth $15 million) to Saudi Arabia, it offsets the import of 1.3 million barrels of oil. Or, every time we sell a Boeing 747 (worth $40 million) to Japan Air Lines, it offsets the import of 200,000 Sony television sets or of 16,000 Honda automobiles.

The United States government remains the number one customer of the aerospace industry (see fig. 61). About 47 percent of all aerospace sales in 1981 went to the government (DOD and NASA). Thirty-nine percent of the sales were to civil aviation customers, and 14 percent were sales of non-aerospace products. There is a downward trend in government sales which began in the late 1960s. At that time, the sales to the government accounted for about 75 percent of all aerospace sales. Most aerospace industry leaders feel that this is a healthy condition and is much better than relying almost entirely on the government for their business.

The area of non-aerospace products is worthy of some discussion because it is a departure from normal aerospace sales. It is also the area which has shown the fastest growth since 1972. Earlier we talked about the spin-off of technology into the econ-

omy. This area of non-aerospace sales represents about $10.5 billion worth of spin-off products into areas such as hospitals and public health, mass transit, public safety, and environmental protection. In the last six years these sales have increased 80 percent, and now account for almost twice as much money as the entire area of space program sales. This is an encouraging indicator to the aerospace industry and these sales should continue to grow in the future as more aerospace technology enters other areas.

One area where this technology is beginning to be felt is in the area of energy. As our energy supplies diminish and the cost of energy increases, we will see more spin-off into this area. Some very obvious applications are the development of better insulations and in the improved production of electrical energy. Let's look at a couple of examples.

As our space program began the use of cryogenics as rocket propellants, the problem of keeping them cold became very serious. The tanks had to be insulated in such a way that the cryogenics did not all boil away. New materials and insulating techniques were developed which were so effective that it was claimed by one manufacturer that "if an ice cube was placed inside one of the propellant tanks of the Saturn V rocket, it would take 100 years to melt." This claim may be exaggerated, but some giant advances were made in insulations which could be applied in the future to insulation problems in other areas.

In the area of power generation, the NASA Lewis Research Center is working on using new technology to improve wind powered generators (see fig. 62). They are looking at better aerodynamics in the

Figure 62.
NASA wind turbine technology

"propeller" blades, reducing friction, and improving the electrical generator. Another area of power generation which may become economical is the use of solar cells to generate electricity. These devises have been used on all satellites to convert sunlight directly into electricity. They are currently not very efficient (about 10 percent) and cannot compare with our present day "cheap" electricity. However, it is hoped that future technology will raise their efficiency to 25 percent. If this happens, and our current energy systems continue to increase in cost, we may see the time when solar cells come into widespread use.

BACKLOG

One area that the aerospace industry uses as an indication of the outlook for the future is what they call backlog. Backlog represents the orders which the manufacturers have received for equipment which will be filled at some time in the future. As long as the backlog of orders is high, the industry knows it will have enough work to keep it busy for quite a while. Figure 63 shows the backlog of orders at the end of 1980 and 1981. The backlog of $99 billion represents an increase of more than $9 billion over year-end 1980. This reflects a great many new orders during 1981 because at the end of 1980 the manufacturers had a backlog of $90 billion, and we

BACKLOG OF MAJOR AEROSPACE COMPANIES
(Millions of Dollars)

YEAR	GRAND TOTAL	TOTAL U.S. GOVERNMENT	TOTAL OTHER CUSTOMERS
1978	57,160	30,223	26,937
1979	78,259	36,136	42,123
1980	90,517	37,200	53,317
1981	98,742	45,821	52,921

Source: A.I.A.

Figure 63.

have already said that during 1981 they sold $63.5 billion worth of equipment. This means that during 1981 the industries must have received $62.5 billion worth of orders.

You can see that the largest gain in backlog is from the United States Government. Increase in government backlog amounted to $8.6 billion, while the backlog from nongovernment customers actually decreased by $400 million.

GENERAL AVIATION

The figures we have looked at so far represent the industries belonging to AIA. The General Aviation Manufacturers Association (GAMA) represents the builders of general aviation aircraft. The number of aircraft produced by GAMA members was down for the second straight year. The general aviation manufacturers sold over 9,457 aircraft in 1981 which were worth about $2.9 billion. This compares with 11,877 aircraft built in 1980 and 17,048 in 1979. Export of general aviation aircraft amounted to $749 million in 1981.

SOCIOLOGICAL IMPLICATIONS

One interesting phenomenon seen in the aerospace industry is an apparent cycle in the number of trained engineers and scientists. This has a dramtic and, in some cases, devastating impact on our educational system. This first became apparent just after Sputnik I was launched in 1957. Prior to this time, there were apparently enough scientists and engineers to fill all available jobs and there was no large demand for them from our colleges and universities. Suddenly, after Sputnik, there was an outcry from industry and government that we were behind the Russians and it was all the fault of our schools because they hadn't been producing enough scientists and engineers. The demand for scientists and engineers skyrocketed and the starting salaries for graduates in these fields followed suit. The result was that these fields became very popular. More and more young people began entering them assured that when they graduated there would be a good job waiting for them. The federal government made huge sums of money available for grants and stipends. As mentioned earlier, at that time 75 percent of the aerospace industry's business was with the United States Government.

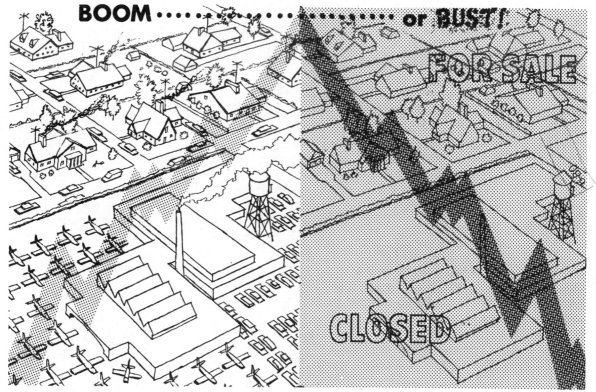

BOOM · or BUST!

FOR SALE

CLOSED

Figure 64.

In the mid-1960s, there was a slowdown in government contracts as fewer new fighters and bombers were being built, and missile programs were phased out. Suddenly these highly skilled scientists and engineers found themselves unemployed. To make matters worse, many of them had become so highly specialized in one particular area that they found that no other industry wanted them. The aerospace industry has always been a highly transient industry. When one manufacturer completed production of a particular fighter or bomber, and began to lay-off people, another manufacturer would get a new contract and hire them. However, in the '60s there were no new contracts and these highly educated individuals found themselves unemployable. Many left their career fields and found work elsewhere. Others found employment with aerospace industries in foreign countries such as Canada, England, Germany, etc. The serious thing was that this was a vital natural resource which

was lost. We had spent millions of dollars and many years to train these people, and then overnight we lost them.

The result was felt immediately in the education community. The word spread very quickly that science and engineering were no longer good fields to enter. Enrollment in colleges of engineering began to drop, resulting in lay-offs of professors. In the high schools, fewer students attended science and mathematics classes. Eventually the pendulum swung back.

As we began to gear up for our Apollo project, and as the war in Vietnam began to escalate, suddenly there was again a shortage of trained scientists and engineers. The entire cycle started over again because the trained people who had been affected by cutbacks earlier had left the aerospace field, and many of them were leery of coming back. It takes a long time to replace these highly qualified people because their replacements must complete many years of high school and college to become trained.

In 1971, just when we had again geared up to produce more scientists and engineers, the United States Government cancelled the American supersonic transport program, and the cycle once again reversed itself. In this case the Boeing Company in Seattle was hit the hardest as thousands of trained engineers and skilled production workers were laid-off. The economy of Seattle was impacted severely. When the major industry in a large city is hit with a big lay-off of workers, the other businesses also suffer. The grocery stores, schools, movie theaters, etc., all have less business and they, in turn, must lay-off people. Hundreds of houses must be sold which ruins the real estate market. Countless automobiles, refrigerators, televisions, etc., are repossessed because the people cannot continue to make their payments.

After another upturn in the mid and late 1970s, we are again entering a period of decline in the aerospace industries. Increased sales of aircraft and missiles to the military is helping, but there is a decline in the civil aviation market. This is felt most by the general aviation manufacturer. Many general aviation aircraft are purchased for personal use or by small businessmen. When economic times get tough, the purchase of a new general aviation aircraft for $50,000 to $500,000 is something that can be delayed. This is why the sales of general aviation aircraft in 1981 were only about one-half what they were in 1978. Projections are that this decline in sales will continue into 1982 and 1983. Cessna, Piper, and Beech Aircraft Companies have had to lay off several thousand employees.

PROBLEM AREAS

Just as we saw in the case of air transportation, the main problems facing the aerospace industry are financial and political in nature.

In the manufacturing of commercial transports, companies like Boeing, McDonnell-Douglas, and Lockheed are finding it very difficult to finance the development of the next generation of commercial airliners.

In the past, new commercial transports were

Figure 65.

spin-offs from the development of military aircraft. For example, the Boeing 707 was an offshoot of the B-47 and B-52 bombers. This meant that the costs for research and development, building the factories, tooling, equipment, materials, and labor were all paid for by the government. When production of the bombers was completed the same technology (tooling, labor, etc.) was used to produce the civilian airliners. This is no longer the case. Experts and industry leaders believe that we can no longer depend on the new technology derived from military aircraft developments for our new generation of commercial air transports as we have in the past.

The cost of developing a new aircraft can run as much as $2 billion and no single company, such as Lockheed or Boeing, can possibly afford these costs. Remember, we said earlier that the net profit for the *entire industry* was only $2.9 billion in 1981. How to finance these costs is a problem for the manufacturers.

One way to obtain part of the money is to demand partial payment from an airline before the aircraft are produced. This payment "buys" the airline a certain place on the production line. The airlines that place their orders first are guaranteed the first production aircraft. The further down the order list, the later the delivery date. This system only provides a fraction of the money required to place a new aircraft into production. The manufacturer must borrow the rest. It is very difficult to compete for the required capital, especially when the bank knows that in order to break even 300 to 400 aircraft must be sold, but there are orders for only 100.

The amount of interest banks charge is also an important factor. In 1981, the interest rate rose to 20 percent. How would you like to pay the interest on a $500,000,000 loan at 20 percent financed over a period of ten years? The manufacturer, of course, passes these interest charges along to the airline purchasing the aircraft. This increases the cost of the airplane by 20 percent which, in turn, forces the airlines to borrow more money.

FOREIGN COMPETITION

The problem of financing faced by our commercial aircraft manufacturers is made even more difficult by the increasing foreign competition. Historically, commercial aircraft manufactured in the United States have dominated the market—both here and in foreign countries (see fig. 66). It is easy to assume that because the United States manufacturers have such a lead over foreign manufacturers, there is no need to worry about foreign competition. This is not true. The foreign nations recognized the economic value of commercial transports, and over the past 10 years they have made increasingly large investments in research and development in this area. By contrast, the United States growth rate in research and development has been declining. The foreign investments in R & D are beginning to pay off as higher technology foreign jets like the A-300B Airbus enter the market. In 1979 Airbus Industrie received 31% of the world's orders for wide body aircraft. By 1981 this had grown to 43% of the world's orders for wide body jets.

Government support in foreign countries goes beyond their contributions to research and development. One other area is in "directed procurement." Most foreign airlines are government owned and the government may tell them what type of airplanes to buy, without regard for which are the best or what type the airline wants. Foreign manufacturers also have a big edge in government subsidy for develop-

U.S. MANUFACTURERS		NON-U.S. MANUFACTURERS	
Model	# Produced	Model	#Produced
Boeing		Comet★	112
707/720★	939	Caravelle★	279
727	1786	Trident★	117
737	823	VC-10★	54
747	540	BAC-111	227
Convair		F-28	165
880★	65	Mercure★	10
990★	37	A-300	164
Lockheed		VFW-614★	10
L-1011	231	Concorde★	12
McDonnell Douglas			
DC-8★	556		
DC-9	1032		
DC-10	358		
U.S. TOTAL	6367	Non-U.S. TOTAL	1150

★ No longer in production

Figure 66. Commercial Jet Aircraft Deliveries through 1981

ment of new aircraft models. Most foreign manufacturers are either nationalized or government controlled. Thus, foreign governments often assume the financial risk of building a new aircraft model by putting up 50-90 percent of the production costs.

Another way that foreign governments assist their manufacturers is by providing customers with very generous loan terms which our manufacturers cannot match. These generous terms may be in the form of a "no down payment" loan, a longer term loan, or a loan at a much smaller interest rate. It has also been reported that in at least one case, a foreign government "closed the sale" of its aircraft to another foreign airline by telling the customer that he would be able to land in their country *only* if he bought their aircraft rather than an American one.

The only U.S. carrier flying the A-300 is Eastern Airlines. The Airbus sale to Eastern included giving Eastern Airlines the use of four A-300s for a six-month trial period at no lease cost. Another incentive provided by Airbus was to defer 29 percent of the interest for up to four years on 12 of the A-300s purchased by Eastern.

These types of "assistance" are in violation of existing international agreements, but there is little that can be done about it.

Whatever the reason—better technology, or other "assistance"—the foreign jet transport is fast becoming very competitive with the American jet transport. The race is on between United States manufacturers and the foreign manufacturers, and the prize is the next generation of commercial jet transports.

JET TRANSPORTS OF THE 1980s

We have already mentioned that the next decade will see the largest growth in air transportation in history. Most estimates are that airline purchases between 1980 and 1990 will run about $125 billion. Some estimates place this figure as high as $150 billion. The competition between aircraft manufacturers for this market is intense and will get even more so. This is true both between United States and foreign manufacturers as well as among the American manufacturers.

European manufacturers are working hard to get a larger share of the world air transport market. American aircraft companies are working just as hard to maintain their dominance in this market. This is more than just a struggle between manufacturers because, as we have already seen, it has a strong effect on the overall economies and the people of the nations involved.

AREAS OF COMPETITION

The needs of the world's airlines during the decade of the 1980s fall into two market areas—(1) the replacement market, and (2) the added capacity market.

The replacement market consists of the present jetliners which are more than 10 years old. At the beginning of 1980 the world's jet airline fleet consisted of 5,500 aircraft. Of these 3,300 were from 9 to 12 years old. There are about 2,000 of these older jets, and they will have to be replaced during the 1980s. This market will make up about 36 percent of the total airline deliveries during the period.

The other 64 percent of all transport aircraft built during the 80s will be the new aircraft needed to carry the estimated 600 million additional passengers who will be flying by 1990. This is called the added capacity market and could amount to as many as 3,600 new aircraft during the 1980s.

In both the replacement market and the added capacity market, the largest demand is for a medium range/medium capacity airliner. This is basically an aircraft with a range of about 2,000 miles and a capacity of about 200 passengers. It is in this area that the most intense competition between manufacturers will occur. The new generation of aircraft that are competing in this area are all wide body aircraft. This is because this type of aircraft has great passenger appeal. The Boeing 727-200, the McDonnell-Douglas DC-10 Model 10, the Lockheed L-1011, and the Airbus Industrie A-300B are all current-day jets that are designed to serve the medium range/medium capacity market. There can be no doubt that a great many of these "present-day technology" aircraft will be purchased to serve the demands of the 1980s. However, it is in the "new technology" generation of aircraft that the greatest impact will be felt.

Many people may expect that the new generation of jetliners will be dramatically different in appearance from their predecessors. They will not, because they are still subsonic airplanes operating at the same 500-600 mph speed and 30,000-40,000

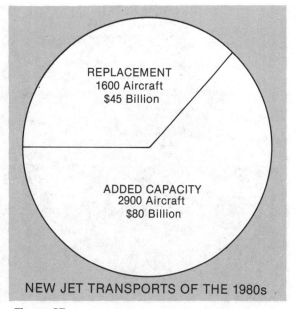

NEW JET TRANSPORTS OF THE 1980s

Figure 67.

Figure 68. Boeing 767

Figure 69. Interior of Boeing 767

foot altitude. The wings will be the same shape, the fuselages will be similar, and the engines will be mounted in the same fashion. However, they are new airplanes. They use advanced technology developed over the last two decades. These advance-technology features are aimed at reducing airline operating costs, lowering maintenance requirements, and improving environmental characteristics. The degree of advanced technology will vary, but generally the jetliners of the new generation will offer some or all of these improvements:

- Dramatic improvements in engine performance with regard to fuel consumption.
- Much lower engine noise levels and reduction in exhaust emissions.
- Longer engine life and reduced maintenance.
- Advanced aerodynamics, particularly in the wings, which contribute to lower fuel consumption.
- Advanced structures for extending airframe life.
- New flight controls and more reliable digital autopilots.
- Greater passenger comfort through better seating arrangements.
- Lower noise levels in the cabin and better pressurization/air conditioning systems.

New United States Transports. Among the new United States jetliners for the 1980s, only one, the Boeing 767 (fig. 68) is currently in service. The 767 was launched by a $1.2 billion order from United Airlines in July 1978. This was the largest single aircraft order in history. The United Airlines order for 30 aircraft was soon followed by an order from American Airlines for 30, and Delta Airlines for 20. As of December 31, 1981, there were 147 of these aircraft on order by U.S. carriers and 40 by foreign airlines.

The 767 is built in two models, the 767-100 which seats about 180 passengers and the 767-200 which seats about 200. All of the early orders were for the 200 model. The aircraft is 165 feet long and has a 155-foot wing span (both about 10 feet greater than the 707). The fuselage is wider than the 707, but not as wide as the wide body 747. The passenger cabin will have seven-abreast seating with two aisles

(see fig. 69). The 767 is powered by two turbofan engines mounted in pylons under the wings. The engines are new technology, high bypass engines which produce little noise but are rated at about 40,000 pounds of thrust each. Boeing claims that the fuel burned per passenger seat is 35 percent lower than in its 727s, and each 767 could save an airline nearly one and one-half million dollars per year in fuel costs. United Airlines was the first airline to fly the 767, which was inaugurated on September 8, 1982, between Chicago and Denver.

Two other new generation United States jet transports were also planned—the Lockheed L-1011 Dash 400 and the McDonnell-Douglas DC-X-200. However, since Boeing was awarded the first orders, the other two manufacturers appear to have stopped their developmental programs. Both the L-1011 Dash 400 and the DC-X-200 were what are called "derivative" airplanes, derived from earlier models. The Dash 400 was a shortened version of the L-1011 *Tristar*. Both of these aircraft did utilize advanced technology but not as much as the 767. Both Lockheed and McDonnell-Douglas may revive their aircraft at a later date.

New Foreign Transports. The only major competition Boeing has in the new technology transport market comes from the European consortium— Airbus Industrie. Airbus Industrie has a new twinjet transport already in development and slated for first deliveries in 1982. The A-310 Airbus (fig. 70) is an advanced technology, scaled down version of the A-300B. It is being offered in two models, the -100 which has a range of about 2,800 miles, and the -200 which has larger fuel tanks and a range of about 3,600 miles. Both versions seat between 215-265 passengers, depending on what type of seating the customer selects. Lufthansa, Air France and Swiss Air have all placed orders for the A-310, and all three have selected American engines (General Electric and Pratt & Whitney) although it is also offered with Rolls Royce engines.

OTHER NEW JET TRANSPORTS

We mentioned earlier that the largest demand for airliners was in the medium range/medium

Figure 70. A-310 Airbus

capacity area. This does not mean that there will be no short range/small capacity jets or long range-/large capacity jets built during the 1980s. As of January 1982, orders for 727-100s and 737s from Boeing total 262 aircraft. Orders for DC-9s from McDonnell-Douglas total 51 aircraft. Even though the manufacturers have raised their production rates for these aircraft, they are still sold out until late 1985. The same thing is true for the jumbo jets. Boeing has more orders for 747s than it can handle (74 units), as does Lockheed for the L-1011 (32 units). There are two United States advanced technology jets which are also in production for the short/medium range market.

McDonnell-Douglas DC-9 Super 80. The first of the

Figure 71. DC-9 Super 80

new technology short/medium range jets to go into service was the DC-9 Super 80 (see fig. 71). The Super 80 is a stretched DC-9, but it also has new turbofan engines which reduce noise and emissions while saving fuel. It is also equipped with a new technology wing which further adds to its fuel savings. The Super 80 carries between 137 and 172 passengers (depending on customer preferences) and has a range of about 1,500 miles. However, it can be built to have a range of about 2,000 miles. Firm orders have been received for 43 of the Super 80s with options for 25 more.

Boeing 757. Boeing's entry into the new technology short/medium range market is the 757 twinjet. This aircraft has the same fuselage width as the Boeing 727 and 737, but it also has an advanced technology wing and new engines (see fig. 72). Boeing claims the 757 will have 40 percent better fuel economy than the jets it replaces. British Airways has ordered 19 with options for another 12, and Eastern Airlines has ordered 21 plus options for another 24. All of these orders are for the 757-200 which carries 174 passengers and has a range of up to 2,500 miles. Boeing is also offering a 757-100 which would have a range of 1,400 miles and carry 164 passengers. Boeing is predicting that the 757 will become one of the best selling aircraft in its history

Figure 72. Boeing 757

and they predict that they will sell 1,200 of them. At the price of about 17 million dollars per aircraft, you can see that 1,200 aircraft amount to a great deal of money.

NEW ENGINES

All of these new advanced technology aircraft mean that there is also a revolution in advanced technology engines with which to power them. The 767 is powered by a Pratt & Whitney JT9D-7R (fig. 73). This engine is rated at 42,000 pounds of thrust. Boeing also offers its customers the choice of the General Electric CF6 engine or the Rolls Royce RB 211. These same basic engines, although available in various thrust ratings, are also used to power the Boeing 747, Lockheed L1011, McDonnell-Douglas DC-10 and the A-300 and A-310 Airbus. The DC-9 Super 80 is powered by two 18,000 pound thrust Pratt and Whitney JT8D Dash 209 engines.

All of these engines are derivatives of tried and true engines which have powered jet transports for two decades. These new engines, however, make use of the newest technology to reduce pollution and noise.

FOREIGN MILITARY SALES

There is a growing movement in this country to limit or even eliminate sales of our military aircraft to

Figure 73. Pratt & Whitney JT9D-7R engine

foreign nations. This issue causes much emotion, both pro and con. The critics of foreign arms sales call the aircraft industry "merchants of death." Those who favor these sales say that if the foreign nations cannot buy weapons from us, they will get them elsewhere. They also say that in doing this they will move away from the United States at a time when we cannot afford to lose friends. Without getting involved in the moral aspects of the question, it is necessary to take a look at the political and economic aspects of this area of our aerospace community.

There are two types of exports of military arms: (1) Foreign Military Sales (FMS) where all arrangements are made on a government-to-government basis; and (2) direct sales, where the manufacturer contracts directly with the foreign government. In either case, the State Department and Congress have the final approval. The sales are allowed only when they serve the best interests of United States foreign policy.

Sales to foreign nations are political in nature, but you cannot overlook the fact that they accounted for over four billion dollars in exports in 1981. This was an increase of 90 percent over 1980. Figure 74 shows the amount of sales in the various categories.

Another factor to consider when discussing foreign military sales is that these sales result in lower cost aircraft and missiles for our armed forces. The cost per unit of an aircraft or missile is determined by the total number manufactured. If only a few aircraft of a certain type are built, each will be more expensive than if a large number are built. This is because the research and development costs are figured into the sales price. In most cases, our sales of military aircraft to foreign nations involve the same type of aircraft that our armed forces are buying. If we sell several hundred to a foreign government, the cost of each aircraft bought by our armed forces will be less.

Many people also are concerned about the

EXPORTS OF AEROSPACE PRODUCTS
(Millions of $)

	1980	1981
TOTAL MILITARY	2,258	4,322
Complete Aircraft	949	1,712
Transports	231	158
Helicopters	88	177
Fighters & Bombers	449	1,006
Parts & Equipment	560	2,054
Rockets and Missiles	749	556

Source: A.I.A.

Figure 74.

"export of technology" as it relates to aerospace exports both military and civilian. For instance, it costs a great deal of money to develop the new technology of an electronic autopilot. If we sell an aircraft equipped with the latest electronic autopilot to a foreign nation, many believe we are exporting our expensive technology in addition to the aircraft. Of course, the foreign government wants to buy the most modern aircraft available. Again, this problem becomes political in nature, and if the technology also involves our national security, it becomes even more touchy. For example: The United States has sold 48 of the new F-14A aircraft to Iran. These aircraft were equipped with the Phoenix missile and the latest fire-control system. This same aircraft, missile, and fire-control system is also used by the United States Navy, and is the most modern available. This was no serious problem so long as we remained friendly with Iran. But now that our friendly relationship has changed, this is a problem. If the Soviets get hold of the F-14A and the Phoenix, it would seriously jeopardize the security of the United States.

These questions have no easy answers, as is the case with most questions related to aerospace. It is important that we are aware of these questions and understand both sides of the issue well enough to make informed judgments.

Chapter 3-6

AEROSPACE EDUCATION AND TRAINING

At the beginning of Part 6 we discussed the concept of aerospace power. We learned that there were three factors that determine our aerospace power—military aerospace activities, civilian aerospace programs, and aerospace education. We also mentioned that the three factors were all interrelated and anything that affected one also affected the other two. In this chapter we are going to discuss the area of aerospace education and its importance. We are also going to look at some aerospace careers and the training requirements for them.

The general learning objective for this chapter is for you to know the aerospace education and training factors that help determine U.S. aerospace power. To reach this objective, you must pattern your study of the material according to the *specific learning objectives* listed in the Appendix of this textbook.

AEROSPACE EDUCATION

The term aerospace education has been in existence for about twenty years. In the beginning, it had a very specific meaning. As more and more people began using it, the meaning began to change and to cover more things. In our use of the term aerospace education in this text, we are returning to the original "pure" definition. We will discuss what aerospace education is and also what it is not.

AEROSPACE EDUCATION DEFINED

Let's begin by giving the definition and then discussing what the definition means.

"Aerospace Education is that branch of *general education* concerned with communicating *knowledge, skills,* and *attitudes* about aerospace activities and the total *impact* of air and space vehicles upon *society.*"

We have italicized the key words in the definition that may need further explanation.

General Education. The field of education is often broken down into two areas—general education and special education. *General education* is the education which a society considers necessary for all of its members. Subjects like reading, mathematics, English, history, etc., are considered by our society as general education courses. *Special education* is the education which is designed to *train* individuals or groups to perform certain tasks. Some examples of this are typing, home economics, driver education, and any vocational courses. If a course is a required course, it is usually in the general education area, and if it is an elective, it is in the special education area.

Knowledge. One of the goals of all education, general or special, is to provide people with information and an understanding of something. Knowledge is the creation of understanding or awareness of a certain topic. Knowledge can be gained either through study or through experience in an area.

Skill. Skill is the ability to use your knowledge—to do something with it. Some types of skills are mechanical and come through training in the special education area. Others are mental and these are the skills which allow you to think or interpret the relationships between things. It takes a lot longer to acquire skills than it does knowledge.

Attitudes. Attitudes are your mental feelings or emotions about something. Some attitudes are taught by our parents, or our teachers, or by our churches. Others are acquired through working with or experience in an area of activity. Attitudes can be positive or negative, but once they are acquired, they are hard to change.

Knowledge and skill should work together to form attitudes, but this is not always the case. In many cases a person can develop an attitude about

something without having much knowledge or skill in the area. Unfortunately, this is often the case in aerospace. For example, many people firmly believe that our armed forces exist only to kill people and fight wars. Another attitude that many people have is that all progress is bad. We often hear this attitude voiced in sayings such as "Remember the good old days?" or, "Interesting, but what good is it?" (See figure 75.)

Impact upon society. This refers to what aircraft and our space programs do for or to society. The term society is one that is interpreted differently by different individuals. Society usually means a group of people having common traditions, interests, and institutions. In the time of the cave man, society was limited to the family unit that inhabited a particular cave. Later it would include all those people who lived under one feudal lord. During the Civil War, the North and the South were certainly different societies. What is our society today? Is it just our nation? Does it include our allies? The charter of the National Aeronautics and Space Administration established that aerospace agency to explore space "for the benefit of all mankind." What do you think society should include in an aerospace age?

AEROSPACE EDUCATION UNDERSTOOD

It is clear that the people who established the definition for aerospace education felt that it was so important that all of our citizenry should study it. It is also evident that when they defined aerospace education they were not talking about any program which trained pilots, navigators, engineers, astronauts, flight attendants, or anybody else. The purpose of aerospace education is not to train anyone to do anything. Rather, its purpose is to teach everyone to understand aerospace developments and appreciate their importance. Aerospace education is designed to provide the citizenry with the knowledge (information) necessary to understand what aerospace is. Once this knowledge is acquired, the citizen should develop the ability to understand the relationship between aerospace and other aspects of our society (skill). When this happens, certain attitudes begin to form which are the result of informed rather than uninformed opinions.

WHY IS AEROSPACE EDUCATION IMPORTANT?

Thomas Jefferson once said: "An informed citizenry is the foundation of democracy." The advocates of aerospace also believe this is true. Understanding aerospace is vital for all citizens because of our unique political system. Americans through their elected Congressmen and Senators ultimately decide the priorities of our nation. The people decide which programs are the most important and which will be funded from the federal treasury. Like many citizens, some elected officials are uninformed about aerospace. These representa-tives have attitudes and beliefs about the importance of aviation and our space exploration program which have been formed out of a lack of knowledge rather than from an informed viewpoint. Ideally, both the citizens and their representatives should be equally informed or they cannot know or cause the right decisions to be made. Because of the absence of an aerospace understanding, elected officials rarely hear reports from their constituents. From that silence, judgments are made and the representa-tives believe they are doing what the voters want. On the other hand, if the citizens understood the importance of aerospace and voiced their opinions, the elected representatives would have to reflect these opinions when voting on aerospace matters.

In most cases, average citizens has a super-ficial knowledge about aerospace because their information is based upon what they have read,

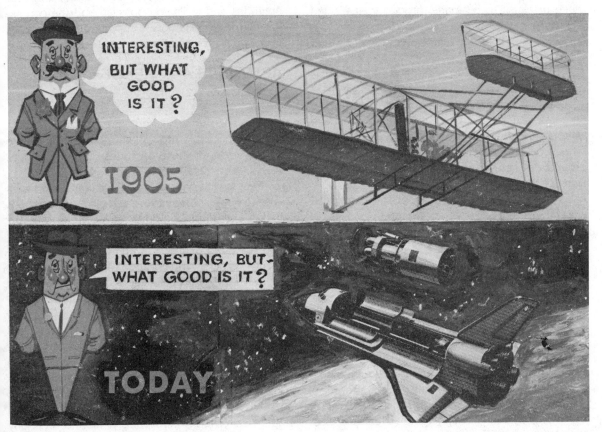

Figure 75.

seen, or heard through the media. In many cases this information is misleading. The only solution to the problem is a citizenry informed about aerospace.

Another freedom which individuals and organizations enjoy in the United States is the right to dissent and to register protests against things to which they are opposed. In order to be effective in this type of action, those individuals and organizations must be informed about aerospace if their protests are to be legitimate and worthy of any action.

Unfortunately, there is nothing which requires that the press or the media, or even the people, know what they are talking about. An uninformed or misinformed citizen has just as many rights as an informed one. If we are to maintain our leadership in aerospace, citizens must be active and informed. It is vital that the people understand the importance of aerospace to our nation so that the decisions they make or cause to be made through their elected officials are informed decisions. Once again, the solution is obvious: an aerospace-informed and active citizenry.

This then is the role of aerospace education. It is not an attempt to sway everyone to believe in all aerospace projects. It is not an attempt to propagandize people into supporting aerospace without question. It is not an attempt to get "equal time" on television. Rather, it is a long-duration program of study devoted to understanding both sides of the aerospace issues and to producing a nation of citizens informed about the aerospace world they live in.

AEROSPACE TRAINING

INTRODUCTION

From the information presented in other chapters, it should be evident that our present-day aerospace society is complex and dynamic; also, that it will become more complex as technology advances and population increases.

The one thing aerospace has produced, more than anything else, is change. The advent of space exploration in 1957, coupled with the beginning of commercial jet aviation in 1958, created an environment where, for the first time in man's history, the quest for knowledge became one of our nation's greatest industries. Suddenly, it was not only acceptable but actually popular to do research, and the effect of this is what many have called the knowledge revolution. The electronic computer was developed, refined, and improved to enable man to store, refine, and analyze the tremendous amount of data created by aerospace-related industries. During the first decade of the space exploration program, man created more new knowledge than he had in his entire past history.

This quest for knowledge placed a great demand on our education community. We needed, and we still need, more and better-trained people to work in our aerospace community. The highly technical nature of aerospace demands training beyond the high school level. However, the special aptitudes and skills you possess and the courses you take in high school are important considerations in preparing for an aerospace career.

APTITUDES AND AEROSPACE CAREERS

The special talents and natural abilities which a person possesses are called aptitudes. Figure 76 shows some of these aptitudes (i.e., mechanical, verbal, numerical, social, artistic, etc.).

People with a good mechanical aptitude find it easy to repair, adjust, or assemble machinery. Verbal aptitude is important in jobs related to any form of communication, such as reading, writing and speaking. Numerical aptitude makes mathematics very easy and is important to people seeking employment using calculators or computers.

There is a definite relationship between aptitudes and a person's success in certain occupations. People working in professions related to their aptitudes are also usually happier in their careers. Figure 76 shows the relationship between various aptitudes and those aerospace occupations in which they are important.

The aerospace industries and government agencies employ aerospace personnel in many thousands of different job categories. Aptitudes in

APTITUDES AND AEROSPACE CAREERS

Aptitudes	Related Vocational Activities	Selected Aerospace Age Careers
MECHANICAL	Equipment Development Aircraft Maintenance Machinery Repair	Aeromechanical Engineer Astronautical Engineer Production Technician Powerplant Mechanic Instrument Repairman
VERBAL	Speaking and Writing Giving Instructions Persuasive Activities	Flight Instructor Public Relations Director Air Traffic Controller Military Information Specialist Airline Sales Representative
SCIENTIFIC	Research and Invention Experimentation Scientific Investigation	Aeronautical Engineer Physical Chemist Research Metallurgist Astrophysicist Aeromedical Lab Technician
MANIPULATIVE	Equipment Operation Machinery Control Instrument Supervision	Aircraft Pilot Flight Engineer Radar Specialist Machine Tool Operator Production Expediter
NUMERICAL	Mathematical Calculations Arithmetic Reasoning Computational Activities	Data Processing Engineer Aircraft Navigator Research Mathematician Industrial Accountant Airline Statistician
ADMINISTRATIVE	Managerial Activities Supervisory Responsibility Secretarial Duties	Research Project Director Management Engineer Airport Operator Military Administrative Officer Stenographer
SOCIAL	Service, Advice, and Assistance to Individuals and Groups	Aviation Psychologist Personnel Manager Flight Nurse Training Director
ARTISTIC	Self-expression Through Design, Drawing, and Other Creative Skills	Design Engineer Airline Architect Photographic Technician Technical Illustrator Scale Model Builder

Figure 76.

the areas listed in the chart may lead to satisfaction and success in hundreds of additional aerospace jobs requiring similar abilities.

Frequently, there are relationships between aptitudes and the school subjects you may like or dislike, those that are difficult and those in which you may excel. Figure 77 shows the association of selected school subjects with representative aerospace occupations in which they have primary importance.

An occupation should provide much more than a means of making a living. It should be interesting and pleasant and provide satisfaction and self-respect in addition to financial rewards. The choice of a particular occupation requires complex decisions involving such factors as general ability, special aptitudes, health, learned skills, and family status, as well as the opportunities for necessary education and employment.

You may wonder how your aptitudes compare with those necessary in particular aerospace jobs. Very probably you are interested in discovering how your personal traits can be used to best advantage. Questions may also arise concerning the educational requirements for different vocations.

Answers to these and many other questions

SCHOOL SUBJECTS AND AEROSPACE CAREERS

SCHOOL SUBJECTS

Related Aerospace Age Occupations	Chemistry	Physics	Bookkeeping	Bus. Machines	Biology	English	Mathematics	Speech	Mechanics	Sheet Metal	Machine Shop	Welding	Radio	Electricity	Mech. Drawing	Woodworking	Journalism	Psychology	Typing	Shorthand	Photography	Nutrition
Aeronautical Engineer	●	●				●	●		●	●	●				●							
Nuclear Engineer	●	●				●	●		●						●							
Flight Test Mechanic	●	●				●	●		●	●	●	●		●	●							
Design Draftsman	●	●				●	●		●	●	●				●							
Instrument Mechanic	●	●				●	●		●		●		●	●	●							
Airline Pilot	●	●				●	●		●				●	●								
Flight Engineer	●	●				●	●		●				●	●	●							
Ground Radio Operator		●				●	●		●				●	●								
Airline Maintenance Inspector	●	●				●	●		●	●	●	●	●	●	●							
Business Pilot	●	●				●	●		●				●	●								
Meteorologist	●	●				●	●		●													
Airframe Mechanic		●				●	●		●	●	●	●			●							
Jet Engine Mechanic		●				●	●		●	●	●	●			●							
Nuclear Weapons Mechanic	●	●				●	●		●				●	●	●							
Air Electronics Officer		●				●	●		●				●	●								
Aircraft Navigator		●				●	●		●				●	●								
Military Pilot		●				●	●		●				●	●								
Electronics Engineer		●				●	●		●				●	●								
Airline Traffic Manager			●	●		●	●	●										●				
Flight Surgeon	●	●			●	●	●											●				●
Scale Model Builder						●	●		●	●	●				●	●					●	
Airline Accountant			●	●		●	●												●			
Stenographer						●													●	●		
Aerial Photographer		●				●	●		●					●							●	
Public Relations Director						●		●									●	●	●			
Physicist	●	●				●	●															
Mathematician		●				●	●															
Chemist	●	●				●	●															
Metallurgist	●	●				●	●		●		●				●							
Mechanical Engineer	●	●				●	●		●	●	●	●			●							
Chemical Engineer	●	●				●	●		●						●							

Figure 77.

---

about selecting the best vocation may be obtained in part from persons now in your own community. With the aid of standard inventory blanks, aptitude scales, interest surveys, and other materials for the measurement of personal traits, your teacher, principal, or school counselor may give you objective information about your interests, personal aptitudes, and general ability.

Vocational guidance services listed in your telephone directory and operated in your community as nonprofit organizations provide excellent assistance of this type. Local offices of your state employment commission offer vocational counseling services in addition to current occupational information. Professional vocational and educational counselors and private employment agencies operated in your community as business enterprises provide similar assistance. Persons entering the military services receive extensive counseling and guidance to help with proper assignment.

Regardless of what choice you make as to what career you want to enter, you are going to have to receive additional education and training. Let's look at some of the advanced training available for persons interested in aerospace.

JUNIOR COLLEGES

The junior colleges, or community colleges, as they are sometimes called, have become very popular in recent years, and more and more are being built every year. Why the popularity? The junior colleges are dispersed within the various states to make them more accessible to prospective students and therefore less costly; students can live at home and commute to school. Also, the junior college attendee is more likely to find a job to pay for, or help pay for, education at this level.

Junior colleges offer the same courses that students take during the first two years at a four-year college, and at most of them, students can specialize. For example, many provide a two-year education that is especially tailored to the future engineer (aeronautical or otherwise), or to the future physician. Credits earned in this manner are transferred to a four-year college or university, and the student proceeds to earn his degree.

In addition to the basic preparatory courses of study which are common to further study in engineering, medicine, business, etc., the junior colleges offer special *terminal* courses. These terminal courses will vary from college to college because they are usually established to fulfill the needs of prospective employers (industries) found within a local, state, or regional area. However, as a result of the growth of new technologies created by aerospace developments, more and more junior colleges offer courses that prepare students for vocations in the aerospace industry (air transport and aerospace manufacturing) and related fields (government and military).

Common to most of the junior colleges will be a continuation of studies in language, mathematics, history and certain other subjects that were begun in secondary school. In any event, the amount of exposure to these basic subjects will depend on which of the curricula a student chooses. Curricula designed to prepare students for studies beyond junior college level place more emphasis on basic subjects. On the other hand, those curricula that are highly specialized and terminal (non degree) place more emphasis on the subjects in which students will specialize.

TECHNICAL/VOCATIONAL SCHOOLS

Technical/vocational schools provide the majority of formal technical educational courses. In this type of school, many people learn the special trades and skills that are applicable to the aerospace industry. A person planning to become an aircraft welder, an electronics technician, or an aircraft powerplant mechanic should seek out the nearest technical/vocational school and obtain details on what the school has to offer. Let's take a quick look at what you would study if you were to decide to specialize as an aircraft airframe and powerplant mechanic:

Aircraft basic science
Aircraft sheetmetal
Aircraft woodwork
Aircraft welding
Aircraft electicity
Aircraft powerplants (introduction)
Induction, fuel and oil systems
Aircraft propellers
Aircraft hydraulics and pneumatics
Turbine-engines (operation, maintenance, overhaul)
Covering and finishing
Assembly and rigging

Auxiliary systems
Radio, electricity and instruments
Powerplant installation and test
Repair stations (organizations, management and operation)
Rocket engines

How long does it take to complete a course of study such as the one described above? Like junior colleges, about two years. This time can be shortened to perhaps fifteen calendar months if the student continues studies without a vacation break.

People who graduate from this type of school go directly into the work force of private industry or government. There usually is a short period of further training sponsored by the employer. This is necessary because, no two companies use the exact same manufacturing or work procedures, and the new employee's skills must be adjusted to his employer's methods of doing things.

INSTITUTES

At various locations across the country, special schools offer only those courses and degrees which are designed specifically for careers found in the aerospace field. This type of school probably uses the title "institute," but may be termed school, college or university.

Institutes, like the technical/vocational schools and terminal courses in junior colleges, place more emphasis on subjects that are essential to doing the job that the student is preparing for; however, there will be several courses in the humanities (rather-than-science subjects) which help give students a more well-rounded education.

Students attending an institute may concentrate in engineering, aerospace engineering, electronic engineering, mechanical engineering, aeronautical engineering, aircraft maintenance engineering technology, aviation management, and mathematics.

Aerospace engineering is a fairly new curriculum which has evolved because of space developments. This type of engineering education prepares a person to work on either aircraft, shuttlecraft, or spacecraft design and production programs—

hence, the title "aerospace." Listed below are the subjects to be mastered over a four-year period by the aspiring aerospace engineer:

Freshman and Sophomore Years:
English composition and literature
Economics
History (U.S.)
Oral communication
Political Science
Technical report writing
Chemistry
Electronic engineering—introduction
Engineering: orientation, drafting
Engineering mechanics: dynamics, statics
Mathematics: calculus, analytic geometry, computer programming, advanced engineering mathematics
Mechanical engineering: engineering materials and design
Physics: mechanics, thermodynamics and electrostatics, atomic physics and quantum mechanics

Junior and Senior Years:
Aerospace engineering: guidance and control systems
Electronic engineering: electrical network analysis, electronic circuits, linear systems analysis
Engineering: engineering design, engineering economy and systems engineering
Engineering mechanics: strength of materials, fluid mechanics, aircraft structures
Mathematics: complex variables, probability and statistics
Mechanical engineering: thermodynamics, engineering metallurgy, heat transfer

The curriculum shown above is an example taken from one institute. A comparable curriculum for the aerospace engineering degree may be slightly different at other institutes. Language studies in composition, technical report writing, and oral communication prepare the aerospace engineer to communicate with fellow engineers and the public. Of course, the several mathematics courses are essential to physics and engineering studies.

FOUR YEAR COLLEGES/UNIVERSITIES

Entry into a college or university is recommended for those who intend to earn a degree and either do or do not know how they will use their education.

The college or university offers a much broader education to its students because they can choose from more electives in both the humanities and science areas. The person who wants to specialize immediately upon beginning the freshman year can do so in somewhat the same manner as found in the institute. Aspiring engineers, for example, begin introductory engineering courses as freshmen. For the person who hasn't decided on a specialized course of study when entering a college or university, the final decision on the area of major study can be postponed until the beginning of the sophomore or junior year. There is only one drawback to this approach for those who decide on an engineering major: It will take additional study to complete the engineering requirements if the prerequisite subjects were not taken during the first one or two years. This means that if one doesn't plan ahead, the total time involved for the basic engineering degree could be as long as six years.

Curricula vary in colleges and universities, too. This is particularly true with the elective courses. Today's forward-looking educators have taken steps to help students understand the aerospace world and the changes brought about by aerospace developments. Many colleges and universities now offer courses especially tailored for this purpose. Some colleges provide flight training as an elective for the entire student body and as a required course for certain major fields of study.

At least one university has developed curricula which are especially designed for aerospace careers. This particular institution now affords an *aerospace minor* for students who are majoring in some other subject, and it provides a special two-year program for students who want to become professional pilots but also want to expand their education beyond that needed to master the art of powered flight. The institution also gives credit for pilot certificates earned. In addition to these special courses, a person can receive a bachelor of science degree in either *aerospace administration* or *aerospace technology* and a master of education degree in *aerospace education.*

The curriculum for aerospace technology was designed for students who intend to become professional pilots or who want to work within the various technical fields found in the aerospace industry. Therefore, it contains a mixture of courses from engineering and other curricula.

Of particular interest is the curriculum for the degree in aerospace administration because it is relatively new and was designed especially to prepare a person for an administrative or managerial position in the aerospace field. Let's see what kinds of courses are given in this curriculum:

Freshman Year
   Theory of flight
   FAA regulations
   English composition
   College algebra
   Plane trigonometry
   Science
   Technical drawing
   General metals
Sophomore Year
   Meteorology
   Navigation
   Flight instruction
   Prose fiction

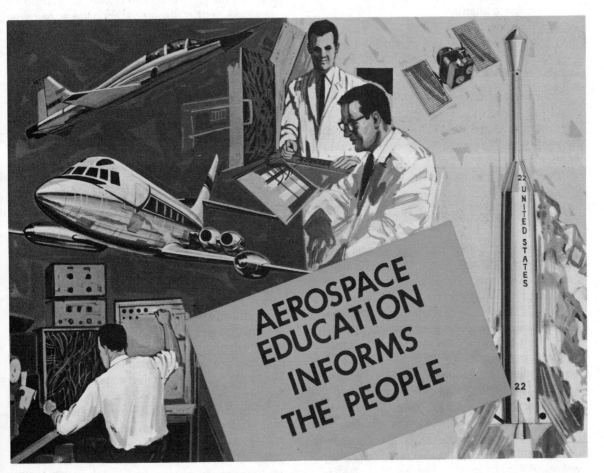

Figure 78.

Poetry
Science
American people (history)
General psychology

Junior Year
Propulsion fundamentals
Aircraft operation & performance
Principles of economics
Statistical methods
Basic electrical fundamentals
Alternating current theory
Principles of accounting
Principles of management
Data processing
(plus electives)

Senior Year
Aerospace vehicles systems
Aerospace internship
Management
(plus a certain number of electives and the courses needed to complete the requirements for a "minor.")

Note that this curriculum gives the student a very broad but in-depth sampling of courses which pertain to specialized areas in the aerospace field. At the same time it provides a good background in those subjects that a person needs to know to become an administrator or manager.

AIR FORCE SCHOOLS

The serious, determined student will find it possible to get the education wanted and needed from civilian schools. If funds are low or nonexistent, the student can work through school, borrow the needed funds (to be repaid after graduation), win scholarships, obtain federal assistance, or enter a co-op plan with an industry (student alternates full time work periods with full time school periods).

What many people have done and continue to do is enter the United States Air Force, or one of the other branches of the armed forces, and continue their education while serving their country. For those who are not "frightened" by the prospect of leading a military life for four or five years, this is a very sensible route to take. After all, the individual's

personal and financial needs are satisfied while gaining further education and training.

Education has always played an important role in the Air Force, but today that role is more important than it has ever been. A broad range of courses are open to airmen and officers to develop the skills and knowledge which will further their service careers or prepare them for employment in their chosen fields if they elect to return to civilian life.

In addition to conducting nearly 4,000 technical training courses, the Air Force provides for the education of Air Force officers through the Air Force Academy, the professional military schools of the Air University, the Air Force Reserve Officer Training Corps program, and the Air Force Institute of Technology. Also, thousands of Air Force personnel further their education on a part-time basis at colleges and schools on or adjacent to many Air Force bases. Others enroll in correspondence courses. The Community College of the Air Force (CCAF) was established by the Air Training Command in 1972 for the purpose of obtaining broader recognition for Air Force training programs in civilian educational institutions and in the employment field.

AIR FORCE RESERVE OFFICER TRAINING CORPS (AFROTC)

The Reserve Officer Training Corps is the primary source of commissioned nonrated officers and a major source of rated officers (pilots and navigators) for the Air Force. The program is offered on the campuses of colleges and universities in 46 states, Puerto Rico, and the District of Columbia. Two commissioning programs are available for college students through AFROTC. Freshmen may enroll in the four-year program and students with at least two years of undergraduate or graduate work remaining may apply for the two-year program. The two programs are open to both men and women.

Both four-year and two-year cadets attend the *Professional Officer Course* (the last two years of the AFROTC program), but four-year cadets also take the General Military Course (the first two years), which consists of one hour each week in the

Figure 79. Air Force ROTC Cadets

classroom and one hour of leadership laboratory (military training and leadership). Classroom instruction time for the Professional Officer Course is three hours weekly, plus one hour of leadership laboratory. Four-year cadets must complete a four-week field training course during the summer between their sophomore and junior years. Two-year cadets complete a six-week field training course (which makes up for the General Military Course) before entering the program.

Scholarships are available to qualified cadets in both the four- and the two-year AFROTC programs. Each scholarship provides full tuition, laboratory expense, incidental fees and a reimbursement for textbooks. While all cadets receive a monthly,

nontaxable subsistence allowance of $100 in their junior and senior years, scholarship cadets receive this allowance for the duration of the scholarship.

In either program, there are certain commissioning requirements. The cadet must successfully complete the Professional Officer Course and field training; must earn at least a baccalaureate degree; must agree to accept a commission in the United States Air Force if it is offered; and must agree to serve for a period of not less than four years on active duty after being commissioned. Pilot candidates must serve six years after completion of pilot training. Navigator candidates must serve five years after completion of navigator training.

AFROTC cadets who volunteer and are qualified

for Air Force pilot training take their first step toward winning their wings through the Flight Instruction Program (FIP) which is provided at no cost to the cadet. The program is conducted during the 24 months prior to the commissioning. It serves as a test of the cadet's aptitude and interest in flying before attending undergraduate pilot training as an officer.

High school students who have successfully completed at least two years of the Air Force Junior ROTC program (AFJROTC) may receive credit for a portion of the General Military Course if they elect to

Figure 80. United States Air Force Academy

enroll in the four-year college ROTC program.

THE AIR FORCE ACADEMY (AFA)

Located near Colorado Springs, Colorado, on an 18,800-acre site, the Air Force Academy ranks among the nation's finest colleges and universities (see fig. 80). Appointees to the Academy receive a four-year college education in addition to military and physical training. The academic curriculum consists of studies in both the humanities and the sciences. Successful completion of the prescribed courses leads to a Bachelor of Science degree and a commission as a second lieutenant in the Air Force or one of the other armed services.

By authorization of Congress, the Academy maintains a strength of 4,500 cadets. This equalizes the student strength of the Air Force, Army, and Naval academies.

Most of the yearly appointments to the AFA are made by United States Senators and Representatives. The nominees are selected by members of Congress from eligible young people in their states or districts who have applied for an appointment. Application for appointment to the Academy must normally be made during the year before the applicant wants the appointment—in other words, during their junior year in high school.

Of special interest to AFJROTC students is the fact that five students from each high school may be nominated to compete for authorized vacancies in the AFA. To be eligible, the student must have successfully completed the AFJROTC program at his/her school and be awarded a certificate of completion and a high school diploma. The aerospace education instructor recommends the best qualified applicants to the high school principal, who, in turn, submits the nomination to the Academy.

A prospective appointee, male or female, to the Air Force Academy must meet the following requirements:

(1) Be at least 17 years old and not have passed his/her 22nd birthday on 1 July of the year of admission.

(2) Be a citizen of the United States. (This does not apply to allied students.)

(3) Be of good moral character.

(4) Be unmarried and have no dependent children. Any cadet who marries while at the Academy will be discharged.

(5) Be in good physical condition.

(6) Have a good scholastic record.

(7) Have demonstrated a potential for leadership in extracurricular activities.

(8) Have a strong desire to become a cadet and have an interest in serving as an Air Force officer.

A successful candidate for admission must assume certain obligations and sign an agreement to that effect. The candidate must agree to complete the course of instruction unless disenrolled by competent authority; accept appointment as a commissioned officer upon graduation and serve in one of the armed services for at least five years; if authorized to resign before the sixth anniversary of his/her graduation, serve as a commissioned officer in the Reserve component of the service until such sixth anniversary is reached; and, if disenrolled from the Academy, be subject to the separation policies employed by all service academies.

The Air Force offers a comprehensive range of academic courses in addition to leadership and military training, physical education, and athletics. Cadets may select their major from numerous courses offered within the fields of science and engineering or social studies and humanities.

The academic program of AFA includes graduate-level courses which may be applied toward a master's degree under a cooperative arrangement between the Academy and various civilian universities in less than one year after graduation. Graduate programs include both science and engineering fields and social sciences and humanities.

In conjunction with the AFA, the Air Force conducts the Air Force Academy Preparatory School for selected members of the Regular and Reserve components of the Air Force and for unsuccessful candidates for AFA whose records indicate that they could improve their chances of receiving an appointment by additional academic preparation. The Preparatory School provides an 11-month course of intensive instruction in English and mathematics to assist students in preparing for

Figure 81. Air University

the entrance examinations. It also prepares the students for the academic, military, and physical training programs of the Academy.

COMMUNITY COLLEGE OF THE AIR FORCE

Since 1972 enlisted men and women in the Air Force have had their own Community College. The Community College of the Air Force helps airmen and noncommissioned officers by translating what they have learned in Air Force technical training and on-the-job training into college-level semester hours. Air Force enlisted members can then credit those hours toward an associate degree related to their Air Force job.

The Community College of the Air Force is a worldwide multicampus college. The seven major technical schools, the professional military education system and the field training detachments are affiliated with the Community College of the Air Force. Enrollment in the college is voluntary, but many enlisted people enroll because they know that planning for the future includes the need to document the technical education they receive in the Air Force.

When an enlisted person enrolls in the Community College of the Air Force, he or she receives a transcript with the credits granted for Air Force courses completed. For example, by completing Basic Military Training, airmen earn four semester hours of Physical Education. The Community College maintains a computerized record of each student's educational progress. This record will automatically pick up all applicable Air Force courses and translate them into semester hours and into civilian educational terminology.

Students are able to add civilian courses which may then be applied toward an associate degree.

Degree programs include a minimum of 64 semester hours of Air Force and civilian instruction including:

24 semester hours in Technical Education directly related to the student's Air Force career area

21 semester hours in the area of General Education. Courses include humanities, math, natural sciences, physical education and communication skills

6 semester hours in Management Education

The remaining hours are technical or general education hours and are usually elective options.

The College offers associate degrees in more than 70 programs in career areas such as aircraft and missile maintenance, electronic and telecommunications, health care sciences, management and logistics, and public and support services.

When a Community College of the Air Force student leaves the Air Force, he or she can take the transcript or can write for one later. It's a document easily understood by potential employers, trade unions, and college officials. The transcript is valuable whether or not the individual completes an associate degree.

In addition to the schools previously discussed, the Air Force, through the Air University at Maxwell AFB, Alabama (fig. 81), provides for the Professional Military Education (PME) of the men and women who elect to make the Air Force a career. The PME schools at Air University include the Squadron Officer School (SOS), the Air Command and Staff College (ACSC), the Air War College (AWC), and the recently opened Senior Noncommissioned Officer Academy.

Appendix
LEARNING OBJECTIVES

PART ONE
The Heritage of Flight
PART OBJECTIVE:
Know the heritage of flight

Chapter 1-1. The Origins of Flight
Chapter Objective:
Know the origins of flight.

TESTING OBJECTIVES:
1. Define "aerospace."
2. Tell how the earliest civilizations regarded flight.
3. Identify the two methods used to fly as described in ancient legends.
4. List two contributions to flight made by the ancient Chinese.
5. Name two recurrent traits of mankind which appear throughout the history of flight.
6. State the method used in early attempts to fly.
7. Identify five of Leornardo da Vinci's contributions to the field of aviation.
8. Tell how the developments which reduced the cost of printing affected the development of flight.
9. Identify the contributions of Cavendish, the Montgolfiers, Thible, deRozier, Garnerin, and Jean and Sophie Blanchard to lighter-than-air flight.
10. Outline Thaddeus Lowe's efforts during the Civil War.
11. List the advantages and disadvantages of using hydrogen gas in balloons.
12. Identify the contributions that Meusnier, Renard, von Zeppelin, and Santos-Dumont made to dirigible flight.
13. Identify the three basic problems of flight.

14. Identify two ways balloonists overcame the problems of development and maintenance of lift.
15. Identify the scientific studies carried out by George Cayley.
16. Describe the contributions to glider flight made by John Montgomery, Otto Lilienthal and Octave Chanute.
17. Describe the work of Samuel Langley.
18. Identify the factors and approach which were instrumental in helping the Wright brothers develop successful powered, sustained, and controlled heavier-than-air flight.
19. State the two major contributions to controlled flight made by the Wright brothers.

Chapter 1-2. The Formative Years: 1904-1919
Chapter Objective:
Know the important developments in aviation during the 1904-1919 time period.

TESTING OBJECTIVES:
1. Outline the Wright brothers' efforts to sell their airplane to the United States Army.
2. Identify the contributions to aviation made by Glenn Curtiss.
3. Describe Calbraith Rodgers' first American transcontinental flight.
4. Identify the first four women to receive a pilot's certificate in the United States.
5. Name the person who first used ailerons to control an airplane.
6. Identify the contributions to aviation made by Louis Bleriot and Louis Breguet.
7. Describe the first international air meet.
8. Describe the "Triple Twin" and "Le Grand" aircraft and the "Gnome" engine.

A-1

9. Identify the problems encountered in the early development of the helicopter.
10. Name the world's first regularly scheduled commercial airline service.
11. Describe the United States' military aviation involvement during World War I.
12. Describe the development of bombers and fighters by Europeans in World War I.
13. Define "Ace" and "Ace of Aces."
14. List the "Ace of Aces" of Germany, France, Britain, and the United States.
15. Describe the composition of the Lafayette Escadrille in World War I.
16. Identify the achievements of Raoul Lufbery, Eugene Bullard, Eddie Rickenbacker, Frank Luke, and Billy Mitchell during World War I.
17. State the importance of air power in World War I in terms of the most important lesson to be learned from the war.

Chapter 1-3. The Golden Age: 1919-1939

Chapter Objective:
Know aviation developments during the Golden Age: 1919-1939.

TESTING OBJECTIVES:
1. Outline the first attempt to fly across the Atlantic by the U.S. Navy.
2. Outline the nonstop transatlantic flights made by Hawker and McKenzie-Grieve and by Alcock and Brown.
3. Describe the condition of aviation in America immediately following World War I.
4. Describe the barnstormers' activities and three stunts they performed.
5. Identify Phoebe Fairgrave Omlie and Bessie Coleman.
6. Describe General Billy Mitchell's efforts to gain support for Army aviators.
7. Name the first two aircraft to fly around the world.
8. Identify the accomplishments in aviation of Russell Maughan and Edwin Nickles.
9. Outline Mitchell's failure and success in achieving some of the changes he wanted in the Army Air Service.
10. Describe the purpose of the Pulitzer Trophy Race.
11. Identify three races from the National Air Races and the important contributions each made to aviation.
12. Identify the purpose of the Schneider Trophy Race.
13. Identify the purposes of the Air Mail Acts of 1925 and 1934 and the Air Commerce Act of 1926.

14. Describe Charles Lindbergh's transatlantic flight, its purpose, and its impact on the American public.
15. Identify the accomplishments in aviation made by Amelia Earhart.
16. Name three general aviation companies in America founded during the Golden Age.
17. Identify the contributions of the NACA, Daniel Guggenheim, and James Doolittle to aeronautics.
18. Identify the two main contributors to rotary-wing aircraft development and the progress they made during the Gold Age.
19. Identify the contributions to rockets and jet research made by Goddard, Oberth, and von Opel in the Golden Age.
20. Identify the purpose of the McNary-Watres Act of 1930.
21. Name the new airliners developed as a result of the McNary-Watres Act.
22. Describe the Pan American Clipper.
23. Name the most famous dirigible of the 1930s.
24. Describe how the Army Air Force prepared for WW II.
25. State the objective of the Civilian Pilot Training Program.
26. Identify the effect that civilian schools for training military pilots had on aviation.
27. Identify the achievements in aviation of Charles "Chief" Anderson, William J. Powell, and Jacqueline Cochran.

Chapter 1-4. World War II

Chapter Objective:
Know aviation developments during World War II.

TESTING OBJECTIVES:
1. Name the Axis powers and describe their preparations for World War II.
2. Name the Allied powers and describe their preparedness for World War II.
3. Identify the events which led to the official beginning of World War II in Europe.
4. Describe the German tactic of Blitzkrieg.
5. Identify the most serious mistake Hitler made in not invading England immediately after the fall of France.
6. Tell how the British military solved the problem of ferrying aircraft during the war.
7. Describe the progress of World War II in 1940 and 1941 on the following fronts: Italian, Mediterranean, Eastern European, Russian, and British.
8. Describe the strategic plans made by the Allies in

preparation for the United States' possible entry into World War II.

9. Describe the Japanese attack on Pearl Harbor on December 7, 1941.
10. Outline the United States military build-up after December 7, 1941.
11. State the basic Allied strategy for winning the war in Europe and the Mediterranean and how the army and air forces each planned to accomplish the strategy.
12. Describe the strategic bombing of Germany by the United States and Britain.
13. Identify the three-part concept of tactical air warfare that resulted from the American tactical operations in Europe and the Mediterranean.
14. Describe the invasion of Europe and its eventual outcome.
15. Identify the stronger, Japan or the Allies, at the time Japan entered World War II.
16. Name the two battles that stopped the Japanese advance in the Pacific during the spring and summer of 1942.
17. Describe the island-hopping campaign in the Pacific during World War II.
18. Describe the bombing tactic used by the United States in the bombing of Japan in 1944.
19. List the two roles served by the island of Iwo Jima.
20. Name the "ultimate" weapon used on Hiroshima and Nagasaki.
21. State three lessons learned from World War II.

Chapter 1-5. The Postwar Years: 1945-1958

Chapter Objective:
Know aviation developments in the postwar years: 1945-1958.

TESTING OBJECTIVES:
1. Name the revolutionary new aircraft that was a product of WW II and the two countries that had this aircraft in operation before the end of the war.
2. Describe the development and use of the V-1 and V-2 "Vengeance" weapons during World War II.
3. Name the two major world political forces at the end of World War II.
4. State the reason United States political leaders cut the size of the Army Air Forces after the end of the fighting in the Pacific.
5. Describe the formation, mission, and capability of the United States Air Force in 1947.
6. State the cause and outcome of the Berlin Airlift.
7. Identify the participants in the Korean War, the importance of airpower, and the lesson learned from it by the United States.
8. Outline the development of USAF strategic

bombers and fighters from the end of World War II through the 1950s.

9. State the outcome of World War II in terms of the effect on people worldwide, women and ex-service people.
10. Outline the post-World War II development of civil aviation in terms of new commercial aircraft and participation of blacks in aviation.
11. List the "big three" of general aviation manufacturers.
12. State the purposes and accomplishments of the X-1, X-2, X-3, and X-5.
13. Name two products of aviation medicine research.

Chapter 1-6. The Aerospace Age: 1958-Present

Chapter Objective:
Know significant developments and events in the Aerospace Age: 1958-Present.

TESTING OBJECTIVES:
1. Name two locations and two vehicles used in the rocket and missile R&D efforts by the United States prior to 1958.
2. Name the first satellite to carry a passenger and the country that launched it.
3. Outline the American reaction to the Russian launches of Sputnik I and II.
4. State the chief reason for the "space race" between Russia and America.
5. State which Federal agencies were put in charge of the American space programs and their respective functions.
6. List the five phases and the major accomplishments of each in the first era of manned spaceflight by the Soviet Union and the United States.
7. Identify two activities of the Soviet Union and of the United States from the second era of manned spaceflight.
8. Name four achievements that Jacqueline Cochran accomplished in the 1960s.
9. Identify the achievements of General "Chappie" James and Jeanne Holm.
10. Identify the role in the space program of Robert H. Lawrence, Jr.
11. Name three major aeronautical research projects since the early 1970s.
12. Name two military aircraft developed since the Korean War.
13. Define and identify a Long-Haul, Short-Haul, Jumbo, and Advanced-Technology Jet and a Supersonic Transport.

14. Name the fastest growing segment in aviation and identify the three main reasons for this growth.

PART TWO
Rocketry and Spacecraft

PART OBJECTIVE:
Know the fundamentals of rocketry and applications of rocketry to spacecraft

Chapter 2-1. Rocket Fundamentals
Chapter Objective:
Know the historical background, fundamental laws, and operating principles of rockets.

TESTING OBJECTIVES:
1. Identify the country that first used rockets in war.
2. Identify Congreve's contribution to rocket flight stabilization.
3. Identify Hale's contribution to rocket flight stabilization.
4. Tell when rockets were first launched from airplanes.
5. Name the *propellant* used in Dr. Goddard's rockets.
6. Name the *propellant* used in Dr. Oberth's rockets.
7. Name the nation which gave rocketry a new start in warfare.
8. Define "gravitation" and "gravity."
9. Define weight, mass, and momentum.
10. Identify Newton's law of motion which *most* applies to rocketry.
11. Name the four *systems* of a rocket.
12. Describe a rocket's airframe.
13. List the basic components of a rocket propulsion system.
14. Identify the three classifications, or groups, of rocket propulsion systems.
15. Name three types of guidance systems.
16. Define payload.
17. Define "specific impulse."
18. Define "density impulse."

Chapter 2-2. Chemical Propulsion
Chapter Objective:
Know the various types of chemical propulsion systems.

TESTING OBJECTIVES:
1. Define "oxidation."
2. Tell what is required for oxidation to take place.
3. Define "propellant," "bipropellant," and "monopropellant."
4. Describe what happens within a charcoal fire.
5. List the qualities of a good propellant.
6. Tell why a rocket propellant does not need air.
7. Identify the only way currently to get more *force* from a load of propellant.
8. Describe the functions of a rocket motor's nozzle throat and nozzle.
9. Name two substances which may be used as *fuel* in solid propellants.
10. Tell what each of the following solid propellant additives does: (a) plasticizer, (b) flash depressor, (c) stabilizer, and (d) opacifier.
11. State how the burning rate of solid propellants may be controlled.
12. Identify the purpose of a "squib."
13. List one advantage and one disadvantage of liquid bipropellants and liquid monopropellants.
14. List the phases of the combustion process that take place within the combustion chambers of a liquid propellant engine.
15. Tell why an *injector* is similar to an automobile carburetor.
16. Define "hybrid propellant."
17. Identify three advantages of a hybrid propulsion system.

Chapter 2-3. Advanced Propulsion Systems
Chapter Objective:
Know the operational concepts of several advanced propulsion systems.

TESTING OBJECTIVES:
1. Describe an "advanced propulsion system."
2. State a need for heavy-lift launch vehicles.
3. Describe a possible use for a manned HLLV.
4. Tell why a manned HLLV might be equipped with an aircraft-type turbine engine.
5. Identify the effect a small amount of thrust will have on a vehicle in space.
6. State two reasons why objects in space can be moved about so easily.
7. Tell why a lot of force or thrust is needed to slow a spacecraft to bring it out of orbit.
8. Describe why low-thrust over a long period of

time is good for long space flights.

9. Name three sources of electricity that might be available to a spacecraft.
10. Describe the characteristics of "thrust" and "propellant" as associated with electric propulsion.
11. Identify three types of electric rocket engines.
12. List two drawbacks to nuclear propulsion.

Chapter 2-4. Guidance and Control

Chapter Objective:
Know how rockets are guided and controlled.

TESTING OBJECTIVES:
1. Identify the source of infrared radiation.
2. Describe a homing guidance system.
3. Describe the three types of homing guidance systems.
4. Define "terminal guidance."
5. Define "command guidance."
6. Identify two means of transmitting commands to a missile with the command guidance system.
7. Tell the purpose of electronic countermeasures (ECM).
8. Describe the "beam rider" type of command guidance system.
9. Identify the advantage of using inertial guidance systems on missiles.
10. List the major parts of an inertial guidance system.
11. Describe how an accelerometer works.
12. Define "initialization."
13. Identify three ways that the direction of a rocket engine's thrust can be changed.

Chapter 2-5. Orbits and Trajectories.

Chapter Objective:
Know the different types of orbits and trajectories.

TESTING OBJECTIVES:
1. Define "orbit."
2. Define "trajectory."
3. In simple terms, describe Newton's law of universal gravitation.
4. Describe the process that keeps an object in Earth's orbit.
5. Name the points in an orbit where the orbiting body is the closest to and farthest from the *Earth.*
6. Name the points in an orbit where the orbiting body is closest to and farthest from the *sun.*
7. Describe the change to a circular orbit if the vehicle's speed is increased.
8. Define "burnout velocity."

9. Describe the effect of Earth's rotational and orbital velocities on the launching of a satellite.
10. Define "total velocity requirement."
11. Describe a ballistic trajectory.
12. Describe a sounding rocket trajectory.
13. State the purpose of a sounding rocket.
14. Name the two *basic* types of orbits.
15. Tell why lower velocities are required for satellites to stay in orbit at higher altitudes.
16. Define "coplanar transfer."
17. Describe the non-coplanar transfer procedure to place a satellite in orbit directly above the equator.
18. Describe a "geosynchronous" orbit.
19. Identify the orbit that provides the best chance to photograph all of Earth's surface.
20. Identify the appropriate orbit for those satellites that need constant sunlight.

Chapter 2-6. Civilian Spacecraft

Chapter Objective:
Know the various actual and proposed unmanned and manned spacecraft programs.

TESTING OBJECTIVES:
1. Define "civilian spacecraft."
2. Define "probe."
3. Name the satellite(s) which was orbited especially for use by amateur radio enthusiasts.
4. Identify the unmanned satellite which is an element of the Space Transportation System.
5. Identify the area of "applications satellites" where the most growth is expected.
6. Give at least two examples of services provided by the Landsat Satellites.
7. Briefly describe the Global Positioning System.
8. Identify what is most closely associated with the environmental satellites.
9. List the names and sponsoring countries of satellites and special units on satellites which can provide global search and rescue services.
10. Identify one contribution made by the Explorer series of satellites.
11. List three types of radiation sensed by orbiting observatories.
12. Name three groups of probes sent to the moon prior to the astronauts' landing on the moon.
13. Identify at least one planet flown by or landed on by each of the following series of probes: the Mariners, the Pioneers, the Vikings, and the Voyagers.
14. Name the probe which is scheduled to arrive at Jupiter in 1988.
15. Describe *two* of Skylab's scientific accomplishments.

16. Identify a primary benefit of the Apollo-Soyuz flight.
17. Describe the duties of the *mission pilot astronaut, mission specialist astronaut,* and *payload specialist.*
18. Briefly describe the *mission profile* of a Space Shuttle flight.
19. Name the spacecraft used in the Soviet's manned satellite programs.
20. Identify future benefits associated with the construction in space of large antennas and space stations.
21. Identify a reason for constructing space colonies.

PART THREE
The Aerospace Community

Part Objective:
Know the composition of the aerospace Community

Chapter 3-1. The Meaning of Aerospace Power

Chapter Objective:
Know the meaning of aerospace power.

TESTING OBJECTIVES:
1. Describe the scope of aerospace.
2. Define "aerospace power."
3. Describe a world power's interest in a strong aerospace oriented economy.
4. Describe how a nation's aerospace power can be increased or decreased.
5. List the three factors of aerospace power.
6. Describe the five elements necessary to possess the capability to act in aerospace.
7. Describe each of the five elements which determine the potential aerospace power of a nation.
8. Define "right to fly."

9. Identify the "five air freedoms."
10. Identify the basis for the international recognition that outer space is free and open to everyone.

Chapter 3-2. Military Aerospace Power

Chapter Objective:
Know military aerospace activities that help determine U.S. aerospace power.

TESTING OBJECTIVES:
1. State the basic task of the "national security policy."
2. Identify the four basic objectives of our military forces.
3. Describe how an economic boycott might be used to resolve conflict between nations.
4. Name the two categories of armed conflict.
5. Define general and limited war.
6. Identify what determines the level of U.S. involvement in armed conflicts.
7. Outline the general strategy followed by the United States in fighting a limited war.
8. Identify the general role or roles of the Army, Marine Corps, Navy, Air Force, and U.S. Readiness Command in fighting a limited war.
9. Define "deterrence."
10. Identify two requirements for deterrence.
11. Describe the Triad.
12. List the strengths and weaknesses of each of the Triad's three systems.
13. State the mission of the USAF Space Command.
14. Identify major elements and problems with SALT I and II.

Chapter 3-3. Civilian Aerospace Programs I

Chapter Objective:
Know the economic and sociological aspects and problems of the civilian aerospace programs that help determine U.S. aerospace power.

TESTING OBJECTIVES:
1. Identify four areas included in civil aviation.
2. Describe the effect of air transportation on our civilization.
3. Describe the economic impact air transportation has had in the United States.
4. Describe three ways airlines increase fuel economy.
5. Describe the growth of the air cargo industry.
6. Identify what part general aviation plays in intercity air passenger service.
7. Describe the air traffic hub system.

8. Identify the percentage of air passengers served by each of the four classes of airports in the hub system.
9. Describe two sociological changes air transportation has produced.
10. Describe the use of two types of non-transportation aircraft.
11. List three problem areas facing air transportation.
12. Describe the two major areas of change that resulted from the Airline Deregulation Act of 1978.
13. Describe the two major problems facing general aviation.

Chapter 3-4. Civilian Aerospace Programs II

Chapter Objective:
Know the governmental agencies and services provided to civil aviation and the importance of our civilian space exploration program to U.S. aerospace power.

TESTING OBJECTIVES:
1. Identify responsibilities of the Federal Aviation Administration.
2. Outline the history of the Federal Aviation Administration.
3. Describe the function of the FAA Air Traffic Control System.
4. State the function of air traffic control towers, air route traffic control centers, and flight service stations.
5. Describe the FAA system of flight standards which ensures that all aircraft are airworthy and all airmen are competent.
6. Outline the function of the National Aviation Facilities Experiment Center.
7. List the responsibilities of the FAA Aeronautical Center.
8. Identify the function of the National Transportation Safety Board.
9. Outline how the Civil Reserve Air Fleet would be used in time of national emergency.
10. Describe Civil Air Patrol's three basic missions.
11. Name three types of support to aviation provided by state governments.
12. Define "basic research," "applied research," and "development."
13. Describe the importance of space technology in the areas of weather satellites, Earth survey satellites, communication satellites, and computers.
14. Define "spinoff."
15. List two spinoffs developed from the space program.

Chapter 3-5. The Aerospace Industry

Chapter Objective:
Know the economics and the problems of the aerospace industry.

TESTING OBJECTIVES:
1. Describe the economics of the aerospace industry in terms of number of employees and payroll.
2. Identify the economic benefit and number one customer of the aerospace industry.
3. Outline the "pendulum" phenomenon seen in the number of trained scientists and engineers in the aerospace industry.
4. Describe the problems faced by our aerospace manufacturers in financing new jet transports.
5. Identify three ways foreign governments assist their aircraft manufacturers.
6. Define "replacement market" and "added capacity market" with regard to the jet transports of the 1980s.
7. Describe the type of aircraft in greatest demand by both added capacity and replacement markets.
8. List some of the new technological improvements which will be on the type of aircraft in the greatest demand.
9. List the advantages of the Boeing 767 as a competitor in the new-technology transport market.
10. Describe the McDonnell-Douglas DC-9 Super 80 and the Boeing 757.
11. Describe two types of exports of military arms.

Chapter 3-6. Aerospace Education and Training

Chapter Objective:
Know the aerospace education and training factors that help determine U.S. aerospace power.

TESTING OBJECTIVES:
1. Define "aerospace education."
2. Identify the basic concepts associated with the key words in the definition of aerospace education.
3. State the purpose of aerospace education.
4. Outline why aerospace education is important to a nation like the United States.
5. Describe the purpose of four-year colleges/universities and two-year vocational/technical schools.

6. Describe the AFROTC and its role in preparing officers for the U.S. Air Force.
7. Identify what an appointee to the Air Force Academy could expect to receive.
8. Describe the services the Community College of the Air Force provides to Air Force personnel.

INDEX